Activity GEMS

for the 6–8 Classroom

EDITED BY

Peggy House
Northern Michigan University, Emeritus
Marquette, Michigan

Sharon Stenglein
Minnesota Department of Education, Retired
Saint Paul, Minnesota

Roger Day
Illinois State University
Normal, Illinois

NCTM NATIONAL COUNCIL OF TEACHERS OF MATHEMATICS

Library of Congress Cataloging-in-Publication Data

Names: House, Peggy, author. | Stenglein, Sharon, author. | Day, Roger P., author.
Title: Activity gems for the grades 6–8 classroom / by Peggy House, Sharon Stenglein, Roger Day.
Description: Reston, VA : National Council of Teachers of Mathematics, [2021] | Series: Activity gems | Includes bibliographical references. | Summary: "This book contains a carefully selected and adapted set of lessons from NCTM's Navigations series, with a special emphasis on incorporating the Effective Mathematics Teaching Practices in NCTM's *Principles to Actions: Ensuring Mathematical Success for All*. Teachers of grades 6–8 students can use these activities to engage their students in exploring, thinking, connecting, discussing, justifying, and advancing in their mathematical understanding and confidence. Each of the Activity Gems includes the following elements: * An overview of how the lesson can help grades 6–8 students develop their mathematical knowledge and abilities, with lists of goals to achieve and all needed materials. * A detailed three-part lesson plan—designed to Engage, Explore, and Extend—including questions a teacher can pose, possible responses and challenges that students may present, and ways to continue the learning beyond the activity. * Activity sheets, classroom images and figures, and any other necessary materials, all available both in an appendix and in downloadable and printable form at NCTM's more4U website. These Activity Gems give grades 6–8 teachers the tools to use purposeful discussion and productive struggle to guide their students toward both conceptual understanding and fluid problem solving"—Provided by publisher.
Identifiers: LCCN 2020026425 (print) | LCCN 2020026426 (ebook) | ISBN 9781680540284 (paperback) | ISBN 9781680540321 (adobe pdf)
Subjects: LCSH: Mathematics—Study and teaching (Middle school)—United States—Activity programs. | Mathematics teachers—In-service training—United States.
Classification: LCC QA13 .H676 2021 (print) | LCC QA13 (ebook) | DDC 510.71/273—dc23
LC record available at https://lccn.loc.gov/2020026425
LC ebook record available at https://lccn.loc.gov/2020026426

The National Council of Teachers of Mathematics advocates for
high-quality mathematics teaching and learning for each and every student.

Printed in the United States of America

Contents

Introduction

> Imagine a classroom, a school, or a school district where all students have access to high-quality, engaging mathematics instruction. There are ambitious expectations for all, with accommodation for those who need it. Knowledgeable teachers have adequate resources to support their work and are continually growing as professionals. The curriculum is mathematically rich, offering students opportunities to learn important mathematical concepts and procedures with understanding. Technology is an essential component of the environment. Students confidently engage in complex mathematical tasks chosen carefully by teachers. They draw on knowledge from a wide variety of mathematical topics, sometimes approaching the same problem from different mathematical perspectives or representing the mathematics in different ways until they find methods that enable them to make progress. Teachers help students make, refine, and explore conjectures on the basis of evidence and use a variety of reasoning and proof techniques to confirm or disprove those conjectures. Students are flexible and resourceful problem solvers. Alone or in groups and with access to technology, they work productively and reflectively, with the skilled guidance of their teachers. Orally and in writing, students communicate their ideas and results effectively. They value mathematics and engage actively in learning it. (*Principles and Standards for School Mathematics*, National Council of Teachers of Mathematics [NCTM] 2000, p. 3)

Forty years ago, NCTM initiated widespread dialogue about the teaching and learning of mathematics with the publication of *An Agenda for Action* (1980) and its leadoff recommendation that problem solving should be the focus of school mathematics. Over the ensuing years the dialogue has been reiterated, refined, and expanded through such vehicles as the *Curriculum and Evaluation Standards for School Mathematics* (1989), *Professional Standards for Teaching Mathematics* (1991), *Assessment Standards for School Mathematics* (1995), *Principles and Standards for School Mathematics* (2000), and other documents both from

NCTM and in collaboration with other educational partners. Among the relevant documents that we consider here, the following are major sources:

Principles and Standards for School Mathematics (NCTM 2000) [PSSM]

Common Core State Standards for Mathematics (National Governors Association Center for Best Practices and Council of Chief State School Officers 2010) [CCSSM]

Principles to Actions: Ensuring Mathematical Success for All (NCTM 2014) [PtA]

Closely aligned and complementary to these reports are two additional NCTM documents, *Curriculum Focal Points for Prekindergarten through Grade 8 Mathematics: A Quest for Coherence* (2006a) and *Focus in High School Mathematics: Reasoning and Sense Making* (2009a), along with *Adding It Up: Helping Children Learn Mathematics* (2001), a report from the National Research Council.

Each of these documents considers the process of teaching and learning mathematics, along with curricular content, and offers a vision of high-quality mathematics programs and the educational experiences, practices, and outcomes that are deemed essential components of such programs. Although the language varies a bit, common themes resonate. Consider, for example, the PSSM Process Standards (see figure Intro.1), the CCSSM Standards for Mathematical Practice (see figure Intro.2), and the PtA Mathematics Teaching Practices (see figure Intro.3). Comparing these three sets of standards or practices, we observe strong convergence on the following:

- Emphasis on reasoning and sense making in order to develop conceptual understanding and facilitate problem solving
- Flexibility in investigating and representing mathematical problems and developing mathematical arguments and proofs
- Connecting mathematical concepts, representations, and processes, and using those connections to extend understanding and solutions
- Communicating mathematical ideas and reasoning, and evaluating the communication of others
- Developing procedural fluency anchored in conceptual understanding and flexible thinking

FIG. INTRO.1

NCTM Process Standards (*Principles and Standards for School Mathematics,* NCTM 2000)

NCTM Process Standards (PSSM)

Problem Solving: *Instructional programs from prekindergarten through grade 12 should enable all students to—*

- Build new mathematical knowledge through problem solving
- Solve problems that arise in mathematics and in other contexts
- Apply and adapt a variety of appropriate strategies to solve problems
- Monitor and reflect on the process of mathematical problem solving

Reasoning and Proof: *Instructional programs from prekindergarten through grade 12 should enable all students to—*

- Recognize reasoning and proof as fundamental aspects of mathematics
- Make and investigate mathematical conjectures
- Develop and evaluate mathematical arguments and proofs
- Select and use various types of reasoning and methods of proof

Communication: *Instructional programs from prekindergarten through grade 12 should enable all students to—*

- Organize and consolidate their mathematical thinking through communication
- Communicate their mathematical thinking coherently and clearly to peers, teachers, and others
- Analyze and evaluate the mathematical thinking and strategies of others
- Use the language of mathematics to express mathematical ideas precisely

Connections: *Instructional programs from prekindergarten through grade 12 should enable all students to—*

- Recognize and use connections among mathematical ideas
- Understand how mathematical ideas interconnect and build on one another to produce a coherent whole
- Recognize and apply mathematics in contexts outside of mathematics

Representation: *Instructional programs from prekindergarten through grade 12 should enable all students to—*

- Create and use representations to organize, record, and communicate mathematical ideas
- Select, apply, and translate among mathematical representations to solve problems
- Use representations to model and interpret physical, social, and mathematical phenomena

FIG. INTRO.2

CCSSM Standards for Mathematical Practice (NGA Center and CCSSO 2010)

CCSSM Mathematical Practices
1. Make sense of problems and persevere in solving them.
2. Reason abstractly and quantitatively.
3. Construct viable arguments and critique the reasoning of others.
4. Model with mathematics.
5. Use appropriate tools strategically.
6. Attend to precision.
7. Look for and make use of structure.
8. Look for and express regularity in repeated reasoning.

FIG. INTRO.3

Mathematics Teaching Practices (*Principles to Actions,* NCTM 2014)

Principles to Actions **Mathematics Teaching Practices**

1 **Establish mathematics goals to focus learning.**

Effective teaching of mathematics establishes clear goals for the mathematics that students are learning, situates goals within learning progressions, and uses the goals to guide instructional decisions.

2 **Implement tasks that promote reasoning and problem solving.**

Effective teaching of mathematics engages students in solving and discussing tasks that promote mathematical reasoning and problem solving and allow multiple entry points and varied solution strategies.

3 **Use and connect mathematical representations.**

Effective teaching of mathematics engages students in making connections among mathematical representations to deepen understanding of mathematics concepts and procedures and as tools for problem solving.

4 **Facilitate meaningful mathematical discourse.**

Effective teaching of mathematics facilitates discourse among students to build shared understanding of mathematical ideas by analyzing and comparing student approaches and arguments.

Principles to Actions Mathematics Teaching Practices *(continued)*

5 Pose purposeful questions.

Effective teaching of mathematics uses purposeful questions to assess and advance students' reasoning and sense making about important mathematical ideas and relationships.

6 Build procedural fluency from conceptual understanding.

Effective teaching of mathematics builds fluency with procedures on a foundation of conceptual understanding so that students, over time, become skillful in using procedures flexibly as they solve contextual and mathematical problems.

7 Support productive struggle in learning mathematics.

Effective teaching of mathematics consistently provides students, individually and collectively, with opportunities and supports to engage in productive struggle as they grapple with mathematical ideas and relationships.

8 Elicit and use evidence of student thinking.

Effective teaching of mathematics uses evidence of student thinking to assess progress toward mathematical understanding and to adjust instruction continually in ways that support and extend learning.

We can compare the enterprise of mathematics education to a woven fabric in which two sets of threads, the *warp* and the *weft* (or *woof*), are interlaced to produce a finished cloth. In weaving, the warp threads are stretched lengthwise on the loom and form the longitudinal elements of the fabric, while the weft threads are woven transversely, over and under the warp, to yield the finished cloth. In mathematics education, the warp can be likened to the curriculum strands, such as the elements elaborated in the PSSM content standards of number and operations, algebra, geometry, measurement, and data analysis and probability, that span the PK–12 curriculum and beyond, while the weft is embodied in the practices of reasoning and sense making essential for mathematical proficiency at all levels. Those process threads have also been summarized succinctly as five interwoven and interdependent strands of mathematical proficiency (*Adding It Up*, National Research Council 2001, p. 115):

1. *Conceptual understanding*—comprehension of mathematical concepts, operations, and relations
2. *Procedural fluency*—skill in carrying out procedures flexibly, accurately, efficiently, and appropriately
3. *Strategic competence*—ability to formulate, represent, and solve mathematical problems
4. *Adaptive reasoning*—capacity for logical thought, reflection, explanation, and justification
5. *Productive disposition*—habitual inclination to see mathematics as sensible, useful, and worthwhile, coupled with a belief in diligence and one's own efficacy

Both components of the woven fabric are essential to the strength, usefulness, and integrity, as well as the beauty, of the finished cloth, just as the components of both content and process are essential for mathematical proficiency and understanding. PSSM stressed that the content and process standards are inextricably linked, and NCTM complemented the publication of PSSM by commissioning the series of 35 *Navigations* books and accompanying CDs as guides to help educators set a course for successful implementation of the PSSM vision by providing examples of high-quality tasks that promote reasoning and sense making across the fabric of mathematics education PK–12.

Yet despite our belief in the essential connectedness of mathematical understanding and competencies, discussions (and assessments) of mathematics education, both among educators and the general public alike, run the risk of focusing disproportionately on the warp of the educational fabric while overlooking the vital role of the weft. With that in mind, our goal with this series of books has been to select activities from throughout the Navigations series (in each of the four grade bands and across mathematics topics) that embody the mathematics teaching practices described in PtA and illustrate how each selected activity can provide opportunities for students to develop the mathematical understanding and proficiency that we value as goals for all students.

We will be paying particular attention to those teaching practices throughout this book. Each activity will establish clear goals that drive the flow of the lesson. The tasks are chosen to promote reasoning and problem solving. Multiple representations of concepts are not only used but are also connected in classroom discussion. Throughout each activity, teachers are guided and encouraged to facilitate mathematical discourse, posing purposeful questions to guide discussions. For these young learners, the emphasis is on developing conceptual understanding, with procedural fluency following as each student is ready.

Perhaps the most difficult practice for many teachers is supporting productive struggle. All teachers have a strong desire to help students. Often, at the first sign of struggle, the teacher steps in and offers assistance to lift students over the trouble spot, despite knowing at some deep level that there can be rich learning for students who figure out a way to climb over the trouble spots on their own or with just a tiny boost. The challenge for teachers is to offer just enough encouragement and a small hint to students so that they can continue finding solutions without taking away the thinking and satisfaction of finally solving the problem on their own.

Finally, effective teachers monitor students' thinking throughout the lesson, adjust as needed, and reflect soon afterward to note suggestions for improving the lesson for the future. Reflecting on the activities sampled in this book and trying them with your own students can provide opportunities for gaining deeper insight into your own students' thinking and understanding. Doing this together with colleagues and examining the teaching practices that you employed and their effects with your own students can contribute even more to your professional growth.

Developing Reasoning and Sense Making in Grades 6–8

Middle-grades students should have a foundation for and experience with reasoning and sense making from elementary school. They ought to have an understanding of additive and multiplicative relationships; they likely will have had many opportunities to make quantitative comparisons and find patterns; and they may have a variety of experiences generating conjectures and making informal arguments.

In the middle grades an emphasis on reasoning continues, with a long-term focus on advancing skills in verification and argumentation, moving from generating specific confirmatory examples to suggesting generalizations that can either be verified and justified or shown not to be true using counterexamples. As originally stated in NCTM's *Principles and Standards for School Mathematics* (NCTM 2000), and reinforced throughout the last two decades (see, for example, NCTM 2009b, NCTM 2014), middle-grades teachers focus on three elements that will help continue students' development of their reasoning and sense-making capabilities: (1) making and investigating mathematical conjectures, (2) developing and evaluating mathematical arguments, and (3) using a variety of reasoning and proof techniques (NCTM 2000, p. 402). The collection of *Navigations* Gems Activities in this volume support teachers in achieving these goals, reinforcing the original intent of the middle-grades *Navigations* authors:

> **Students in grades 6–8 should develop arguments to support their conclusions in solving problems involving a variety of mathematical topics. Although mathematical argument in the middle grades usually lacks the formality and rigor customarily associated with mathematical proof, it should include the formulation of plausible conjectures, testing of those conjectures, and presentation of associated reasoning for evaluation by others. (NCTM 2009c, p. 8)**

Middle-grades students continue to use concrete representations and will extend those to visual, numerical, and algebraic models. They will observe and describe patterns and suggest extensions and generalizations of those patterns, all the while communicating with one another and offering feedback on the work of others. Teachers' efforts in supporting these student actions are consistent with the outcomes described in *Principles to Actions* Mathematics Teaching Practices (see figure Intro.3) and are practices that, as illustrated in figure Intro.4, are interconnected and mutually supportive.

FIG. INTRO.4

Mathematics Teaching Framework (from Berry 2019)

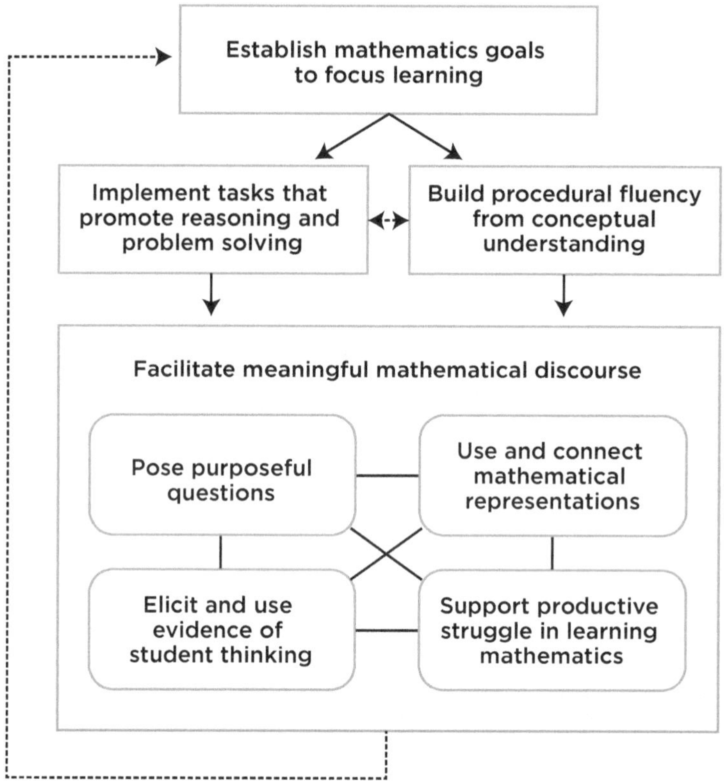

The original NCTM Navigations series offered a rich collection of activities to support teachers and students, addressing content and practice, goals and outcomes, through implementation of the strategies reiterated in the framework shown earlier. The *Navigations* Gems assembled in the current volume provide examples of how we envision middle-grades teachers and students actively exploring, thinking, connecting, discussing, justifying, and advancing in their mathematical understanding and confidence.

1

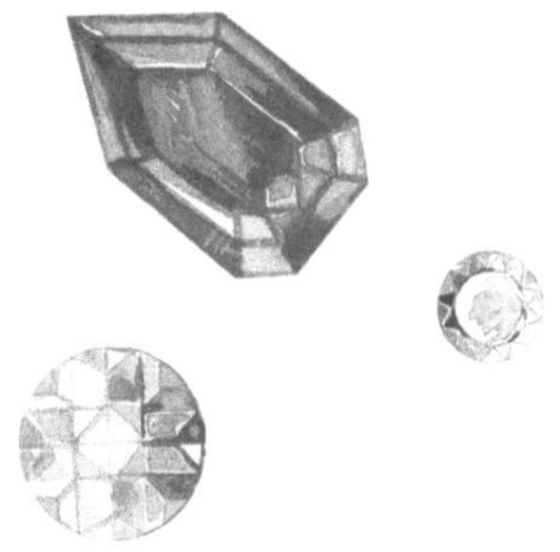

Reasoning about Sums of Consecutive Numbers

OVERVIEW

During the primary and elementary grades, major emphasis is placed on learning numbers and developing proficiency with the basic arithmetic operations. As the curriculum in the middle grades expands to include more algebra, geometry, and other topics, there is a danger that numbers and operations may be overshadowed on the mistaken assumption that students have by now mastered these topics and should focus elsewhere. But, in fact, number and operations remain central themes as students expand their knowledge to include integers and rational numbers and as they develop facility working with fractions, decimals, and proportional reasoning.

Derived from "Reasoning about Sums of Consecutive Numbers" in *Navigating through Problem Solving and Reasoning in Grades 6–8* (NCTM 2009b, pp. 12–16).

In the middle grades, students have numerous opportunities to develop and use number concepts in a variety of contexts and applications. They are able to focus more directly on properties of numbers than they were in earlier grades, and they can explore interesting number patterns and relationships. This activity invites students to reason and think analytically about sums of consecutive numbers, to note patterns, and to investigate whether and why those patterns make sense. Such exploration of numbers and their relationships promotes the development of number sense. Because this activity and the questions it raises will probably be new for most students, you are encouraged to work through it yourself before presenting it to the students.

"Reasoning and proof should be a consistent part of students' mathematical experience in prekindergarten through grade 12. Reasoning mathematically is a habit of mind, and like all habits, it must be developed through consistent use in many contexts." (NCTM 2000, p. 56)

GOALS

- Solve problems using numerical and algebraic expressions and equations.
- Work with concepts related to consecutive addends, divisibility, and powers of 2.
- Make conjectures, determine their validity, and support or contradict them by making mathematical arguments.
- Explain problem-solving strategies and justify solutions.

MATERIALS NEEDED

Copies of the activity sheet Sum-thing about Consecutive Numbers, one for each student

Copies of the Recording Sheet for Sum-thing about Consecutive Numbers, one for each student

Engage

In this activity, students will investigate the counting numbers from 1 to 35 to determine which of those numbers can be written as a sum of consecutive counting numbers. As they do, they will look for patterns, make conjectures, and present explanations and arguments to support or refute those conjectures.

Introduce the activity with a brief discussion of the meaning of *consecutive numbers*: two or more integers for which the *absolute difference* between any two of them is 1. Relate this to the number line and the fact that the distance between any two consecutive integers is 1. We refer to this as "absolute difference" because the distance is not concerned about the direction of movement from one integer to its neighbor—that is, the absolute difference between 4 and 5 is 1, regardless of whether one is moving from 4 to 5 or from 5 to 4 [$|4 - 5| = |5 - 4| = 1$]. Also tell the students that in the initial activity they will be working with only the *counting numbers*, that is, the set {1, 2, 3 . . .}.

Show the students the following three examples of sums of consecutive counting numbers:

$$3 + 4 = 7$$

$$2 + 3 + 4 = 9$$

$$4 + 5 + 6 + 7 = 22$$

Here 7, 9, and 22 are the sums of two, three, and four consecutive numbers, respectively. Ask the students to each write one or two more examples of sums of consecutive counting numbers, and call on several students to share their examples. Be sure that the students demonstrate understanding of the task and of the meaning of consecutive numbers before proceeding with the activity.

Explore

Give each student a copy of the activity Sum-thing about Consecutive Numbers and pose the following challenge: Consider the counting numbers from 1 through 35. We want to see how many of them can be written as a sum of two or more consecutive counting numbers. Use the chart in question 1 on the activity sheet to record all the consecutive sums that you can find. Some of the numbers may be written as sums in more than one way. For example, 9 is shown earlier as a sum of three consecutive numbers (2 + 3 + 4), but 9 is also the sum of two consecutive numbers (4 + 5). In the chart, record *all* the ways you can find for the numbers from 1 to 35.

Let the students work individually for 5 or 10 minutes, then arrange them in twos or threes so they can share and discuss their findings. Allow time for the teams to continue working together to complete the chart in question 1 for the numbers 1 through 35.

The next step in the investigation is to ask the students to examine the sums they have recorded earlier to see if they can discover any patterns or relationships. To facilitate that exploration, give each student a copy of the Recording Sheet for Sum-thing about Consecutive Numbers and have them organize their earlier work in a table where for each number from 1 through 35 (the rows), the possible sums are recorded in the columns according to the number of addends in each case. Table 1.1 shows a copy of a completed table.

Table 1.1. Numbers 1–35 as Sums of Consecutive Numbers

Number	Two Addends	Three Addends	Four Addends	Five Addends	Six Addends	Seven Addends
1						
2						
3	1 + 2					
4						
5	2 + 3					
6		1 + 2 + 3				
7	3 + 4					
8						
9	4 + 5	2 + 3 + 4				
10			1 + 2 + 3 + 4			
11	5 + 6					
12		3 + 4 + 5				
13	6 + 7					
14			2 + 3 + 4 + 5			
15	7 + 8	4 + 5 + 6		1 + 2 + 3 + 4 + 5		
16						

Table 1.1. Numbers 1–35 as Sums of Consecutive Numbers *(continued)*

17	8 + 9					
18		5 + 6 + 7	3 + 4 + 5 + 6			
19	9 + 10					
20				2 + 3 + 4 + 5 + 6		
21	10 + 11	6 + 7 + 8			1 + 2 + 3 + 4 + 5 + 6	
22			4 + 5 + 6 + 7			
23	11 + 12					
24		7 + 8 + 9				
25	12 + 13			3 + 4 + 5 + 6 + 7		
26			5 + 6 + 7 + 8			
27	13 + 14	8 + 9 + 10			2 + 3 + 4 + 5 + 6 + 7	
28						1 + 2 + 3 + 4 + 5 + 6 + 7
29	14 + 15					
30		9 + 10 + 11	6 + 7 + 8 + 9	4 + 5 + 6 + 7 + 8		
31	15 + 16					
32						
33	16 + 17	10 + 11 + 12			3 + 4 + 5 + 6 + 7 + 8	
34			7 + 8 + 9 + 10			
35	17 + 18			5 + 6 + 7 + 8 + 9		2 + 3 + 4 + 5 + 6 + 7 + 8

When the students have finished organizing their sums in the previous step, direct them to examine their tables and write descriptions of any patterns that they observe. Have the students share their observations and collect them in a classroom display, but do not delve into them yet. Right now, we want to collect as many observed patterns and conjectures as we can; later we will examine them to see what is happening and why. Here are some of the observations that students have reported:

> *"People who reason and think analytically tend to note patterns, structure, or regularities in both real-world and symbolic objects; they ask if those patterns are accidental or if they occur for a reason; and they conjecture and prove."* (NCTM 2000, p. 56)

1. We noticed that all the odd numbers from 3 on can be written as a sum of two consecutive numbers. And we also noticed that every time you go from one odd number to the next, the two addends increase by one. For example, 3 = 1 + 2, 5 = 2 + 3, 7 = 3 + 4, and so on.

2. We noticed that, starting with 3, every second number can be written as a sum of two consecutive numbers; starting with 6, every third number (6, 9, 12 . . .) can be written as a sum of three consecutive numbers; starting with 10, every fourth number (10, 14, 18, 22 . . .) can be written as a sum of four consecutive numbers. A similar pattern continues for all the columns.
3. We saw something that links the first two patterns. You showed us that for the sums of two consecutive numbers, every time you go to the next odd number, the addends start one number higher. The same kind of pattern is true down all the columns. For instance, $6 = 1 + 2 + 3$, and for the next numbers in the column, $9 = 2 + 3 + 4$, then $12 = 3 + 4 + 5$, and so on. You can always get the next case just by starting the addends one number higher. And that works for four or five or any number of consecutive addends. You could keep going like that forever.
4. We saw that all the numbers that are sums of three consecutive addends are divisible by 3: 6, 9, 12, 15, and so on. And all the numbers that are sums of five addends are divisible by 5: 15, 20, 25, 30, 35. We only have two examples of numbers with seven addends (28 and 35), but they're both divisible by 7.
5. We noticed something else about some of the odd numbers. Look at 15: $15 = 3 \times 5$, and 15 is a sum of three consecutive numbers and of five consecutive numbers. Same thing for 35: $35 = 5 \times 7$, and 35 is a sum of both five and seven consecutive numbers. But sometimes it doesn't seem to work that way, like for 21—it's a sum of three consecutive numbers, but not of seven—and we wonder why. Maybe we just don't have enough information.
6. But there's more to what you just said. Some of the odd numbers, like those you mentioned, are sums in more than one way. But we noticed that prime numbers on the list, from 3 on, are sums of only two consecutive numbers and never more than that.
7. We couldn't find any consecutive numbers that give sums of 1, 2, 4, 8, 16, or 32. Oh, wait! Those numbers are all powers of 2: 2^0, 2^1, 2^2, 2^3, 2^4, 2^5. Something must be going on here. We wonder what.

Congratulate the students for their observations. They are beginning to think like mathematicians, who continually look for patterns and for reasons to explain them. Depending on their background and prior experiences, the students will vary in their ability to note and articulate patterns, and you may need to assist them in formulating their observations. For example, some may not immediately recognize the powers of 2, or they may be unfamiliar with using exponential notation to represent powers; that can be an opportunity for you to introduce those ideas to the class.

"The role of the teacher is to engage students in tasks that promote reasoning and problem solving and facilitate discourse that moves students toward shared understanding of mathematics." (NCTM 2014, p. 11)

Before you delve further into the reasons underlying the students' observations, ask them to look at question 3 on the Sum-thing about Consecutive Numbers sheet, which challenges them to apply the patterns they have observed to five other numbers—45, 57, 62, 75, and 80—and use their observations to write those numbers as sums of consecutive addends in as many ways as they can. Give them sufficient time to work, individually or in teams, to discover the sums and to write which pattern they used to determine each case; then have them share their discoveries with the class. Figure 1.1 shows the possible sums. Note that one of the numbers, 75, can also be written as a sum of 10 consecutive numbers, which exceeds the number of columns on the students' chart and does not reflect any of the observed patterns reported earlier. Do not be surprised if the students do not find that case; if they do not, you can use it as an opportunity to challenge them to "look for one more solution for 75."

FIG. 1.1

Sums of consecutive addends for five numbers

45 is the sum of two, three, five, and six consecutive addends:
(22 + 23), (14 + 15 + 16), (7 + 8 + 9 + 10 + 11),
(5 + 6 + 7 + 8 + 9 + 10)
57 is the sum of two, three, and six consecutive addends:
(28 + 29), (18 + 19 + 20), (7 + 8 + 9 + 10 + 11 + 12)
62 is the sum of four consecutive addends:
(14 + 15 + 16 + 17)
75 is the sum of two, three, five, six, and ten consecutive addends:
(37 + 38), (24 + 25 + 26), (13 + 14 + 15 + 16 + 17),
(10 + 11 + 12 + 13 + 14 + 15),
(3 + 4 + 5 + 6 + 7 + 8 + 9 + 10 + 11 + 12)
80 is the sum of five consecutive addends:
(14 + 15 + 16 + 17 + 18)

Now that the students have discovered a number of patterns and shown that they can apply those patterns in new situations, it is time to look deeper into what is happening, to ask whether their observations will always apply, and why they are (or perhaps are not) true. You might choose to look at the first observed pattern together to see why it makes sense and to model an approach for the students before you ask them to examine other patterns on their own.

The first observation noted that all odd numbers, starting with 3, can be written as a sum of two consecutive numbers. Why is that true? Let's begin by recalling what we know about even and odd numbers: We know that all even numbers are multiples of 2 and that all odd numbers are one more (or one less) than a multiple of 2. We can represent evens and odds visually (see figure 1.2), and we can express the same properties algebraically as $N_{even} = 2n$ and $N_{odd} = 2n + 1$ for any integer value of n. Since we are always adding two consecutive numbers, one of them will be even and the other will be odd, and the sum of an even number and an odd number is always an odd number. To show that algebraically, we have $(2n) + (2n + 1) = (4n + 1)$. To reverse the process, if we start with any odd number, N, and divide it by 2, we will always have a remainder of 1. For example, 35 ÷ 2 = 17, remainder 1. The two addends are 17 and (17 + 1), which gives 35 = 17 + 18.

FIG. 1.2

Visual representation of even and odd numbers

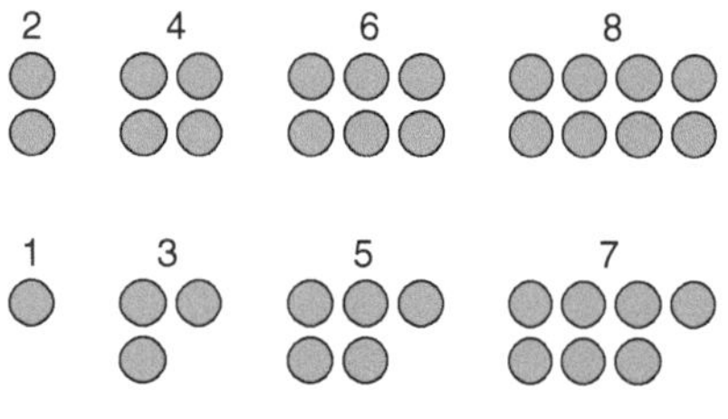

The goals throughout this activity have been to encourage the students to look for patterns, to make conjectures based on the observed relationships, and to develop explanations and arguments to either support or contradict their conjectures. We saw earlier an example of making sense of the observation about the sums of two consecutive numbers. One way to approach the challenge of analyzing the rest of the discoveries that the students reported is to assign each small group the task of examining one of the posted patterns and preparing a presentation to the class. Allow ample time for the groups to discuss their assigned task and to prepare their reports. As you circulate throughout the classroom, be prepared to answer questions the students may have for you and to make helpful suggestions, if appropriate. Following are summaries of some of the reasoning and explanations that students have reported about sums of consecutive numbers.

> *"Effective teaching of mathematics consistently provides students, individually and collectively, with opportunities and supports to engage in productive struggle as they grapple with mathematical ideas and relationships."* (NCTM 2014, p. 10)

Some students looked at the second observed pattern—that, starting with 3, every second number is a sum of two consecutive addends; starting with 6, every third number is a sum of three consecutive addends; starting with 10, every fourth number is a sum of four consecutive addends, and so on. They focused first on the starting number in each column—3, 6, 10, 15, 21, and 28—and recognized them as belonging to the sequence of triangular numbers (see figure 1.3). [If your students are unfamiliar with the triangular numbers, take the time to introduce them and explore some of their properties, because those numbers will arise often and figure prominently in problems the students will encounter throughout their mathematical studies.]

FIG. 1.3

The first five triangular numbers

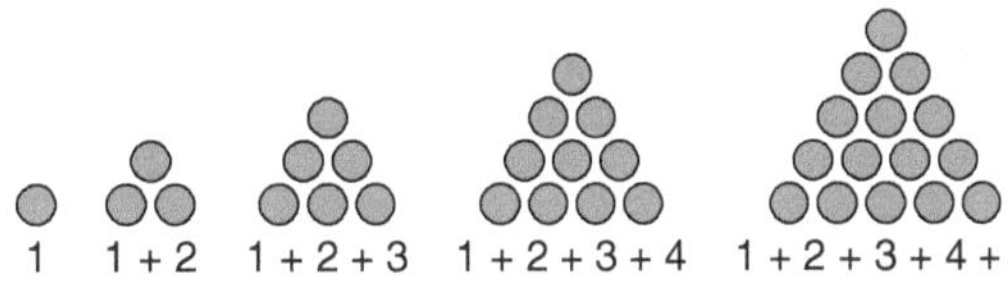

Once the students recognized the appearance of the triangular numbers, they were able to make sense of the rest of the pattern by using the visual representation in figure 1.4. They then used figure 1.5 to demonstrate why the four-addend column started with 10 and why every fourth number after 10 could also be written as a sum of four consecutive addends. Their representation also allowed them to explain the third pattern posted earlier: You can always get the next case just by starting the addends one number higher.

FIG. 1.4

Visualizing patterns observed in the table of sums

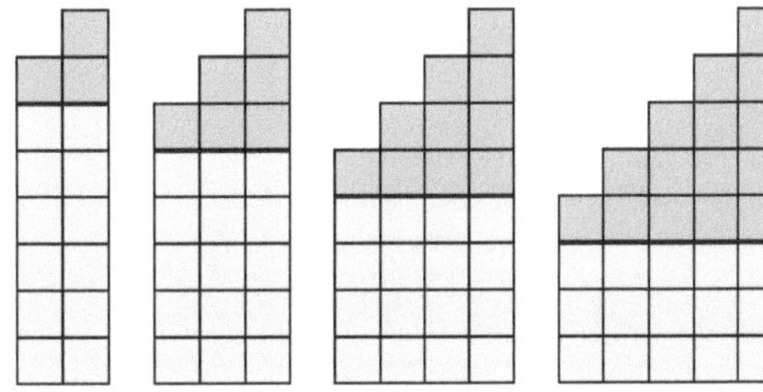

FIG. 1.5

Representing sums of four consecutive numbers

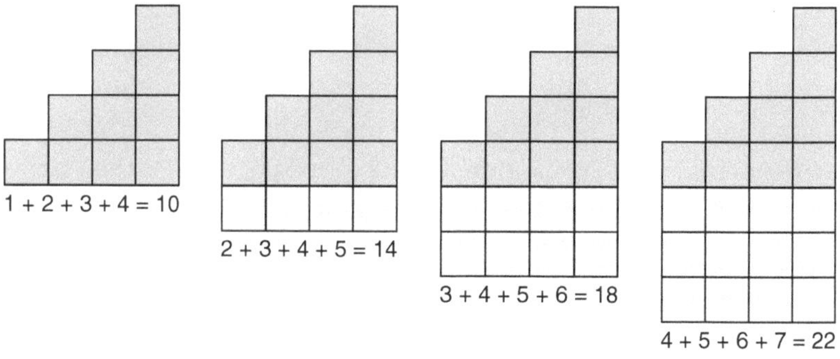

> *"The role of the student is to be actively involved in making sense of mathematics tasks by using varied strategies and representations, justifying solutions, making connections to prior knowledge or familiar contexts and experiences, and considering the reasoning of others."* (NCTM 2014, p. 11)

After the students understood what was happening in the previous example, they also showed how they could reverse the relationship to decide whether a given number could be a sum of four consecutive addends: Subtract 10 from the number in question and see if the remainder is a multiple of 4. They illustrated their strategy with the earlier problem of expressing 62 as a sum of four consecutive addends: $62 - 10 = 52$ and $52 \div 4 = 13$. Hence, following the pattern shown in figure 1.5, add 13 gray rows below the triangular array to get $14 + 15 + 16 + 17 = 62$. The strategy is adaptable to any number of addends: To determine if a given number, N, can be written as a sum of n consecutive numbers, subtract from N the nth triangular number, then see if the remainder is a multiple of n. It also allows one to determine if a number can be written as a consecutive sum in more than one way, as illustrated in figure 1.6 [$18 - 6 = 12$, and $12 \div 3 = 4$; $18 - 10 = 8$, and $8 \div 4 = 2$].

FIG. 1.6

Eighteen as a sum of three and of four consecutive addends

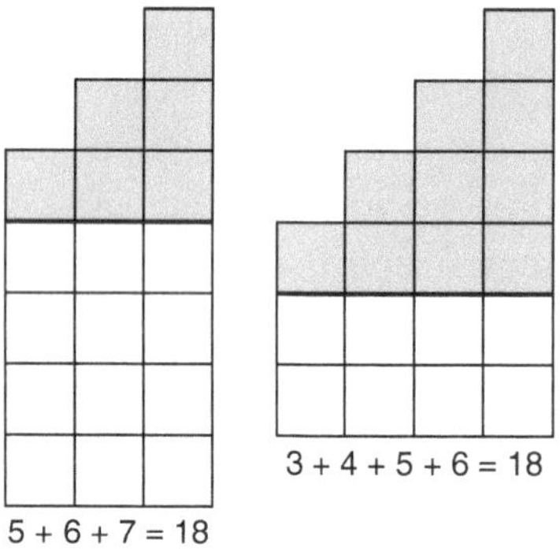

Another group of students examined the fourth observation—that if a number, N, is a sum of an odd number, n, of consecutive addends, then N is divisible by n. They began with $15 = 3 \times 5$, and recognizing that 15 could be a sum of three 5s or of five 3s, they developed the "balancing act" illustrated in figure 1.7.

FIG. 1.7

Fifteen as a sum of three and of five consecutive addends

5 + 5 + 5 = 15	3 + 3 + 3 + 3 + 3 = 15
4 + 5 + 6 = 15	1 + 2 + 3 + 4 + 5 = 15

Because there are an odd number of addends, there is always a middle term that functions as a pivot point in the expression. After locating the middle term, the addends to the left and right are adjusted in pairs, each time decreasing the term on the left while increasing the corresponding term on the right, as shown in figure 1.7.

A few students even noticed that if the middle addend is itself an odd number, they could use the balancing-act strategy a second time to yield another sum of consecutive numbers. They demonstrated with the number 45 from problem 3 on the activity sheet:

$$14 + 15 + 16 = 45$$
$$5 + 6 + 7 + 8 + 9 + 10 = 45$$

Here the 15 in the center position of the first expression is decomposed into (7 + 8), and the continued balancing results in the pairs (6 + 9) and (5 + 10), or three 15s. It was the application of that strategy to the 5-addend expression for 75 that led to the discovery of the 10-addend expression in figure 1.1.

Extend

Many of the patterns that the students observed were explored and explained in the previous discussion, but a few unanswered questions remain. One was posed in observation 5, when the students noted that "21 is a sum of three consecutive numbers, but not of seven, and we wonder why." An answer to their question can be found if we extend the set of possible addends from the counting numbers to the integers. Using the balancing-act strategy on the number 21 and allowing the consecutive addends to be integers leads to the following:

$$3 + 3 + 3 + 3 + 3 + 3 + 3 = 21$$
$$0 + 1 + 2 + 3 + 4 + 5 + 6 = 21$$

Note that the previous line is equivalent to the expression from the six-addend column on the chart. A more graphic example is shown if we consider the number $27 = 3 \times 9$:

$$3 + 3 + 3 + 3 + 3 + 3 + 3 + 3 + 3 = 27$$
$$-1 + 0 + 1 + 2 + 3 + 4 + 5 + 6 + 7 = 27$$

Here we see that the first three terms sum to zero, so the expression we are left with is the one already noted for six consecutive counting numbers. The students can try other examples. In each case the expression they get using integers reduces to an expression with the same or fewer counting-number addends. The important point is that their pattern, or "rule," which seemed to fall short in some situations does indeed hold true if they apply it using the integers instead of only counting numbers.

The extension to integers also provides insight into the sixth observation earlier, that the prime numbers are sums of only two, and never more than two, consecutive numbers.

Consider, for example, the prime number 11; it has only two factors and can only be written as 11 × 1. Thus, we get

$$1 + 1 + 1 + 1 + 1 + 1 + 1 + 1 + 1 + 1 + 1$$

$$-4 + -3 + -2 + -1 + 0 + 1 + 2 + 3 + 4 + 5 + 6,$$

all of which simplifies to 5 + 6 = 11. Again, the students can check other examples for reinforcement.

The remaining unanswered questions concern numbers that are sums of an even number of consecutive addends. Consider first any number, N, that is not a power of 2, such as 26 or 27. When those numbers are written as a sum of an even number of consecutive addends, there are two middle terms, as shown here:

$$5 + (6 + 7) + 8 = 26 \qquad 2 + 3 + (4 + 5) + 6 + 7 = 27$$

As these examples show, the sum of the two middle terms is a divisor of N ($6 + 7 = 13 = 26 \div 2$; $4 + 5 = 9 = 27 \div 3$). This gives a clue to the relationship between the number, N, and the number of addends, n: 26 is a sum of four addends, and $26 \div 4 = 6\frac{1}{2}$, whereas 27 is a sum of six addends and $27 \div 6 = 4\frac{1}{2}$. When the quotient of $N \div n = q\frac{1}{2}$, that quotient is an "imaginary" pivot point for the sum [$6\frac{1}{2}$ for the pair (6 + 7); $4\frac{1}{2}$ for the pair (4 + 5) in the two cases]. The rest of the expression parallels the balancing-act relationship observed for an odd number of addends. It also explains why 57, in the numbers from question 3 of the activity sheet, could be a sum of six addends but not of four: $57 \div 6 = 9\frac{1}{2}$ (and the two middle terms are 9 + 10), but $57 \div 4 = 14.25$, so the four-addend case does not exist. The students should apply this approach to verify some of the other entries in their table.

Finally, there is the case of the powers of 2, for which no sums of consecutive addends were found. Why not? The answer to this question requires algebra that may be beyond the mathematical background of some of your students, and for them you can opt to defer the question at this time. But for students with sufficient algebraic knowledge, we can use the triangular-number approach discussed earlier to answer the question.

First, we need to find an expression for the nth triangular number. Figure 1.8 shows one way to determine this by writing the nth triangular number first as $T_n = 1 + 2 + 3 + \cdots + (n - 1) + n$ and again as a sum with the terms reversed. Adding the two expressions term by term yields n partial sums of $(n + 1)$ as the value of $2T_n$, from which we derive the expression for T_n. To help the students understand the generalization, you might want to have them apply it to a few specific cases. For example:

FIG. 1.8

Finding an expression for the nth triangular number

Determine the value of the nth triangular number as follows:

$$T_n = 1 + 2 + 3 + \cdots + (n - 2) + (n - 1) + n$$
$$T_n = n + (n - 1) + (n - 2) + \cdots + 3 + 2 + 1$$
$$2T_n = (n + 1) + (n + 1) + \cdots + (n + 1) + (n + 1)$$
$$= n(n + 1)$$
$$T_n = \frac{n(n + 1)}{2}$$

$$
\begin{aligned}
T_5 &= 1 + 2 + 3 + 4 + 5 \\
T_5 &= 5 + 4 + 3 + 2 + 1 \\
2T_5 &= 6 + 6 + 6 + 6 + 6 \\
&= 5 \times 6 \\
T_5 &= \frac{5 \times 6}{2} = 15
\end{aligned}
$$

Using the triangular-number strategy developed earlier in this activity to see if a power of 2 (call it 2^k) can be written as a sum of n consecutive addends, 2^k must equal the nth triangular number plus a multiple of n, or

$$
\begin{aligned}
2^k &= T_n + n \cdot a \\
&= \frac{n(n+1)}{2} + n \cdot a \\
2^{k+1} &= n(n+1) + 2na \\
&= n[(n+1) + 2a]
\end{aligned}
$$

Now, if n is an even number, then $(n + 1)$ and $[(n + 1) + 2a]$ are both odd; and, if n is odd, then $(n + 1)$ and $[(n + 1) + 2a]$ are both even. In either case, we have (even) × (odd) = odd = $2^{(k+1)}$, which is impossible.

> *"An effective teacher provides students with appropriate challenge, encourages perseverance in solving problems, and supports productive struggle in learning mathematics."* (NCTM 2014, p. 11)

Not all of your students may be ready for all of the explanations developed here in the Extend section. That will depend on their algebraic background, and you can decide how far to pursue the inquiry at any given time.

SUMMARY

This activity helps build students' number sense by returning them to the familiar operation of addition and encouraging them to explore more deeply, going beyond "getting the answer" to looking for patterns and relationships, then reasoning and making sense of the connections that they observe. The insights the students develop as a result of formulating conjectures and then explaining and justifying those conjectures help build their confidence and promote their ability to reason mathematically. Repeated opportunities such as this to explore relationships, make conjectures, and justify results help students see and expect that mathematics makes sense and that they can understand and use it.

2

Squaring Off with Rational Numbers

OVERVIEW

Rational numbers are complex and abstract, best understood over an extended period. The middle-grades years are an especially important time for building understanding using a variety of models and representations. As middle-school students expand the sets of numbers with which they are fluent and examine rates, ratios, and proportional relationships, the idea of multiple representations of a rational number is a central concept. This activity allows students to step back from their initial experiences with fraction, decimal, and percentage equivalents and to examine the concepts at a deeper level. The primary vehicle for this deepening will be through shading a rectangular grid, but a grid that does not have one hundred squares. This forces students to rethink their understanding and strategies for finding equivalencies and the underlying ideas of fractions, decimals, and percentages.

Derived from "Representing Shaded Areas of Rectangular Grids" and "Shading Areas of Rectangular Grids" in *Navigating through Number and Operations in Grades 6–8* (NCTM 2006, pp. 26–33).

"Rational numbers can be understood only in a whole system of contexts, meanings, operations, and representations." (Lamon 2001, p. 150)

Although some students may have already been introduced to rules for converting fractions to decimals by dividing the numerator by the denominator, in this activity students will not use that procedure; instead, they will dig deeper into the meaning of the relationships using diagrams. Students who approach mathematics problems as tasks to be completed as quickly and "efficiently" as possible may be impatient with this, but searching for alternative strategies should give them a more robust understanding of these concepts. The diagrams offer all students a tool for sense making. However, since the goal of the lesson is conceptual understanding, using the visual tool of a nonstandard grid will force them to confront the basic concepts.

"This task promotes problem solving because students are positioned to explore the situation without being told in advance what to expect." (NCTM 2014, p. 21)

Prior to using this lesson with students, the teacher should work through the activity sheet Shading Areas of Rectangular Grids. This will prepare for introducing the ideas of the entire activity with the class.

In the first part of the activity, students are presented with a grid that has some squares shaded, and they are asked to find the fraction, decimal, and percentage represented by the shading. In the second part, they will be given a blank grid and asked to create a shading to represent a percentage, decimal, or fraction. This latter problem is considerably more difficult, though discussion during the first part will help make it more accessible to students.[1]

Students will be "describing and justifying their mathematical understanding and reasoning with drawings, diagrams, and other representations." (NCTM 2014, p. 29)

GOALS

- Solve multistep mathematical problems posed with rational numbers in any form (whole numbers, fractions, and decimals), using tools strategically.
- Identify shaded regions of rectangular grids by using fractions, decimals, and percentages.
- Shade regions of rectangular grids to represent given fractions, decimals, and percentages.
- Recognize that fractions, decimals, and percentages are different ways of representing the same quantity.
- Use rectangular grids as tools for making sense of abstract mathematical ideas.
- Communicate mathematical thinking.
- Develop general strategies, such as "chunking" and unit rate, for representing rational numbers on a rectangular grid.

MATERIALS NEEDED

Representing Shaded Areas of Rectangular Grids activity sheets for each student

Shading Areas of Rectangular Grids activity sheet for each student

Grid paper

Colored pencils or markers

[1] This activity has been adapted from Foreman and Bennett (1996).

Engage

Distribute copies of the Representing Shaded Areas of Rectangular Grids activity to each student. Together examine the first problem (see figure 2.1), which asks the students to express the shaded region as a fraction, a decimal, and a percentage. Ask students to work with a partner to solve it. While you allow 5 to 10 minutes for students to determine a solution, look around the classroom for students with several different types of solutions. Select a few students to present their solutions. Some students might not notice that there are 80 squares on the grid rather than 100 and say that the fraction is 16/100, with a corresponding decimal and percentage. Other typical answers for this problem are 16/80, which can be simplified to 4/20 or 1/5. Either of these simplified fractions is easily convertible to decimal and percent form. Some students may remember that 1/5 is 0.20 or 20 percent from previous experience.

The description of the work of these seventh-grade classes is adapted from "The Case of Randy Harris" that appears in Smith et al. (2005) and "The Case of Ron Castleman" in Stein et al. (2000).

FIG. 2.1

Problems from Representing Shaded Areas of Rectangular Grids

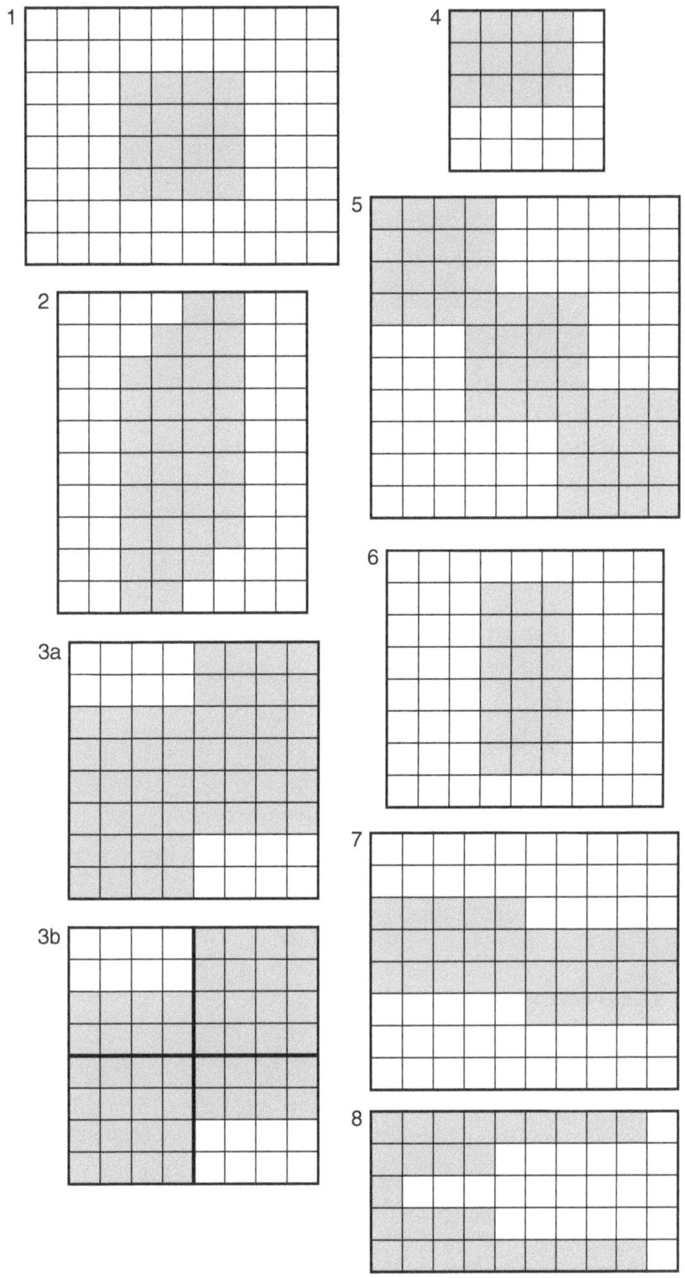

Ask students to explain their thinking and, even more important, to connect their explanation to the diagram. (Examples of student responses are given here and throughout the lesson.)

Marcus and Rashid noticed that each of the columns with filled-in squares represents half of the column. And because there are 10 columns, each column represents 10 percent of the whole. Since half of 10 percent is 5 percent, putting the four partial columns together gives a total of 20 percent.

Mario and Claire tried to determine what each square on the grid is in terms of percentages. They explained that since there are only 80 squares to be divided among 100 percent, each square would then get at least 1 percent, with another 20 percent still to be distributed. Each square would get an additional $\frac{1}{4}$ percent, giving a total of $1\frac{1}{4}$ percent per square. To describe the 16 shaded squares would be $16 \times 1\frac{1}{4}$ percent, or 20 percent. It may well be that no students use this strategy.

While you circulate around the classroom, you might ask one or more groups to think of the value of a shaded square when there are 80 squares on the grid. Then walk away to let them think about a solution. Avoid doing the thinking for the students.

Also, for this problem and others, ask students to relate their values for a fraction, decimal, and percentage to the grid as a way to check for reasonableness. Ask questions related to the size of the numbers: *Are they small and close to 0? Or large and close to 1? What other benchmark values can you use for comparison in order to determine whether your answers make sense and are reasonable?* For this problem, one-fifth, or 0.20, or 20 percent seems about right for the proportion of shaded squares compared to the whole.

A common misconception you may have occasion to clarify during the lesson is the difference between 0.20 and 0.20 percent. Looking at a grid of 100, where each square is 1 percent, gives a starting place to clarify this idea.

Explore

Now ask students to continue working with their partners on problems 2–8. For each problem they should be ready to explain their thinking and connect it to the diagram. Encourage all students to find more than one way to solve each problem. While they are working, observe students' solution strategies and have in mind students to invite to share. After they have had time to solve the first few problems, ask several more students to share solutions.

For number 3, Sharice noticed that rather than counting all the shaded squares, it was easier to determine that 16 squares were *not* shaded. The grid contains 64 squares, so this means that 48 *are* shaded. Since 48/64 is reducible to 3/4, she knows that the decimal would be 0.75 and the percentage would be 75.

Owen had a slightly different approach. He noticed that by drawing lines dividing the grid into four sections, he could easily "see" the quarters. Two were filled in, and combining the shaded parts of the other two filled in another quarter for a total of 3/4 filled. (See shape 3b.)

After looking at several more problems, collect all the different strategies described by the class. State these strategies in writing and post them in a prominent place for all to see. Use your students' names. This list will be helpful for the rest of the lesson. Examples are given here.

Mario and Claire's method: Since the whole grid represents 100 percent, find out what percentage is represented by each square, and multiply this number by the number of shaded squares.

Marcus and Rashid's method: Figure out how many rows or columns are taken up by the shaded squares, and if there are 10 rows or 10 columns, find out how many 10ths are filled by the shaded squares if they are all put together.

Sharice and Owen's method: Examine the diagram for other unique features, such as visualizing grid 3 as being divided into four subsquares, of which three are filled.

Ask students to complete the rest of the problems using the diagrams rather than any rules. Remind them that several strategies are listed; they are free to find and use others as well. Some students may need clarification about what is the unit in each case and the meaning of the decimal and percent notation.

Solutions for Representing Shaded Areas of Rectangular Grids

1. *1/5, 0.2, 20%*
2. *17/40, 0.425, 42.5%*
3. *3/4, 0.75, 75%*
4. *12/25, 0.48, 48%*
5. *23/50, 0.46, 46%*
6. *1/4, 0.25, 25%*
7. *3/8, 0.375, 37.5%*
8. *27/50, 0.54, 54%*

When you have finished a discussion of all eight problems in part 1, take some time to summarize the methods the students have used and some of the variations on those methods. This could be either a summary for part 1 or an introduction at the beginning of part 2.

"Teachers focus students' attention on the structure or essential features of the mathematical ideas that appear, regardless of the representation." (NCTM 2014, p. 29)

Extend

Propose the following problem to students. (It is not on either of the activity sheets.)

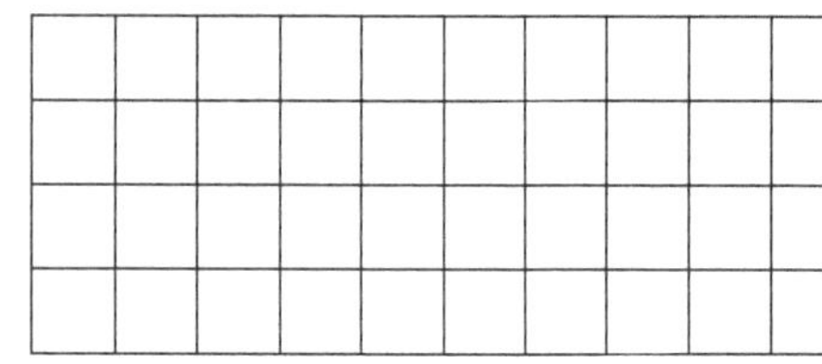

Shade six small squares in the rectangle shown here.

Using the diagram, explain how to determine each of the following:

a. The percentage of the area that is shaded
b. The decimal part of the area that is shaded
c. The fractional part of the area that is shaded

This will introduce students to the part of the activity where they do the shading, which is more demanding. Resist any temptation to "help" students by asking them to determine the fraction first, because that reduces the cognitive demand considerably. How they place the six shaded squares will make a difference in solving the problem. Encourage struggling students to try a different arrangement, and also to refer to the methods used in part 1 of the activity.

"... explicitly encourage students to persevere; find ways to support students without removing all the challenges in a task." (NCTM 2014, p. 49)

Examples of approaches, always using the diagram, are the following:

1. Determine that each square has a value of $2\frac{1}{2}$ percent. Because six squares are shaded, multiplying $2\frac{1}{2} \times 6$ gives a total of 15 percent. This works for a random scattering of shaded squares as well as a more orderly placement.
2. Placing four of the six squares in the first column and the other two in the second allows a student to think in terms of percentages. Because there are 10 columns, each has a value of 10 percent. One column of shaded squares is 10 percent, and the second, which is half full, is half of that, or 5 percent, giving a total of 15 percent.
3. Place the six shaded squares in the first two rows, three in each row, as shown in the diagram method 3. This can be called the "postage stamp" arrangement. Then partition the figure into six corresponding parts. All six parts together comprise 90 percent, and the last column is 10 percent. So that shaded part is 1/6 of 90 percent, which is 15 percent.

These three strategies roughly correspond to the three methods given earlier. [*Solutions: 15* percent, *0.15, 6/40 or 3/20*]

Distribute the sheet Shading Areas of Rectangular Grids and ask students to work through the three problems. All the work done thus far should enable most students to work independently on these problems. For this set, it is helpful to have two pairs of students work together, with each pair starting separately and then consulting with the other pair after a time. Each of the methods discussed earlier are possibilities for one or more of the problems.

FIG. 2.2

Two methods for placing six squares on the grid

Method 2

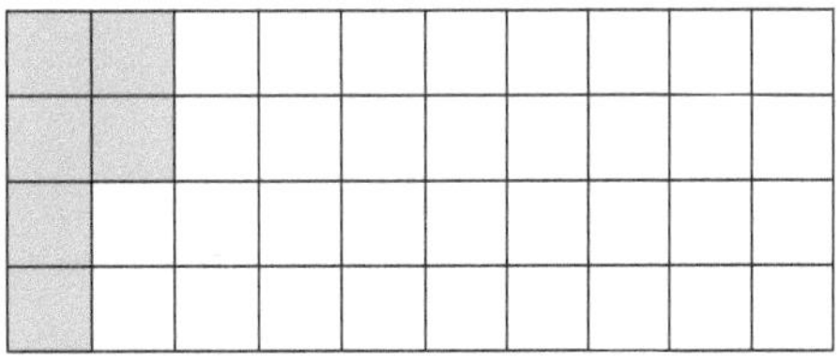

Method 3

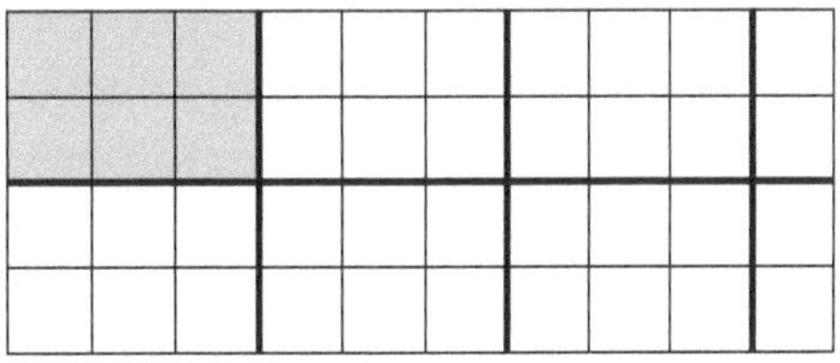

Other problems you could pose, possibly as a short quiz or exit slip, are these:

- Is 1/5 greater than 25 percent? [*No, 1/5 is equal to 20 percent.*]
- What is the order, from smallest to largest, of this set of numbers: 1/8, 10 percent, 1/9, and 0.11? [*10 percent, 0.11, 1/9, 1/8*]

Solutions for Shading Areas of Rectangular Grids

1. *a. Students' choices of areas to shade will vary, but they should cover 58/80 of the rectangle. The diagram shows one example.*

   b. 29/40 of the area is shaded.

   c. 72.5 percent of the area is shaded.

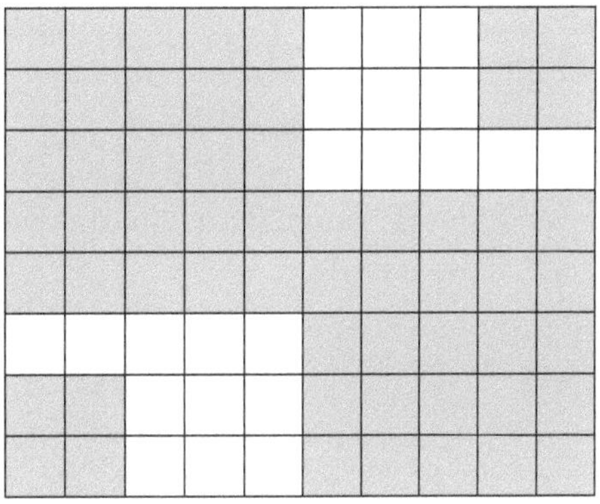

2. *a. Students' choices of areas to shade will vary, but they should cover 36/96 of the rectangle. The diagram shows one example.*

   b. 37.5 percent of the area is shaded.

   c. 0.375 of the area is shaded.

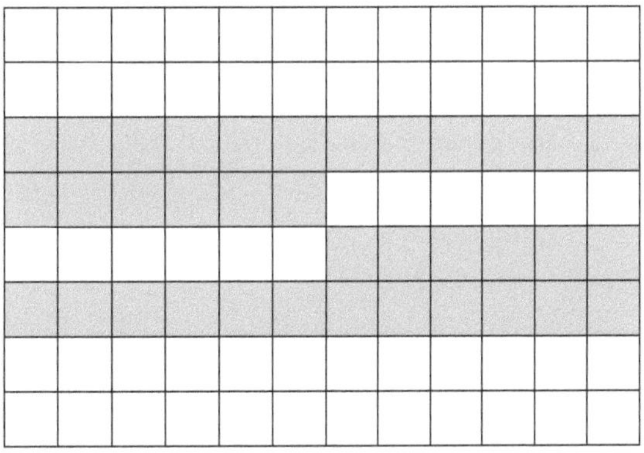

3. *a. Students' choices of areas to shade will vary, but they should cover 63/72 of the rectangle. The diagram shows one example.*

   b. 7/8 of the area is shaded.

   c. 0.875 of the area is shaded.

Susan Lamon (2001) analyzes the teaching of fractions and discusses the research indicating that students' understanding of meanings and operations with rational numbers is greatly enriched when instruction goes beyond the predominant part-whole approach. Fraction models include these:

- Part/whole: 2 parts out of 3 equal parts
- Ratios and rates: 2 parts per 3 parts
- Operator: 2/3 of something
- Quotient: 2 divided by 3
- Measurement: 2 (1/3 units)

The following problems from Lamon (2001) illustrate these various models for rational numbers. They are challenging, but they encourage students to have a broad and flexible approach to rational numbers.

1. Does the shaded area [of the circle] show 1 (3/8 pie), 3 (1/8 pies), or $1\frac{1}{2}$ (1/4 pies)? Does it matter?

2. You have 16 candies. You divide them into 4 equal-size groups, select one group, and make it three times its size. What single expression would have accomplished the same result?

3. You have taken only one drink of juice, represented by the unshaded area in the jar. How much of your day's supply, consisting of two bottles of juice, do you have left?

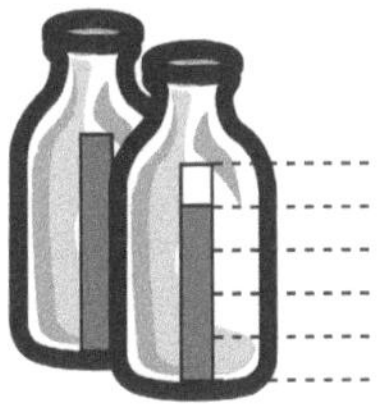

4. If it takes 9 people $1\frac{1}{2}$ hours to do a job, how long will it take 6 people to do it?
5. Without using common denominators, name three fractions between 7/9 and 7/8.
6. Yesterday Alicia jogged 2 laps around the track in 5 minutes, and today she jogged 3 laps around the track in 8 minutes. On her faster day, assuming that she could maintain her pace, how long would it have taken her to do 5 laps?
7. Here are the dimensions of some photos: (a) 9 cm × 10 cm, (b) 10 cm × 12 cm, (c) 6 cm × 8 cm, (d) 5 cm × 6.5 cm, and (e) 8 cm × 9.6 cm. Which one of them might be an enlargement of which other one?

These are challenging problems; do not expect all students to solve all of them.

"When rules and procedures are not learned with meaning, students forget them or do not always realize when to use them. However, when children are accustomed to thinking and reasoning without rules, which numbers they are given makes little difference." (Lamon 2001, p. 16)

Solutions to problems 1–7

1. Yes, it matters. The picture shows 3 (1/8 pies). Children cognitively differentiate the three quantities named here. At the abstract symbolic level, the quantities are indistinguishable, but in instruction, where contexts should be used to build an understanding of fractions, saying that these are the same contradicts children's intuitive understanding.
2. Dividing by 4 and then multiplying the result by 3 is the same as multiplying by 3/4.
3. The 1/5 bottle that you drank is 1/10 of your juice supply, so 9/10 remains.
4. If the number of people is $\frac{2}{3}$ the original number, the time is $\frac{3}{2}$ the original time because the number of people working and the time it takes to do a job are inversely related. It will take 6 people $2\frac{1}{4}$ hours to do the job.
5. A number of strategies are possible here. For example, 7/9 and 7/8 can be represented as 70/90 and 70/80, and three values between the two fractions might be 70/87, 70/85, and 70/83.

6. Yesterday, Alicia jogged $\frac{2}{5}$ of a lap per minute, and today she jogged $\frac{3}{8}$ of a lap per minute. At yesterday's rate, it would take her $12\frac{1}{2}$ minutes to do 5 laps.
7. Ratios of corresponding sides show that (b) is an enlargement of (e).

SUMMARY

In this lesson students have approached equivalent representations of fractions, decimals, and percentages using various-sized grids as the basis for the visual representation of rational numbers. This leads them to think deeply about the meaning of each form of number. They develop flexibility in solving problems and understanding various forms of rational numbers by using multiple strategies to solve the problems.

In the second part of the lesson, we see that reversing the direction of the mathematical activities increases both the complexity of the problem and the extent to which students can enrich their concepts of the various forms of the numbers. Students are asked to begin with a fraction, decimal, or percent and to represent it on a nonstandard grid—that is, one with a number of squares other than 100. This causes them to wrestle with the basic meaning of the multiple forms of rational numbers, leading to a better understanding of ideas and relationships.

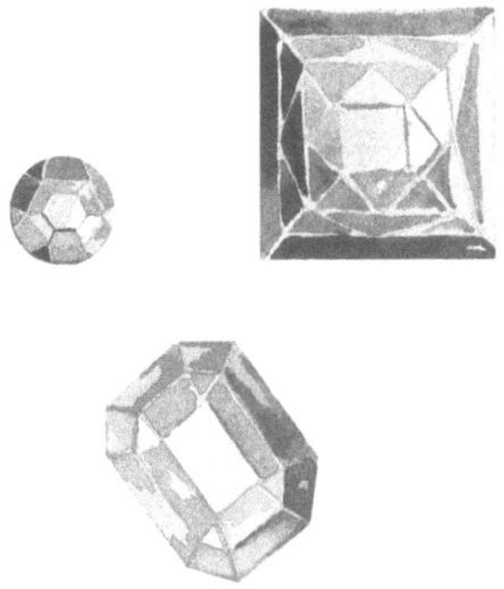

3

Rates and Unit Rates

OVERVIEW

This activity focuses on the meaning and use of rates. The notion of a rate is a significant concept encountered throughout school mathematics and used extensively in commercial and personal applications. We frequently encounter rates in our everyday lives, from common uses in conversation—"At this rate, we won't be home until it's dark!"—to the posted prices we see, such as for gasoline ($2.599 per gallon), to the use of rates in comparing prices at a food store—"Is the five-pound package of flour a better buy than the two-pound bag?" Throughout this activity, you and your students will review the concepts and calculations of rates and then focus on using unit rates for making comparisons.

Derived from "Using a Unit Rate to Solve Problems" in *Navigating through Number and Operations in Grades 6–8* (NCTM 2006b, pp. 104–6).

> *"Many concepts encountered in the middle grades involve proportions, including similarity, the relationship between the circumference and diameter of a circle, and probability."* (NCTM 2006b, p. 75)

Proportional reasoning is at the foundation of the concept of rate, and students' middle-grades mathematics experiences are typically designed to reinforce and extend students' developing knowledge of ratios and proportions. Rates and unit rates are an important component of that middle-grades focus.

GOALS

- Discuss what is meant by a rate.
- Identify rates in contextual situations.
- Calculate unit rates and use unit rates for comparisons.

MATERIALS NEEDED

Copies of the activity sheet Using a Unit Rate to Solve Problems for each student

Calculators

Engage

Your students may or may not have been formally introduced to the concept of a rate in mathematics. The discussion here illustrates how you might engage your students to help them review, as well as to help you assess, what they already know about rates.

> *"Effective teaching of mathematics uses purposeful questions to assess and advance students' reasoning and sense making about important mathematical ideas and relationships."* (NCTM 2014, p. 35)

To begin, arrange your students in small groups or, alternatively, conduct an all-class discussion.

Ms. G: Here are several statements that share a common mathematical theme (see table 3.1).

Table 3.1
Here's a 5-pound sack of potatoes selling for $3.49.
Sonny's mom drives a commercial truck across the country. She told Sonny that last week she drove 48 hours and logged 2,688 miles.
Lonnie took a keyboarding test and typed 384 words in 8 minutes.
Last week, I saw a sign that advertised unleaded gasoline for $1.979 per gallon.

Ms. G: What do you notice about the information in these statements?

Fritz: There's a comparison going on in each statement. Like, in the first one, the statement compares pounds of potatoes to some amount of money.

Ms. G: Is Fritz correct? What are the other comparisons here?

Eddie: Well, in the second statement, there's info about hours driven and miles driven.

Laurie: In the third one, the statement looks at the number of typed words and time in minutes.

Ms. G: How about the last one?

Syd: I think it includes information about the cost of gasoline and amount of gasoline.

Ms. G: So, someone who's not chimed in yet, give me another example of a statement that would fit in with all of these. Ken?

Ken: I'm on the track team, and we talk about how many laps we run and the time to do that. Yesterday, Connie ran 10 laps and it took her 12.5 minutes.

Lisa: My dad's on a special diet because of some health conditions. He mentioned the other day that the doctor wants him to eat 1,200 calories per day this month.

Ms. G: Those are both good examples. Let's add them to our original examples (see table 3.2).

Table 3.2

Here's a 5-pound sack of potatoes selling for $3.49.
Sonny's mom drives a commercial truck across the country. She told Sonny that last week she drove 48 hours and logged 2,688 miles.
Lonnie took a keyboarding test and typed 384 words in 8 minutes.
Last week, I saw a sign that advertised unleaded gasoline for $1.979 per gallon.
Yesterday, Connie ran 10 laps and it took her 12.5 minutes.
Lisa's dad eats about 1,200 calories per day.

Ms. G: So, it sounds like all of these statements are making some sort of comparison. Do you notice anything different among the statements?

Kyle: Well, it's pretty obvious, but each of the comparisons is different. I mean, the stuff being compared is different in each statement and so are the numbers.

Ms. G: Good point Kyle. Anything else?

Jan: It seems there's something different about Lisa's example and the gasoline example compared to the others. Those two just look or sound different.

Ms. G: What do the rest of you think about what Jan just said?

Eddie: I noticed that, too. I think the difference is that only one of the things in each of those two statements has a number in it, but in the others, there are two numbers. Like, with the potatoes statement, there's five pounds and there's $3.49. In Lisa's example, there is one number—1,200 calories.

Ms. G: Is Eddie accurate here? Just one number?

Sissy: Well, maybe yes and maybe no! Lisa's statement only shows one number, but wouldn't it be the same if it read, "Lisa's dad eats about 1,200 calories per 1 day"?

Ms. G:	And what about the gasoline statement? Same thing?
Jorge:	Yes, it would be, "Last week, I saw a sign that advertised unleaded gasoline for \$1.979 per 1 gallon."
Ms. G:	Can someone state another example like that?
Sharon:	How about, "During the summer, Eric mows lawns. He charges \$25 per lawn."

This discussion highlights the focus of this activity: mathematical rates. A *rate* is a comparison, using a ratio, of two quantities where the quantities are described using units. Referring to the first example in the tables earlier, $\frac{5}{3.49}$ is a ratio but without units. When we write or say $\frac{5 \text{ pounds}}{\$3.49}$, we still have a ratio, but more particularly, we call it a rate, because the quantities have units associated with them—in this case, pounds and dollars. Of course, we could have written a different rate using the same quantities, namely, $\frac{\$3.49}{5 \text{ pounds}}$. Thus, we see that when given two quantities (with units) to compare, we can write two rates.

Typically, when we speak of such rates, we use a "this-per-that" pattern. Again, using the earlier example, we can say "five pounds per \$3.49" as well as "\$3.49 per five pounds." If we focus only on the units of comparison, the first is expressed in "pounds per dollars" and the second as "dollars per pounds."

Lisa's example and the example about the cost of gasoline focus on a particular type of rate often used for making comparisons, estimations, and predictions—that of a *unit rate*. A unit rate compares a certain quantity to one unit of another quantity. The gasoline example compares dollars to pay for 1 gallon of gasoline; Lisa's example compares 1,200 calories to 1 day. We would say, "Gasoline costs \$1.979 per gallon" and "The diet requires 1,200 calories per day."

Now is a good time to solidify these definitions with your students. Some students may be familiar with rates and unit rates, and others may not recognize those terms. To reinforce these ideas, you can have students create their own rates and unit rates, different from those in table 3.2. Here are more examples, should you need some (see table 3.3).

Table 3.3

The bug took 12 seconds to travel 4 cm.	12 seconds per 4 cm	$\frac{12 \text{ seconds}}{4 \text{ cm}}$
Hallie drank 600 ml of water on her bike ride of 20 km.	600 ml per 20 km	$\frac{600 \text{ ml}}{20 \text{ km}}$
Sixty hot dogs were eaten by the 45 campers.	60 hot dogs per 45 campers	$\frac{60 \text{ hot dogs}}{45 \text{ campers}}$
The grocery store advertised 3 pints of blueberries for \$2.	3 pints per \$2	$\frac{3 \text{ pints}}{\$2}$

To wrap up the Engage portion of the activity, or to launch the Explore portion, ask your students this question: *What would we need to do to represent a* rate *as an equivalent* unit rate? *Said another way, by example, could we express "The bug took 12 seconds to travel 4 cm" as a unit rate, and how do we do that?*

Explore

Again, arranging your students in small groups, ask them to discuss the question just posed.

Ms. G: What would we need to do to represent a *rate* as an equivalent *unit rate*? By way of example, in your small group, try to express "12 seconds per 4 cm" as a unit rate, and be prepared to describe how you did that.

Walk around your room, responding to questions and gathering evidence to use in a subsequent all-class discussion. After several minutes—or when most or all groups have a response—regroup as an entire class.

"As different ways to think about proportions are considered and discussed, teachers should help students recognize when and how various ways of reasoning about proportions might be appropriate to solve problems." (NCTM 2000, p. 221)

Ms. G: Someone tell me what your group determined.

Leona: We noticed that for "12 seconds per 4 cm" we'd want 1 cm instead of 4 cm, so we need to determine the number of seconds that would make these two rates equal:

$$\frac{12 \text{ seconds}}{4 \text{ cm}} \text{ and } \frac{?? \text{ seconds}}{1 \text{ cm}}$$

We solved this kind of problem when we worked with fractions. I think we called them equivalent fractions. To go from 4 cm to 1 cm, we divide by 4, so we gotta use the same operation between the numerators: 12 seconds divided by 4 is 3 seconds, so

$$\frac{12 \text{ seconds}}{4 \text{ cm}} \text{ and } \frac{3 \text{ seconds}}{1 \text{ cm}}$$

are two rates that are the same, and the second one is a unit rate.

Fritz: I think we did sort of the same thing in a different way, cuz we noticed we needed to compare some number of seconds to 1 cm. We drew a picture and showed 12 seconds on top and 4 cm below (figure 3.1a).

Fritz: Then we cut up the 4-cm part into equal 1-cm pieces (figure 3.1b) and did the same on the top, realizing we needed these to be equal 3-second portions (figure 3.1c). So, the unit rate is 3 seconds per 1 cm.

Ms. G: Any others?

Nina: Well, we just divided 12 by 4, kinda like reducing a fraction.

Ms. G: So, what's going on with these different methods you all have described?

Monty: I think that going from the rate we have to a unit rate, you need 1 in the denominator of the equivalent-fraction unit rate. To get that, just divide the numerator by the denominator in the fraction representing the original rate.

FIG. 3.1

Representing a unit rate

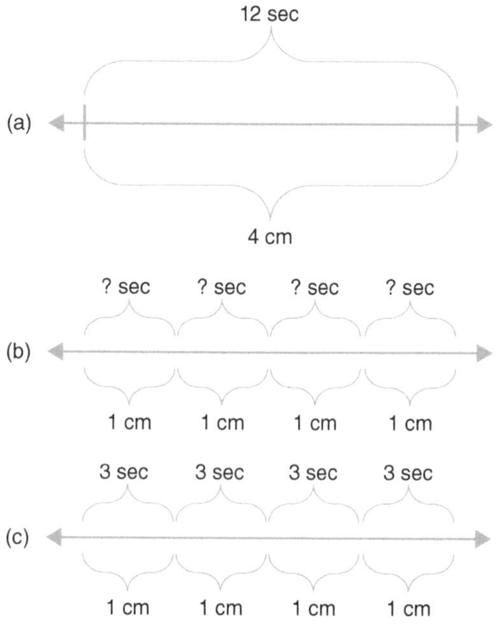

Your students may have come up with these same sorts of methods, and with others as well. The key element is in Monty's explanation: To move from a "this-per-that" rate to an equivalent unit rate, we have to divide—separate, apportion—the "that" quantity (denominator) into one-unit chunks. The number of one-unit chunks is just the original quantity in the denominator, so we separate the "this" quantity (numerator) into that same number of chunks. Division is an accurate and efficient tool for getting this done.

Table 3.4 shows the unit rates associated with the information in table 3.3. You can use this with your students, asking them to return to table 3.3 and calculate the unit rate for each rate shown in the table. Be sure to discuss with students their methods for determining these unit rates.

Table 3.4

The bug took 12 seconds to travel 4 cm.	$\frac{\text{12 seconds}}{\text{4 cm}}$	$\frac{\text{3 seconds}}{\text{1 cm}}$	3 seconds per cm
Hallie drank 600 ml of water on her bike ride of 20 km.	$\frac{\text{600 ml}}{\text{20 km}}$	$\frac{\text{30 ml}}{\text{1 km}}$	30 ml per km
Sixty hot dogs were eaten by the 45 campers.	$\frac{\text{60 hot dogs}}{\text{45 campers}}$	$\frac{1\frac{1}{3}\text{ hot dogs}}{\text{1 camper}}$	$1\frac{1}{3}$ hot dogs per camper
The grocery store advertised 3 pints of blueberries for $2.	$\frac{\text{3 pints}}{\$2}$	$\frac{1\frac{1}{2}\text{ pints}}{\$1}$	$1\frac{1}{2}$ pints per dollar

At this stage of the activity, you want to be sure that your students know the meaning of rate and unit rate, that they can determine a unit rate from a given rate, and that they can explain their calculations. Some of your students may have noticed or commented on the usefulness of these unit rates. If not, now is the time to ask.

Ms. G: So, let's look at one of these unit rates: $1\frac{1}{3}$ hot dogs per camper. In your small group, discuss the meaning of this unit rate.

Move among the groups to address questions and to gather evidence for eventual discussion.

Ms. G: Kim, what did your group decide?

Kim: My group thought this unit rate was some sort of average. We don't know that each and every camper ate exactly $1\frac{1}{3}$ hot dogs. In fact, that would be quite unlikely! What we do know from the unit rate is that, on average, each camper ate $1\frac{1}{3}$ hot dogs.

Nigel: We looked at it like that as well, thinking about dividing up the 60 hot dogs so every one of the 45 campers had exactly the same amount. That would be the unit rate, $1\frac{1}{3}$ hot dogs per camper.

Ms. G: And how might we use this unit rate, once we have an idea about what it means?

Chris: Well, if you're ordering hot dogs for another event, the unit rate might help. If you were expecting 300 people, and you figured they'd be eating hot dogs at the same rate as the campers, this could give you an estimate: 300 people × $1\frac{1}{3}$ hot dogs per person tells us we'd estimate a need for 400 hot dogs.

You can also use this discussion to help your students recognize that every comparison gives us two rates and each rate has an associated unit rate that could serve different purposes. The unit rate applied earlier, $1\frac{1}{3}$ hot dogs per camper, was used to estimate the number of hot dogs required for 300 people. If our question had been to estimate the number of people that could be served by a known number of hot dogs, the other unit rate, $\frac{3}{4}$ camper per hot dog, would have been more useful. For instance, if the camp's stockpile included 200 hot dogs, then we could estimate that 200 hot dogs × $\frac{3}{4}$ camper per hot dog, or 150 campers, could be served.

Here is another example to use with your students. The unit rate "3 seconds per cm" tells us that it takes 3 seconds to move 1 cm. This unit rate could help us address questions such as *How long would it take to go 50 cm?* [*150 seconds*]

The original rate, $\frac{12 \text{ seconds}}{4 \text{ cm}}$, can also be written as $\frac{4 \text{ cm}}{12 \text{ seconds}}$ with an associated unit rate of $\frac{1}{3}$ cm per second. This unit rate can be used to address questions such as *How far will the bug crawl in 10 seconds?* [$3\frac{1}{3}$ *cm*]

Your discussions and your students' practice have helped prepare them for the tasks described on the three activity sheets titled Using a Unit Rate to Solve Problems (see figure 3.2). For each of the three contextual situations, a description is given that includes two quantities. Students are to use those quantities to identify the two possible rates we could write and then to determine the unit rate associated with each of the two rates. Concluding questions with each contextual situation focus on the use of the unit rates. Students must select an appropriate unit rate, use it, and explain their choice.

You can use these activity sheets in a variety of ways. You might distribute one sheet at a time to individuals or small groups, discussing students' responses one sheet at a time. You could also use the first two sheets for reinforcement and then use the third sheet as an assessment tool.

FIG. 3.2

Unit-rate problems

Using a Unit Rate to Solve Problems

1. Marcus runs around the track every day after school. He believes that with practice he can be a track star. He can run 12 laps around the school's track in 30 minutes.

2. Michelle, an exchange student from France, will be in the United States for the next four months. In France, she buys everything in euros. When she came to the United States, she had to exchange her euros for U.S. dollars. She went to the bank and exchanged her money at the rate of 4.5 euros for 5 dollars.

3. The Martinez family is planning to drive from New York to Florida during winter break to visit the Kennedy Space Center. The scale on the map that they are using to plan their trip is 2.5 cm = 125 miles.

Extend

A natural extension to this activity is to use unit rates to compare situations that use the same pair of quantities. For instance, an example included in the introduction to this activity asked: *Is the five-pound package of flour a better buy than the two-pound bag?* Of course, we need more information here—the price of each bag of flour. Let's suppose the five-pound package sells for \$3.49 and the two-pound bag for \$1.59. Which bag is the better buy—assuming "better buy" means costs the least per pound? This assumption is important, because it indicates we need a "dollars per pound" unit rate for each bag of flour.

We can answer that question by comparing the unit rates, in dollars per pound, for each of the two bags of flour. Table 3.5 summarizes the calculation information.

Table 3.5

Five pounds of flour for \$3.49	\$3.49 / 5 pounds	\$0.698 / 1 pound	about 70¢ per pound
Two pounds of flour for \$1.59	\$1.59 / 2 pounds	\$0.795 / 1 pound	about 80¢ per pound

The unit rates show us that the price per pound for the five-pound bag of flour is less than the price per pound for the two-pound bag. This tells us the five-pound bag is a better buy, assuming you need or want five pounds of flour. If all you need is two pounds and the rest cannot be used, price per pound is not the only factor to consider in making your decision. Table 3.6 shows additional questions, with solutions, to ask your students as a way to motivate unit-rate comparisons.

Table 3.6

Two sizes of apple juice are on sale. A 16-ounce bottle sells for \$3.39, and a 25-ounce container is \$4.59. Which container has a lower cost per ounce?	$\frac{\$3.39}{16 \text{ ounces}} = \frac{\$0.2119}{1 \text{ ounce}}$ and $\frac{\$4.59}{25 \text{ ounces}} = \frac{\$0.1836}{1 \text{ ounce}}$	The 25-ounce container has a lower cost per ounce. On that basis, the 25-ounce container is a better buy.
Last week Fran worked out on her bicycle on Monday and Thursday. On Monday, she rode 80 km in 2 hours and 45 minutes. On Thursday, it took her 1 hour and 50 minutes to cover 62 km. On which day did Fran ride 1 km in the shortest time?	$\frac{165 \text{ min}}{80 \text{ km}} = \frac{2.0625 \text{ min}}{1 \text{ km}}$ and $\frac{110 \text{ min}}{62 \text{ km}} = \frac{1.7742 \text{ min}}{1 \text{ km}}$	Fran rode 1 km at a faster rate on Thursday, because the unit rate for that day, 1.7742 minutes per km, is the smaller of the two unit rates.
Lonnie's sister is planning to rent an apartment next year. Currently, she's considering three apartments. One has 680 square feet of living space and rents for \$1,180 per month. A second apartment rents for \$1,350 per month and has 752 square feet. Her third option has 590 square feet, and its rent is \$1,075 per month. If we do not consider utilities, insurance, or other costs, which apartment has the smallest cost per square foot?	$\frac{\$1{,}180}{680 \text{ ft}^2} = \frac{\$1.735}{1 \text{ ft}^2}$ and $\frac{\$1{,}350}{752 \text{ ft}^2} = \frac{\$1.795}{1 \text{ ft}^2}$ and $\frac{\$1{,}075}{590 \text{ ft}^2} = \frac{\$1.822}{1 \text{ ft}^2}$	The apartment that rents for \$1,180 per month has the smallest cost per square foot.
Jackie and her brother were comparing their weights over time, as their parents kept measurements of height and weight for every birthday. On her 8th birthday, Jackie weighed 56 kg, and on her 13th birthday, she weighed 68 kg. Her brother weighed 42 kg on his 7th birthday and 59 kg on his 15th birthday. Whose growth rate was the greatest for the time spans shown?	$\frac{12 \text{ kg}}{5 \text{ years}} = \frac{2.4 \text{ kg}}{1 \text{ year}}$ and $\frac{17 \text{ kg}}{8 \text{ years}} = \frac{2.125 \text{ kg}}{1 \text{ year}}$	Jackie's growth rate in kg per year from her 8th birthday to her 13th birthday was greater than her brother's growth rate from his 7th birthday to his 15th birthday.

"Once you know how your students are thinking about proportions, you can guide them to explore all aspects of the multiplicative structure of proportion. As they expand their repertoire of solution techniques, they strengthen the connections among division, fractions, and rational numbers, and they lay the groundwork for working with slopes and rates of change in functions. You can help your students navigate their routes to reason." (Riehl and Steinthorsdottir 2014, p. 228)

SUMMARY

This activity was intended to help reinforce for students the concept of a rate and to use rates to determine and compare unit rates. Rates and unit rates serve an important purpose inside and out of the mathematics classroom, and during the middle grades, these concepts are part of students' development of proportional reasoning, a big idea in mathematics.

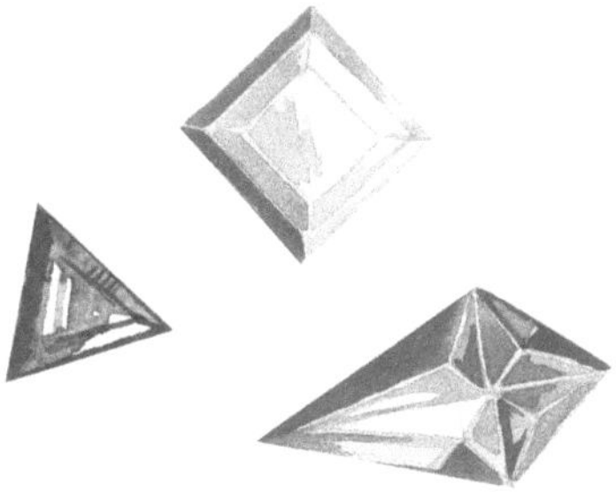

4

From Stories to Graphs and Graphs to Stories

OVERVIEW

The core of algebraic thinking focuses on relationships among quantities and the ways in which quantities change relative to one another. Algebraic thinking requires an understanding of patterns, relations, and functions; the ability to describe and model mathematical situations; and the ability to represent and analyze quantitative relationships and change in various contexts. Students in the middle grades explore patterns expressed in tables, graphs, words, or symbols, with an emphasis on patterns that exhibit linear relationships (constant rate of change). Throughout their lessons they should explore many examples of quantities that change and the graphs that represent those changes, answer questions about the relationships represented in the graphs, and learn to distinguish rate of change from accumulation (total amount of change). And although the emphasis will be on linear relationships, as students begin to develop an understanding of slope and y-intercept, they should also encounter nonlinear examples so that they learn to differentiate, at least informally, among patterns of change. The examples included in this Gem illustrate the type of discussions that should occur frequently and regularly throughout the mathematics program as middle-grades students mature mathematically.

Derived from "From Stories to Graphs" and "From Graphs to Stories" in *Navigating through Algebra in Grades 6–8* (NCTM 2001, pp. 27–35).

GOALS

- Identify the independent and dependent variables in problems.
- Sketch a graph to represent a story context that involves change over time.
- Describe the story context on the basis of a graph that depicts changes over time.

MATERIALS NEEDED

Copy of the activity sheet From Stories to Graphs for each student

Copy of the activity sheet From Graphs to Stories for each student

Graph paper

Engage

In life we frequently encounter situations in which two or more quantities change, and very often the change in one quantity affects the pattern of change in other quantities. Present the students with situations such as the following and have them discuss what is changing, how it is changing, and how change in one quantity affects changes in another. The italicized notes are representative of the responses they may give.

> *"The role of the teacher is to engage students in tasks that promote reasoning and problem solving and facilitate discourse that moves students toward shared understanding of mathematics."* (NCTM 2014, p. 11)

- You ride your bike for 30 minutes and cover 3 miles. You continue riding for another 30 minutes and cover a total of 6 miles. [*Time and distance are two quantities that are changing. The longer you ride, the greater the distance you cover, so distance depends on time. Since you covered 3 miles in each of the 30-minute segments, your speed or rate of pedaling was quite uniform.*]
- The volume of the sound you hear from the TV as you move away from it. [*Volume and distance are the changing quantities. The closer you are to the TV, the louder the sound; the farther you are, the lower the volume. The two quantities vary or change inversely—that is, the greater the distance, the lower the volume, and vice versa.*]
- The temperature of a cup of hot coffee that is left for 2 hours on the kitchen table. [*Time and temperature are both changing. As the time increases from when the coffee was poured, the temperature begins to decrease. But the temperature of the coffee will only decrease until it reaches room temperature; after that, temperature will remain constant even though time continues to increase.*]
- The speed of a car approaching a red light. [*Three things are changing in this situation: the speed of the car, the distance to the red light, and time. If the driver steps on the brake at a certain time, from then on, the speed of the car will decrease, as will the distance to the light.*]
- Make up other examples of your own, perhaps relating to recent classroom events or items in the news.

Explore

Select one of your examples and ask the students to consider how the changes would be represented in a graph. For example, consider the first scenario about bike riding. Pose questions such as these:

- What are the quantities that are changing, that is, the *variables*? [*distance and time*]
- When we graph two variables, we represent the independent variable on the horizontal axis, or x-axis, and the dependent variable on the vertical axis, or y-axis. In this situation, which variable should be represented on which axis? [*Time is the independent variable; it is represented on the* x-*axis. Distance is the dependent variable and is shown on the* y-*axis.*]

Allow time for the students to sketch a graph (see figure 4.1a). As you observe them working, check to be sure that they have selected a suitable scale for their graph and that the axes are correctly labeled. When their graphs are ready, continue the discussion:

- Call on someone to show their graph and explain how the key elements of the situation (3 miles in 30 minutes, 6 miles in 60 minutes) are represented on the graph. (See figure 4.1b.)
- What is the significance of the straight line in the graph? [*The straight line tells us that your rate or speed was quite constant since you covered the same distance, 3 miles, in each half-hour.*]
- What was the rate? [*6 miles per hour.*]
- Why does the line "go up" as you move to the right across the graph? [*As you move to the right on the graph, time increases; and as time increases, so does the distance traveled.*]
- What other information can you tell from the graph besides what is stated in the story? [*You can tell approximately how far you went in other times. For example, in 20 minutes you rode about 2 miles.*]

"Effective teaching of mathematics uses purposeful questions to assess and advance students' reasoning and sense making about important mathematical ideas and relationships." (NCTM 2014, p. 10)

FIG. 4.1A

Graph of bike ride

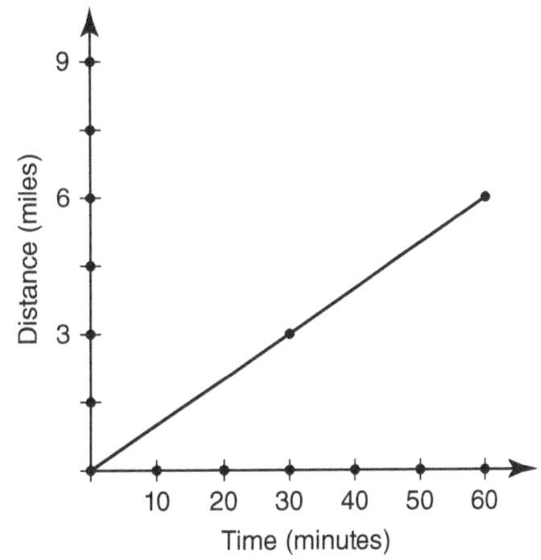

FIG. 4.1B

Graph of bike ride

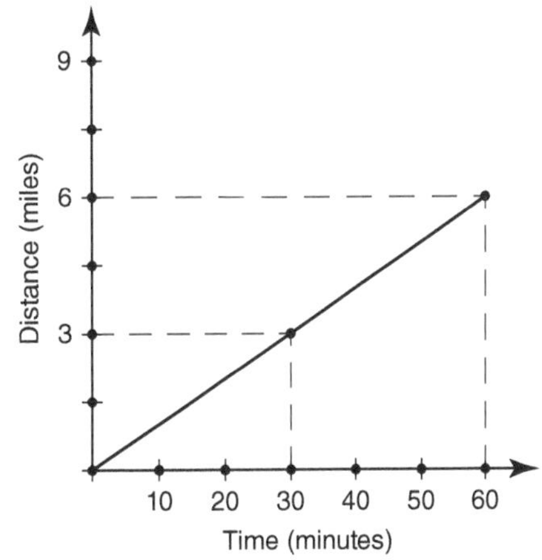

- Can we conclude that you rode exactly 1 mile every 10 minutes? [*No. We know only two things for sure: 3 miles in 30 minutes and 6 miles in 60 minutes. Along the route, you probably had variations in your speed, for example, going slower uphill and faster downhill. If we had more data points, we might see that the "line" is actually "wavier" than what we can show here.*]
- Pose various "What if?" questions and ask how the graph would change in each case. For example: What if you rode the 6 miles in less than 60 minutes? What if you rode the first 3 miles in 30 minutes as before, but then got tired and rode the last 3 miles at half that speed? What if you rode the same as in the original problem but stopped for a 10-minute rest after mile 3?

"Effective teaching of mathematics uses evidence of student thinking to assess progress toward mathematical understanding and to adjust instruction continually in ways that support and extend learning." (NCTM 2014, p. 10)

When the students have demonstrated a basic understanding of the relationship between the story and its graph and their ability to interpret and answer questions about the situation, distribute copies of the From Stories to Graphs activity sheet. Allow time for the students, working independently, to sketch a graph for each of the three stories presented, then have them share their graphs with a partner or in small groups. Call on students to explain how their graphs represent the changing situations and continue to ask "What if?" questions to assess their understanding of each problem. The three stories and a sample graph for each are shown here.

1. In a walking experiment, Josephine walked a total distance of 40 feet. At the halfway point, she had walked for 25 seconds. She stopped for 5 seconds to tie her shoe and then continued walking for 25 more seconds. Sketch a graph that shows Josephine's distance from the starting point over time. (See figure 4.2.)
2. You are gathering data in the school cafeteria from 8:00 a.m. to 3:00 p.m. Sketch a graph that tells a story about the number of cans of soda in a vending machine over that time. Write a paragraph that tells the same story in words. (See figure 4.3.)
3. You are mowing the lawn. As you mow, the amount of grass to be cut decreases. You mow at the same rate until about half the grass has been cut. Then you take a break for a while. Then, mowing at the same rate as before, you finish cutting the grass. Sketch a graph that shows how much uncut grass is left as you mow, take your break, and finish mowing. (See figure 4.4.)

FIG. 4.2

Graph of Josephine's walk

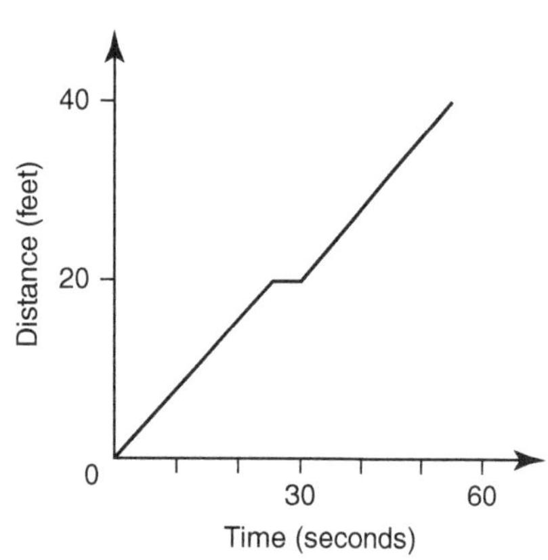

FIG. 4.3

The soda machine story

There is not much action right away, but then a few teachers come in to get sodas. Things continue to be slow; at various times, a student or two and a few teachers stop by for sodas. Then around 10:00 a.m. during a small rush between classes, several students get sodas. Just before noon, there is a steady stream of students and teachers visiting the soda machine. After lunch break is over, there is another lull. Then, at a class bell, there is another small rush for sodas right before the last class. Students are dismissed, and several stop to get sodas on their way out.

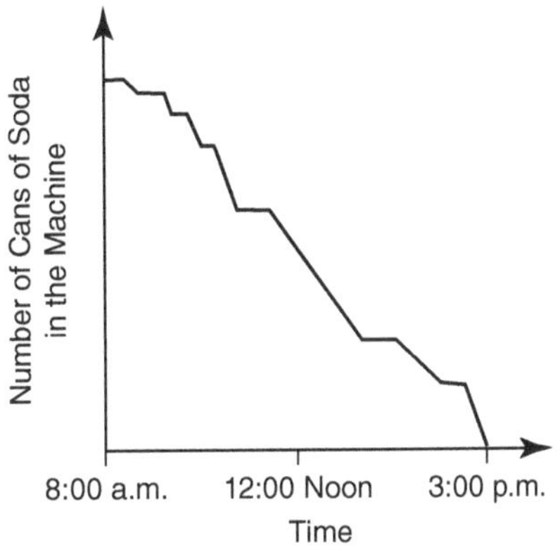

Problems such as these and the accompanying interpretation and discussion should be frequent occurrences throughout the curriculum; they are not merely a one-day lesson. Also, the analysis should flow both ways: from stories to graphs, as in the examples earlier, and from graphs to stories, as in the following problems. To begin that exploration, distribute copies of the From Graphs to Stories activity sheet and give the students time to discuss each problem and create appropriate stories that they will present and explain to the class. Sample stories for each of the four graphs are shown.

FIG. 4.4

Amount of uncut grass

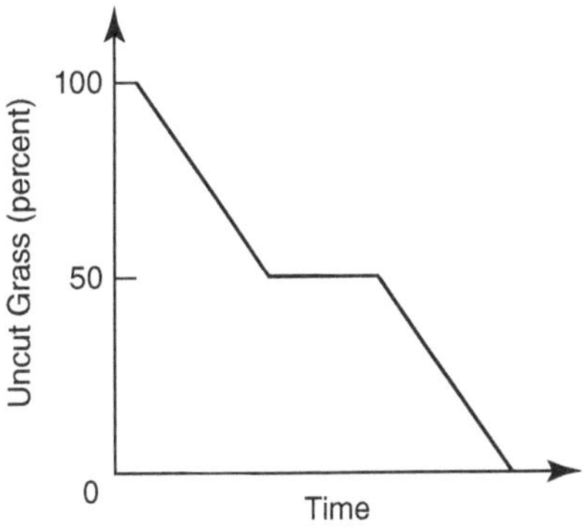

1. John and his father participate in a 100-meter race. John started the race 3 seconds after his father began to run. The graph provides information about how far John and his father ran over time. Write a story about who won the race; be descriptive about how the race was run. If the two lines describing how each person ran were parallel, what would the graph tell you about who won the race? (See figure 4.5.)
2. The graph in figure 4.6 represents the relationship between the profit and the amount of lemonade sold at a lemonade stand. Write a story about how the lemonade stand's profit is determined. Include an explanation of what is indicated when the line is below zero and when the line crosses the horizontal axis. (This graph assumes that the seller is not paid and that there is no overhead.)

FIG. 4.5

The 100-meter race

Both John and his father ran a steady pace for the duration of the race. John's father finished the race at about 17 seconds; John finished before his father, at about 16 seconds. If the two lines were parallel, it would mean that both John and his father had run the race at the same pace and completed it in the same amount of time. However, John's father would have won because he started before John.

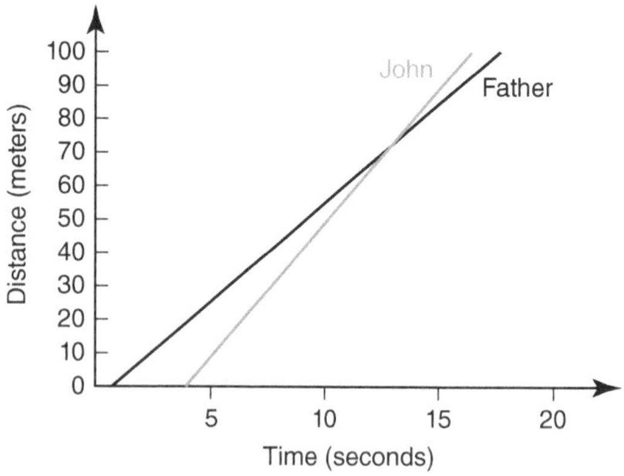

FIG. 4.6

Lemonade sales

The profit starts out below zero before there is any lemonade sold. This is because you need cups, lemons, sugar, ice cubes, and water to make the lemonade. Once glasses of lemonade are sold, there is a point when you have sold enough lemonade to pay for your costs (when the line crosses the horizontal axis). Then you start to make a profit. The profit decreases suddenly because you have to buy more supplies. Then you continue to make a profit at the same rate as before.

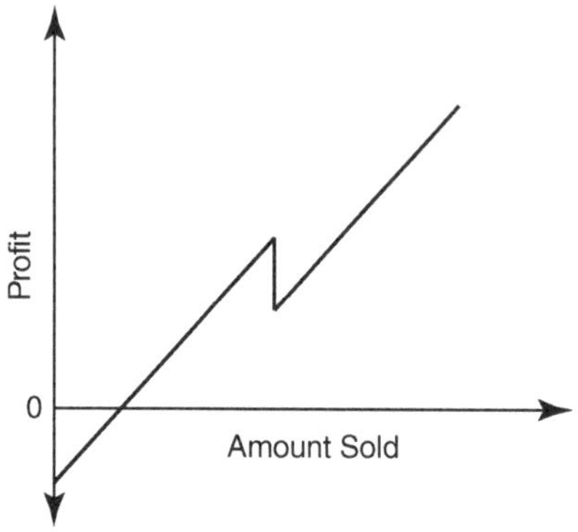

3. The graph in figure 4.7 represents a flag being raised on a flagpole. Write a story that describes what is happening to the flag, gives an estimate of the height of the flagpole, and explains the shape of the graph.
4. Graphs can be used to depict the story of a race. Here is a graph (figure 4.8) that represents a swimming race that occurred between two middle-grades students. Write a story that describes what happened in this race.

FIG. 4.7

Raising the flag

When you raise a flag, you pull steadily with both hands together for a short time, then move your hands up the rope that is used to raise the flag. The graph shows a steady pace at raising the flag in a cycle of pull-move hands-pull-move hands until the flag reaches the top of the flagpole. If we estimate that the flag is raised about three feet at each stage, the flagpole is about fifteen feet in height.

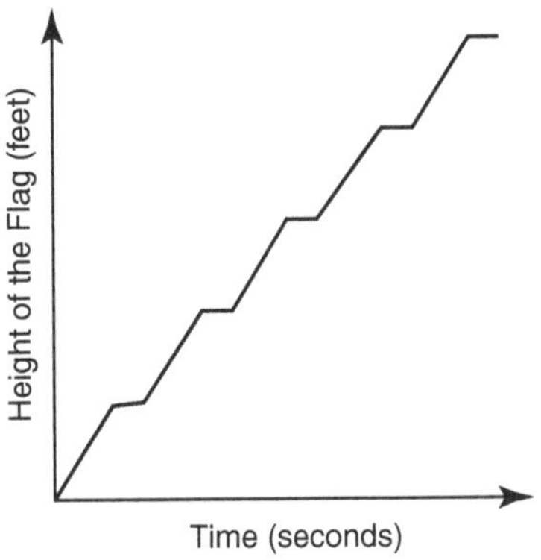

FIG. 4.8

The swimming meet

Cindy started off swimming faster than Kelly; she was ahead of Kelly when they completed the first lap across the pool. On the way back, in her second lap, Cindy slowed down and completed the race in more than 60 seconds. Kelly seemed to spurt ahead, moving past Cindy near the end of the race, and finishing the race in under 60 seconds.

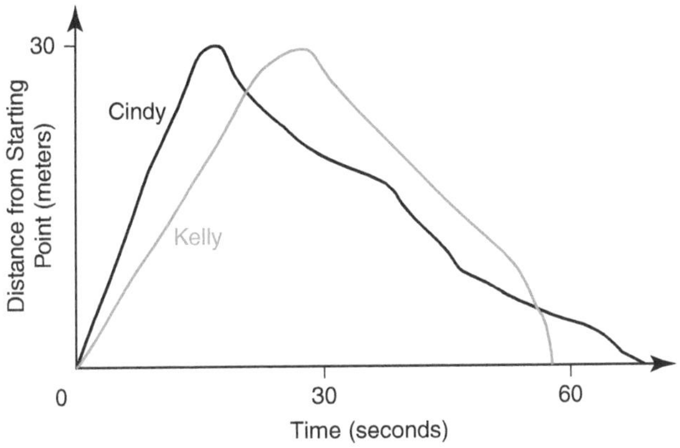

Extend

Engage the students frequently in discussions such as those earlier as they progress through the middle grades. They should also have experience creating their own stories and graphs, which can be posted in the classroom and shared as challenges to classmates.

There are rich opportunities here to collaborate with science teachers on making sense of experiments that students can do to gather data, graph results, and explain phenomena.

For example, in physical science class, students might investigate Hooke's law (figure 4.9) by conducting the following experiment:

> Hang a spring from a hook and measure the length of the spring. Now add one weight (one washer) and again measure the length of the spring. Continue to add one washer at a time until you have 10 or 12 sets of data. (Stop, however, if the spring nears its elastic limit.) Do the entire experiment two more times using different springs. Try to select springs that appear to have different stiffness. Organize all of your data first in a table and then in a graph. What do the results tell you about the relationship between weight and stretch? What are the variables in this situation? Which are the dependent and independent variables?

FIG. 4.9

Hooke's law describes the relationship between the length of a spring and the amount of force applied to it

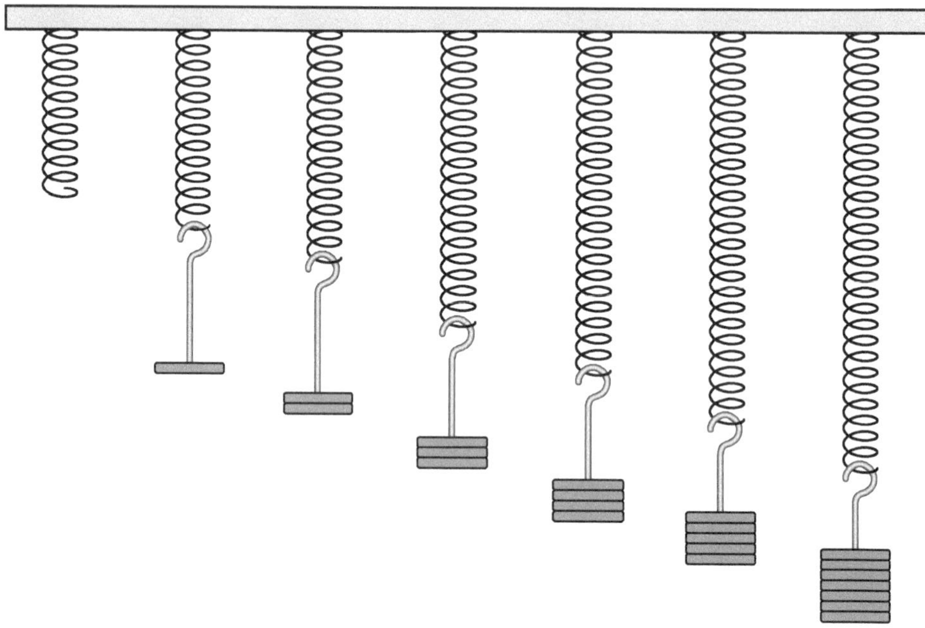

SUMMARY

Problems involving variables as changing quantities are common in middle-grades mathematics, and students should expect to ask and answer questions about such relationships, including these:

- What changes? What remains the same?
- How does it change? Over what time period? [*Rate of change*]
- What is the direction of change? [*Increasing or decreasing? Direct or inverse relationship?*]

- On what does the change depend?
- Is there a pattern to the change?
- What is the shape of the graph?

"Effective teaching of mathematics engages students in making connections among mathematical representations to deepen understanding of mathematics concepts and procedures and as tools for problem solving." (NCTM 2014, p. 10)

Contextualized problems such as those illustrated in this activity engage middle-grades students in exploring notions of dependence and independence as variables change in relation to one another and in recognizing the equivalence of graphical, tabular, symbolic, and verbal representations of those situations. As the students continue to mature mathematically, they will learn to use functions to model patterns of change, and they will acquire greater facility with linear equations and the ability to demonstrate how the values of slope and y-intercept affect the line. Although at this time the emphasis is on contexts that are modeled by linear relationships, students also explore examples of nonlinear relationships, and they use their models to develop and test conjectures, laying a foundation for later study of nonlinear functions.

5

Tiling Tubs and Plotting Land

OVERVIEW

As students move from a focus on arithmetic in the elementary grades toward an algebraic approach, generalizing in problem situations, there are several key components of their work.

Derived from "Tiling Tubs" and "Plotting Land" in *Navigating through Algebra in Grades 6–8* (NCTM 2001, pp. 63–65).

One key is to represent problem situations using expressions containing variables and numbers. This is best done from a problem in context, so the variable expressions can rise organically from the situation. Another key is to be able to determine when various expressions are equivalent, that is, when they name the same number no matter what value is substituted into the expression. A third critical key in recognizing equivalent expressions is the distributive property. This important property relates multiplication and addition and is of central importance to the study of algebra. It is not important at this point that students be able to name the property but that they gain experience with it and are able to use it correctly. Most students need lots of practice using this property.

Five representations of a problem

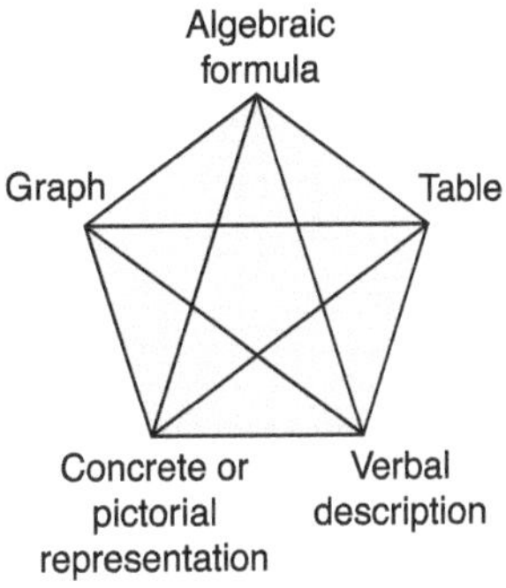

> *"In the middle grades, greater emphasis is placed on the relationships among the five representations of a problem."*
> (Navigating through Algebra in Grades 6–8, p. 59)

A primary means of giving every student access to problems such as these is having experiences with verbal, pictorial, and graphical representations prior to using algebraic symbols. There is ample room for this in the activity sheets.

For this activity, students should work in pairs with each student working independently but comparing and discussing answers as indicated.[1]

GOALS

- Write expressions to describe the relationship among variables in a situation.
- Determine when expressions are equivalent.
- Recognize and generate equivalent forms for simple algebraic expressions.
- Explore the use of the distributive property.

MATERIALS NEEDED

Tiling Tubs activity sheet for each student

Plotting Land activity sheet for each student

Graph paper

Blank paper

Engage

Imagine that you have a rectangle that has width W and length L. Tanya says the perimeter of the rectangle is $2L + 2W$. Carter claims it is $2(L + W)$. How could you convince them that these expressions are equivalent? [*Substituting any value for L and W yields the same result.*]

Suppose a neighbor has asked you to help her construct a tile border for her square backyard pool. She plans to use it for colorful fish. The border will be made of tiles that are 1 foot square. If the pool has sides of length 1 foot, how many tiles would you need for the border? Make a sketch on graph paper to help you figure it out. What if the sides were 2 feet? 3 feet? [*The answers are 8, 12, and 16 tiles.*]

FIG. 5.1

Square pool and border

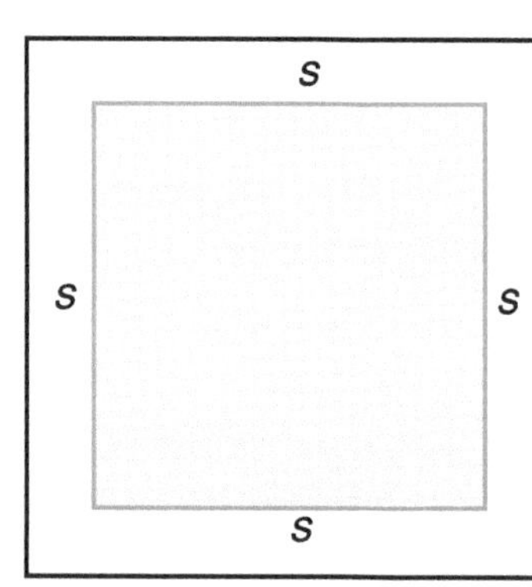

Explore

Your neighbor has not decided how large she wants to make the pool. Use the worksheet titled Tiling Tubs to help her.

As you circulate around the classroom while the students are working on the Tiling Tubs sheet, observe the various ways students have of representing and counting the tiles.

[1] This activity has been adapted from Lappan et al. (1998b, pp. 20–30).

Make note of students with differing representations. When students have finished, choose students to present a variety of expressions to the class. You can also do this by taking photos of their work and projecting them. In either case, each student should explain their representation to the class, using a diagram or other means to illustrate and justify that their representation does represent the tile border.

> *"Teachers must decide what aspect of a task to highlight, how to organize and orchestrate the work of the students, what questions to ask to challenge those with varied levels of experience, and how to support students without taking over the process of thinking for them and thus eliminating the challenge."* (NCTM 2000, p. 19)

These explanations should be offered one at a time, and this is a good opportunity for students who are more reticent to represent their findings. You might also have some students present in pairs, with a partner for support. There is no required method of sequencing, but you might start with the students' most common expressions first or with the simplest explanations, such as Case 1 and Case 2 presented next. Here are seven possible expressions with their accompanying diagrams (figure 5.2). If some are not generated by any of your students, when they finish their reports, introduce those they did not generate as being the work of students in other classes and ask them to try to figure out what that student might have been thinking.

FIG. 5.2

Seven visions of the pool-tiling problem

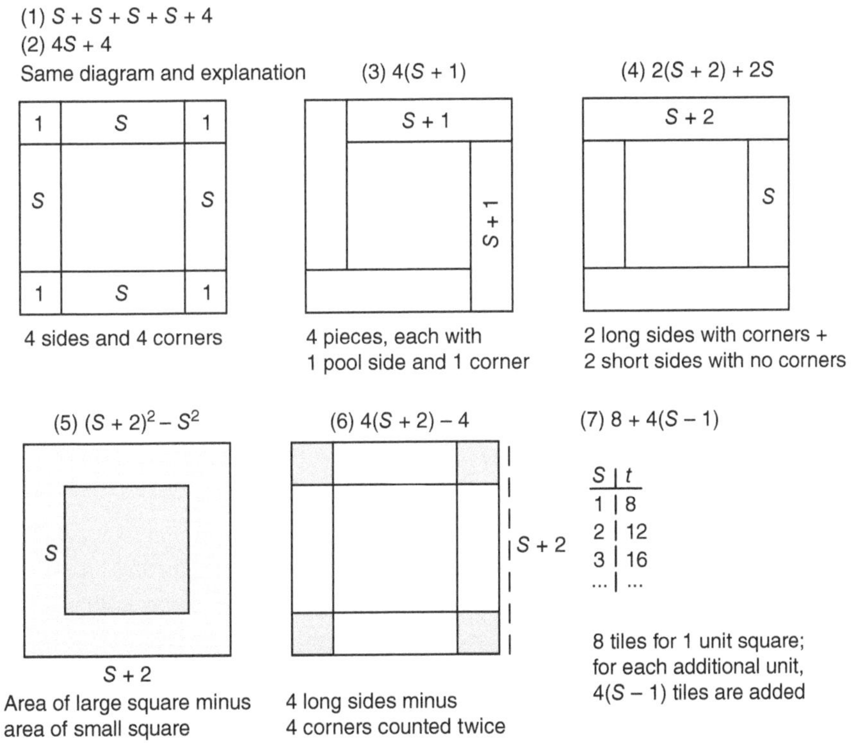

"Because of the absolute nature of mathematics, people have access to mathematical ideas only through representations of those ideas." (National Research Council 2001, p. 94)

In an effective classroom, students will be "describing and justifying their mathematical understanding and reasoning with drawings, diagrams, and other representations" and "sketching diagrams to make sense of problem situations." (NCTM 2014, p. 29)

A big question at this point is whether each of these representations is equivalent mathematically. Earlier we decided that the way to test for equivalence is to find out whether two or more expressions name the same number when values are substituted into each expression. Suppose the pool has a side length of 10 feet. Evaluate each of the expressions generated by the class for that value. Try several more values. Can you now conclude that all the expressions are equivalent? Explain why or why not. [*Yes, all the expressions yield the same value, 44, when using 10 feet for the side.*]

Note that in most of the explanations in figure 5.2, the thinking is clearest when the expression is not in simplest form. So, for example, in Case 4, $2(s + 2) + 2s$ is clearer than $2s + 4 + 2s$, or $4s + 4$.

The same neighbor you helped with the pool is happy with your work and has asked you to help with a garden she is creating. She wants part of it to be for vegetables and part for flowers. If the garden were divided as in figure 5.3, with the shaded part for vegetables and the unshaded part for flowers, find the garden area for vegetables, the area for flowers, and the total garden area. [*150 sq. ft., 100 sq. ft., 250 sq. ft.*]

FIG. 5.3

Vegetable and flower garden

Now turn to the Plotting Land activity sheets. Monitor students as they work on the problems. As students complete the problems, call them together for a class discussion on the two ways to determine total area suggested by the distributive property. They may think that it is always best to add first and then multiply, as in $20 \times (15 + 12) = 20 \times (27) = 540$ rather than $20 \times (15) + 20 \times (12) = 300 + 240 = 540$. However, in many problems, such as $8 \times (x + 5)$, where it is not possible to add x and 5, either form is equally efficient, either $8 \times (x + 5)$ or $8x + 40$. Keep in mind that referring to the two parts of the garden will help students remember that the second expression is $8x + 40$ rather than $8x + 5$, a common error.

Answers for Plotting Land:

1. *123 m^2*

2. *127 m^2*

3. *250 m^2*

4. a. *Shaded: 10 $m \times 15$ m*

   Unshaded: 10 $m \times 10$ m

   b. *Shaded: 150 m^2*

   Unshaded: 100 m^2

   c. *250 m^2*

5. a. $20(15+12) = 20(27) = 540 \text{ ft.}^2$ *or*

   $20(15) + 20(12) = 300 + 240 = 540 \text{ ft.}^2$

   b. $40(25+15) = 40(40) = 1{,}600 \text{ ft.}^2$ *or*

   $40(25) + 40(15) = 1{,}000 + 600 = 1{,}600 \text{ ft.}^2$

   c. $a(20) + a(15) = 20a + 15a = 35a$ *or*

   $a(20+15) = a(35) = 35a$

   d. $b(c) + b(d) = bc + bd$ *or*

   $b(c+d)$

6. *a, c, d*

7. *b*

8. 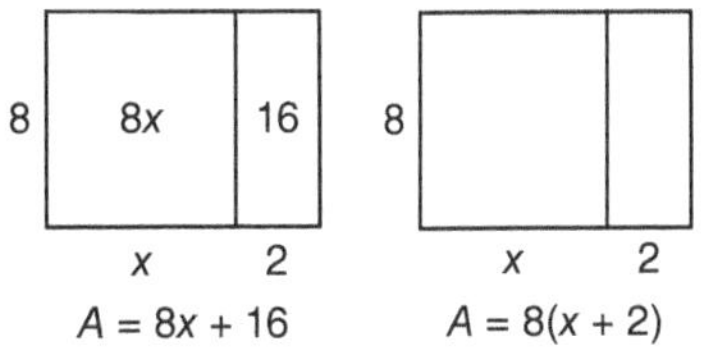

Extend

Since we know students need lots of practice with the distributive property, these first three problems address that property.

1. Suppose that instead of a pool for fish, your neighbor decides to have a larger pool for swimming. She still wants to have a border made of 1-foot tiles, but the pool will be rectangular instead of square (see figure 5.4). If the pool is 25 feet long and 10 feet wide, how many tiles will she need? [*54 tiles*]

   FIG. 5.4

   Rectangular pool

   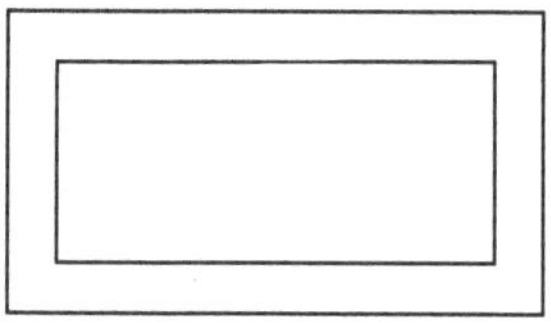

   Write an expression for the number of tiles needed for a pool L feet long and W feet wide. Can you write it in another way? Explain why the two expressions are equivalent. [*Answers will be similar to one of the forms shown earlier for a square tub, but with* $2L + 2W$ *replacing* $4s$*—for example,* $2L + 2W + 4$ *or* $2(L + W + 2)$.]

Throughout this lesson, students "build procedural fluency from conceptual understanding. [They] are demonstrating flexible use of strategies and methods while reflecting on which procedures seem to work best for specific types of problems . . . and [they] are striving to use procedures appropriately and efficiently." (NCTM 2014, pp. 47–48)

2. Suppose that at the corners, each tile is triangular, made from cutting a square tile in half (see figure 5.5). If the pool is 25 feet long and 10 feet wide, how many tiles are needed for the border? [*72 tiles*]

   FIG. 5.5

   Pool with modified corners

   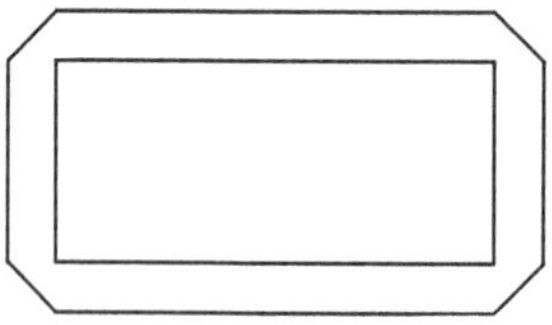

   Write two expressions for the number of tiles needed for a similar pool L feet long and W feet wide. [$(2L + 2W + 2)$ *or* $2(L + W + 1)$.]

In their efforts to elicit and use evidence of student thinking, teachers will "gather evidence of student understanding at strategic points during instruction" and encourage students to reflect "on mistakes and misconceptions to improve mathematical understanding." (NCTM 2014, p. 56)

3. Owen is trying to calculate the total surface area of water in this pool, shown in figure 5.6.

   FIG. 5.6

   Owen's pool

   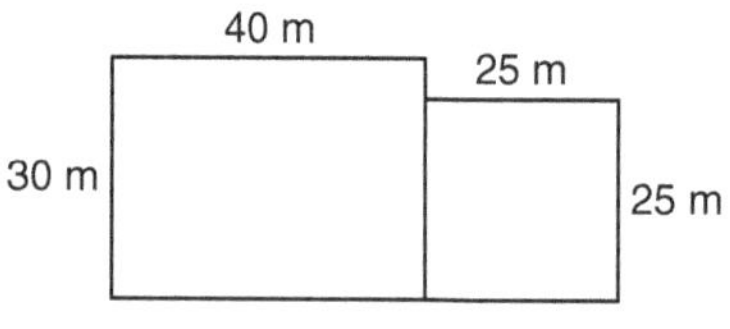

   He writes: $SA = 30 \times (40 + 25) = 30 \times (65) = 1{,}950$ sq. m. Is he correct? If yes, explain his thinking. If not, explain his error in thinking. [*No. He incorrectly assumed that the 25 m part of the pool had the same width as the 30 × 40 part. The correct area is* $(30 \times 40) + (25 \times 25) = 1{,}200 + 625 = 1{,}825$ *sq. m.*]

   Students may also need additional practice on developing algebraic expressions from situations, the topic addressed in the Tiling Tubs activity. The following problems give further suggestions for similar situations.

4. Select a month on the calendar, and then select a 4-by-4 grid of 16 days. Draw a rectangle around it.

   - Find the sum of the dates along the two diagonals.
   - Find the sum in the four corners.
   - Find the sum of the four numbers in the center 2-by-2 region.

   What do you observe? Do the relationships hold for other 4-by-4 grids on the calendar? Can you explain this?

   If the students are struggling to explain, you could suggest calling the first number by a variable and then naming the rest of the days by their relationship to the first number (such as x, $x + 1$, $x + 7$, etc.). Then ask: How could you represent the numbers in the diagonal? The four corners? The center square?

September 2020

		1	2	3	4	5
6	7	8	9	10	11	12
13	14	15	16	17	18	19
20	21	22	23	24	25	26
27	28	29	30			

5. For additional practice with similar problems, a rich source comes from Think of a Number puzzles. Here is an example:

   - Write down any whole number.
   - Add to it a number that is 1 less than the number.
   - Add 9 to this number.
   - Divide the sum by 2.
   - Subtract the original number.
   - What is the final result?

   [*For this problem, the result will be 4, no matter what the original number is.*]

How can this be possible when everyone started with a different number? Algebra can be used to solve the problem. Students should try to represent the steps of the problem with variables and to determine what it is that causes everyone to have a result of 4. After more practice with different problems, ask students to create their own number puzzle and have several other students solve it.

You can continue this with unending variations (including starting with fractions or decimals). For additional problems of this type, see the articles by O'Connor and by Koirala and Goodwin (available at this book's more4U page).

Students can also create their own Think of a Number puzzle. Further contextual problems leading to algebraic expressions are found in *Navigating through Algebra in Grades 6–8.*

SUMMARY

The goal of this lesson has been to give students experience in representing problem situations using algebraic expressions that make sense to them, to determine equivalence among various forms of the algebraic expressions, and to become comfortable correctly using the distributive property. Most students will need additional practice beyond what is given in this lesson.

Further problems can be found in *Principles and Standards for School Mathematics* (NCTM 2000, pp. 158–163), journal articles, and other curriculum materials.

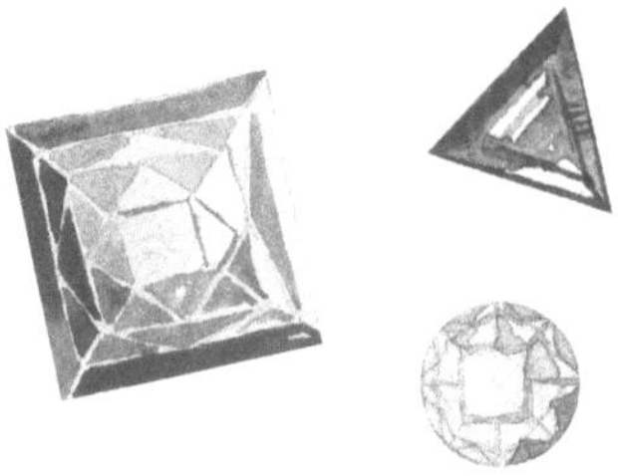

6

Scale Factors and Measurement Relationships: Ratio, Length, Area, and Volume

OVERVIEW

Derived from "Scale Factors and Measurement Relationships" in *Navigating through Problem Solving and Reasoning in Grade 6* (NCTM 2006a, pp. 43–53).

Students are likely to have had many everyday experiences with similar figures, even if they have not recognized them as such. For instance, many children have played with toys that are scale models of actual objects. Model trains and dolls are other examples. A number of films involve scale relationships, including *Honey! I Shrunk the Kids* and the Harry Potter and Lord of the Rings series of movies. Many classic stories and folktales involve elves or giants who are similar to ordinary humans but on a much smaller or larger scale. Students often enlarge or shrink an image on a computer screen or copy machine. They may have seen scale models for proposed buildings or other projects that architects or engineers construct by applying scale factors to the dimensions of planned structures.

Activities that focus on measurement relationships among similar figures offer middle-grades students opportunities to explore ideas related to proportional reasoning, a topic that is central to the middle-grades mathematics curriculum. The activities in this multiday investigation go beyond simply equating two ratios and solving for a missing term. Rather, they require students to recognize "quantities that are related proportionally and using numbers, tables, graphs, and equations to think about the quantities and their relationship" (NCTM 2000, p. 217). Early, often informal, experiences with proportional reasoning should prove helpful to students as they explore increasingly abstract proportional relationships in middle school, where they work with linear functions of the form $y = kx$.

Prior to engaging in this investigation, students should have had some experience with the concepts of perimeter, area, surface area, and volume, including finding perimeters and areas on a dot grid. They also should have had some experience finding the surface areas and volumes of rectangular prisms, as well as writing and simplifying ratios.

This set of activities—which combines the number concepts of similarity and scaling with the geometry and measurement concepts of length, perimeter, area, surface area, and volume—is one way to address the problem faced by many teachers of having more content than they have time for in a given school year.

Teachers should work through each of the activities prior to doing the lesson with students. Though there is nothing surprising or terribly sophisticated, the progression of ideas is important for the teacher to fully understand.

During the first of these activities, students can work individually or in pairs. If you do not have a generous supply of cubes, two pairs can work together during part two, returning to individuals or pairs for part three.

GOALS

- Use scale factors to construct figures that are similar to a given figure.
- Compare the perimeters, areas, and volumes of similar figures.
- Determine how the perimeters, areas, and volumes of similar figures are related to their scale factors.
- Use the relationships between the perimeters, areas, and volumes of similar figures to solve real-world problems.
- Determine the scale factor from measurements that are equivalent according to a scale, such as "1 inch equals 25 miles" on a map.

MATERIALS NEEDED

A copy of each of the activity sheets for each student:

- Scale It Up, Scale It Down
- Perimeters and Areas of Similar Figures
- Surface Areas and Volumes of Similar Figures
- Scale Models
- One or two sheets of grid paper
- Rulers or straightedges

For each pair or group of students:

- 150 one-centimeter cubes or other small cubes

The teacher should, if possible, have available the following literature resources:

- *Gulliver's Adventures in Lilliput* (Beneduce 1996)
- *Gulliver in Lilliput* (Hodges 1995)

(The previous two books are written for younger readers and are easier for students to understand than Jonathan Swift's original *Gulliver's Travels.*)

- *Jim and the Beanstalk* (Briggs 1997)
- *Cut Down to Size at High Noon* (Sundby 2000)
- "One Inch Tall" from *Where the Sidewalk Ends* (Silverstein 1974)

The Silverstein poem is also reprinted in *Principles and Standards for School Mathematics* (NCTM 2000, p. 246). There are many other books dealing with ratios and scale factors; the ones listed are included in the activities of this lesson.

Engage

Middle-school students have had experience with measurement ideas, including length, perimeter, and area. They may also have worked with surface area and volume, but ideas of similarity and scale factors may be new to them. Now they are going to apply a scale factor to every dimension of an initial figure, which allows the formation of another figure that is an enlargement or a reduction of the original. This scale factor is the basis of the relationships between the respective perimeters, areas, and volumes of the two similar figures. Students will discover in the course of this set of activities that all the relationships depend on the scale factor, though in a different way for each measurement.

Jim and the Giant

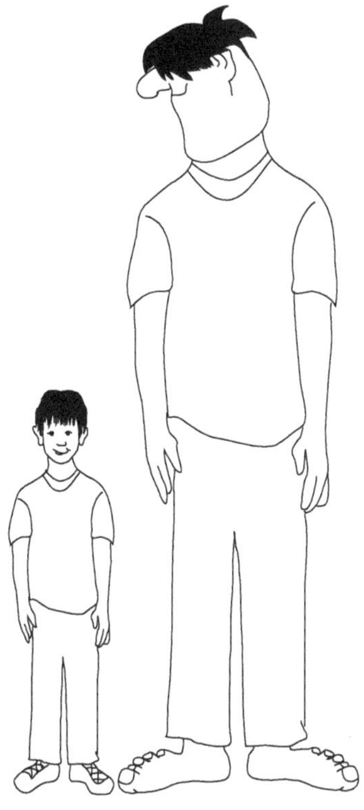

The students will begin with two- or three-dimensional figures and construct similar figures by applying a given scale factor. Multiplying all the dimensions of the original figure (called the *preimage*) by the same scale factor produces a new figure (called the *image*) that is similar to the original. The new figure is also commonly called a size change, or *dilation*, of the original. When a scale factor is greater than 1, the resulting figure is an enlargement of the original; when the scale factor is between 0 and 1, the resulting figure is a contraction, or reduction, of the original.

To introduce the first task, use *Jim and the Beanstalk* to generate a discussion among the students of a case of scale factors and their influence. In the story, Jim carries items such as eyeglasses, dentures, and a wig up the stalk to the giant. First read the story to the class. Then ask questions such as "How would the area of a lens in eyeglasses for the giant compare with the area of a lens in glasses for Jim? Glasses for you?" Allow several minutes for students to discuss this with their partner and then gather a few reports from pairs.

FIG. 6.1

Shapes for scaling

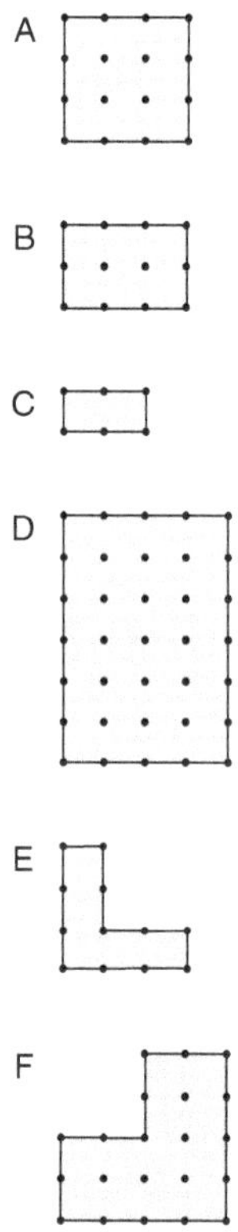

Now pass out the activity sheets Scale It Up, Scale It Down, and Perimeters and Areas of Similar Figures.

> *"It is important that students understand the mathematical purpose of a lesson and how the activity contributes to and supports their mathematical learning."* (NCTM 2014, p. 13)

On Scale It Up, Scale It Down students will construct a figure that is similar to a given figure. The directions for this sheet are in question 1a of the Perimeters and Areas of Similar Figures sheet: "The activity sheet Scale It Up, Scale It Down shows six geometric figures on dot grids (see figure 6.1). Column 2 in the table below shows scale factors for all the figures. For each figure (called a *preimage*) locate the appropriate scale factor and use it to draw a similar figure (called an *image*) on the same grid as the preimage on Scale It Up, Scale It Down." Students must measure the length of each side of the preimage and multiply it by the given scale factor to determine the length of the corresponding side of the image. Give students a few minutes to begin making a scale drawing for figure A. Make sure all students understand how to determine the length of a side of a figure on a dot grid. Some might be tempted to count the number of dots on a side. Instead, they need to count the horizontal or vertical distances between dots. Check work as you walk around to guarantee that all are clear on using the scale factor to create a new image on the same small grid.

> *"Effective teachers understand how contexts . . . and language can be used to create mathematical tasks that draw on students' prior knowledge and experience or that offer students a common experience from which their work on mathematical tasks emerges."* (NCTM 2014, p. 17)

Ask several students to show their images to the class and to share their strategies. Watch for any students who attempt to add the scale factor to each side rather than multiplying. Once any questions have been clarified, continue with the remainder of the activity sheets.

Explore

Students should continue drawing their similar figures for figures B–F on the Scale It Up, Scale It Down sheet. Figure D is the first instance where students encounter a scale factor less than 1 and therefore the first time the image will be smaller than the preimage. Figures E and F might be more challenging than A–D because they are not simple rectangles.

Next they should turn to the Perimeters and Areas of Similar Figures sheets, completing the table as directed in part b. Students can find the perimeter and area for figures A–D by counting squares on the grid, by beginning at one vertex and moving sequentially around the figure, or by applying a formula. For E and F, they may partition the figure into parts or create a rectangle around the figure and then subtract the extra squares. Most students will be able to find ways to determine perimeter and area on their own.

When students have completed the table in question 1b (see table 6.1), call the class together and discuss the results. This is an opportunity to clarify any lingering questions or misunderstandings.

Table 6.1. Solutions for Question 1 on Perimeters and Areas of Similar Figures

Figure	Scale Factor	Length of Longest Side in Preimage (Linear Units)	Length of Corresponding Side in Image (Linear Units)	Perimeter of Preimage (Linear Units)	Perimeter of Image (Linear Units)	Area of Preimage (Square Units)	Area of Image (Square Units)
A	2	3	6	12	24	9	36
B	3	3	9	10	30	6	54
C	4	2	8	6	24	2	32
D	$\frac{1}{2}$	6	3	20	10	24	6
E	2	3	6	12	24	5	20
F	$\frac{3}{2}$	4	6	16	24	12	27

As they work to complete questions 2–6 on the Perimeters and Areas of Similar Figures sheets, encourage students to clearly state the patterns they observe and the conclusions they can draw. Questions 2–4 ask for the ratios of length, perimeter, and area between preimage and image. [*Length and perimeter ratios equal the scale factor; area ratios equal the square of the scale factor.*] Question 5a, which is "What conclusions can you draw about corresponding sides, perimeters, and areas of similar figures?" is asking them to clearly articulate what they discovered in the previous three questions. Students without much experience with variables and exponents might have difficulty formulating a conclusion. Question 5b tells them to consider a 250 percent enlargement of a figure with a given perimeter and area and asks them to predict the perimeter and area of the enlargement. The question is designed to determine whether the students understand the implications of the conclusions they drew in response to part a. [*The perimeter of the image will be* $13 \times 2.5 = 32.5$ *units; the area of the image will be* $16 \times (2.5)^2 = 100$ *square units.*] Some may forget to square the scale factor in order to find the area. They also must know how to translate 250 percent into a scale-factor number.

> *"What is critical is that a task provide students with the opportunity to engage actively in reasoning, sense making, and problem solving so that they develop a deep understanding of mathematics."* (NCTM 2014, p. 20)

Students may still not understand *why* the scale factor is squared for area. The numbers appear in the chart, but students do not necessarily see why the result makes sense. Sometimes a visual explanation helps. For example, using shape A, we can view the following enlargements (figure 6.2):

FIG. 6.2

Enlargements of shape A

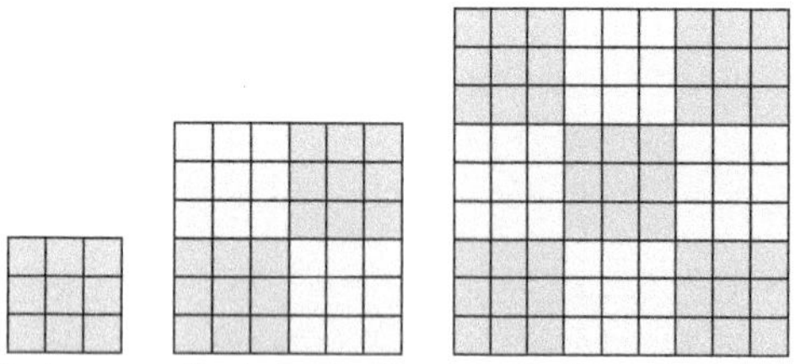

We can see how the scale factor 2 (3) places two (three) copies in both horizontal and vertical directions—hence 2 × 2 = 4 (3 × 3 = 9) copies in all, and so on. Also, the visual helps show why the side lengths and perimeter are doubled (tripled) for scale factor 2 (3).

Question 6, about the prices of different-size pizzas, is optional but is very interesting. Even if students do not yet understand how to find areas for circles, if they extend the conclusions from the work they have just done, they will know that with a scale factor of 2, the area of the larger pizza will be four times the smaller. You might want to use question 6 as homework or as a vehicle for a discussion on the pros and cons of pricing pizzas by a strict proportional scheme. In a typical pizza parlor, is the price of different sizes proportional to the scale factor? Why or why not?

> *"Students who learn to articulate and justify their own mathematical ideas, reason through their own and others' mathematical explanations, and provide a rationale for their answers develop a deep understanding that is critical to their future success in mathematics and related fields."* (Carpenter, Franke, and Levi 2003, p. 6)

When students have completed questions 2–6, call the class together. For questions 2–4, and again for 5a, ask several students to share the patterns they have observed and the conclusions they have reached. This summary serves to solidify in every student's mind the important ratios that are the essential part of this entire activity:

1. The ratios of the lengths of the corresponding sides of similar figures are the same as the scale factor.
2. The ratios of the perimeters are also the scale factor.
3. The ratio of the areas is the square of the scale factor.

As you move into the second part of this activity, select another one of the suggested literature resources to remind students of the overarching idea of scaling up or down. You might select the poem "One Inch Tall" (Silverstein 1974). The first image in the poem suggests that if you were one inch tall, you would be able to ride a worm to school. Would this really be true? Common earthworms are about five inches long with diameters of about one-fourth of an inch. Take 5 or 10 minutes to have students discuss with their partners or group the plausibility of this means of transportation. Collect comments after the discussion, remembering that the purpose of this is to think about the idea of scale factors, not to determine exact scale factors.

Now distribute the Surface Areas and Volumes of Similar Figures activity sheets, together with the cubes for each group of two or four students. Again, ask students to follow the directions on the sheet to build figure A (a rectangular prism with dimensions of 1 × 2 × 3 centimeters) and its image using a scale factor of 2 (see figure 6.3), and use a discussion of the preimage and image figures to clarify any misunderstandings and to answer any questions. Then complete the table for figures B–E, one row at a time (see table 6.2). Note that for this sheet, rather than building all the scale images first, they will be done one at a time, with one row of the table filled in for each image before moving to the next. Students should understand that each face of a cube has an area of one square unit, and each cube has a volume of one cubic unit. It should be straightforward to students to count the surface areas and volumes once they have constructed each figure with their cubes.

FIG. 6.3

Cube constructions for figure A

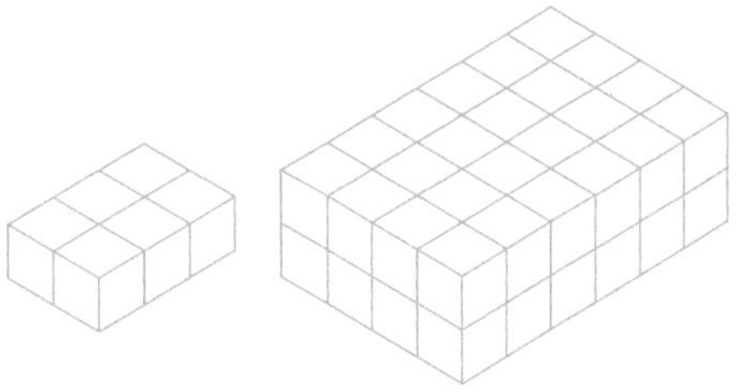

Table 6.2. Solutions for Question 1 Measurement Chart for Surface Area and Volumes of Similar Figures

Figure (Preimage)	Dimensions of Preimage (Centimeters)	Scale Factor	Surface Area of Preimage (Square Centimeters)	Surface Area of Image (Square Centimeters)	Volume of Preimage (Cubic Centimeters)	Volume of Image (Cubic Centimeters)
A	1 × 2 × 3	2	22	88	6	48
B	1 × 2 × 1	3	10	90	2	54
C	1 × 1 × 1	4	6	96	1	64
D	2 × 2 × 4	$\frac{1}{2}$	40	10	16	2
E	4 × 2 × 4	$\frac{3}{2}$	64	144	32	108

Using cubes to construct both the preimage and the image is a powerful way to visualize what is happening and help students "see" the change with both their eyes and minds. When they move on to questions 2–4, they calculate surface area and volume for each of their figures; they observe patterns for surface area and volume and describe how those measurements relate to scale factors. When the students have had time to complete questions 2–4, initiate a whole-class discussion, selecting students you have identified as you observe their work. This can be an opportunity to highlight various ways of expressing the relationships, some simpler, some more sophisticated. They should observe that—

1. the ratio of the surface area of the image to the surface area of the preimage is the square of the scale factor, and
2. the ratio of the volume of the image to the volume of the preimage is the cube of the scale factor.

Encourage the students to discuss and try to determine why the surface-area ratio is the same as for area in the previous activity [*they are both two-dimensional measurements*] and why the ratio for the volume is the cube [*because the scale factor applies to all three dimensions*]. Question 5 asks students to apply what they have learned about scale factors of volumes to a building.

"Teachers support students in exploring tasks without taking over students thinking."
(NCTM 2014 p. 24)

Extend

The third and final component of this set of activities offers an opportunity to summarize and apply the lessons learned so far. Students will use the activity sheets Scale Models to reason about scale factors, particularly those where the given scale uses different units of measure and needs conversion to become a scale factor, which is a ratio expressed using the same measure but with no units. For example, suppose a map has a scale of 1 inch to 10 miles. If we said the scale factor was 1/10, then a town that was 10 miles away would be only 10 inches away, making for some serious crowding! Instead, we need to convert one of the measures, in this case 10 miles, to inches. This looks like the following:

$$\frac{1\text{ inch}}{10\text{ miles}} = \frac{1\text{ inch}}{10 \times 5{,}280\text{ feet}} = \frac{1\text{ inch}}{52{,}800\text{ feet}} = \frac{1\text{ inch}}{52{,}800 \times 12\text{ inches}} = \frac{1\text{ inch}}{633{,}600\text{ inches}}$$

Now, since both measures are in the same units, we can identify a scale factor of 1/633,600. The town that is really 10 miles away is also 633,600 inches away, a more plausible distance.

Students should not have too much difficulty with questions 1–2, which ask for similar unit conversions to determine scale factor. Before beginning question 3, it will be helpful to students if you are able to read from one of the *Gulliver's Travels* books. This will prepare them with the context of that problem.

A comfortable bed for Gulliver

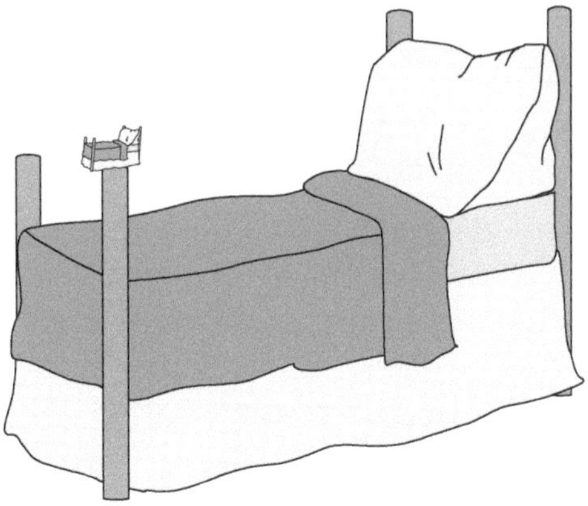

A delightful story to introduce question 4 is *Cut Down to Size at High Noon* (Sundby 2000). In this story, which takes place in the western town of Cowlick, a newcomer competes with the barber to scale objects of local significance up or down in elaborate hairstyles. The challenge in question 4 is to create an original design and make a scale image of the design on grid paper. This pulls together the work of the whole set of activities and allows for some originality and creativity for students.

Solutions for "Scale Models"

1. The scale factor is $\frac{1}{87}$. The students know that 1 foot equals 12 inches, so they can convert 7.25 feet to inches and then form a ratio:

$$\frac{1\text{ inch}}{7.25\text{ feet}} = \frac{1\text{ inch}}{87\text{ inches}} = \frac{1}{87}$$

2. The scale factor is $\frac{1}{1{,}584{,}000}$. The students know that 1 mile equals 5,280 feet and 1 foot equals 12 inches, so they can convert 25 miles to 132,000 feet and to 1,584,000 inches. Then they can form a ratio:

$$\frac{1\text{ inch}}{25\text{ miles}} = \frac{1\text{ inch}}{1{,}584{,}000\text{ inches}} = \frac{1}{1{,}584{,}000}$$

3. a. The scale factor is $\frac{1}{12}$. The students know that 1 foot equals 12 inches, so they can convert 6 feet to 72 inches and then form a ratio:

$$\frac{6\text{ inches}}{6\text{ feet}} = \frac{6\text{ inches}}{72\text{ inches}} = \frac{1}{12}$$

   b. Students will suggest various dimensions. The area of the top of the Lilliputian's mattress is $\frac{1}{144}$, or $\left(\frac{1}{12}\right)^2$, times the area of the top of Gulliver's mattress. The students have previously discovered that the area of the image is the square of the scale factor times the area of the preimage.

c. Students will suggest various dimensions. The volume of the Lilliputian's living room is $\frac{1}{1{,}728}$, or $\left(\frac{1}{12}\right)^3$, times the volume of Gulliver's living room. The students have previously discovered that the volume of the image is the cube of the scale factor times the volume of the preimage.

4. Students' answers will vary, depending on their drawings and the scale factors that they select. The area of the image should be the product of the area of the preimage and the square of the scale factor.

Students may have asked during this lesson what the result is if a negative scale factor is applied to a figure. It does two things: scales the figure up or down depending on whether its absolute value is greater than 1 or less than 1 and reverses the figure vertically. If the scale factor is 1, what would happen? [*The figure is simply copied.*] What would happen if the scale factor is 0? [*The figure would disappear.*] What would happen if the scale factor is –1? [*The figure would be the same size, but reversed, i.e., "upside down."*] Another way of saying this is that applying a negative scale factor results in a reflection across a horizontal line. Students might wish to experiment with this idea on grid paper.

The Overview section of this activity referred to characters of elves and giants encountered in folktales and movies. Let's take a closer look at that in light of what we have learned about scale factors, using an activity called The Jolly Green Giant that students enjoy (from House 1980).

> *"For every type of animal there is a most convenient size, and a large change in size inevitably carries with it a change of form."* (Haldane 1926)

A once-popular advertising campaign featured the Jolly Green Giant and his elf-friend Sprout. Both Giant and Sprout appear very human-like, except one is much larger and the other much smaller. Suppose that Giant is 10 times the height of a man (say 20 meters for convenience), and suppose Sprout is 1/10 human size (say 20 cm.). Consider the likelihood of these creatures actually existing. Since both Giant and Sprout appear to be proportioned like humans, assume that not only their height but also their width and thickness are in the given ratios. That raises interesting questions, such as these:

- How will the cross section of Giant's, Human's, and Sprout's bones compare? Since the body's strength is proportionate to the cross section of the bone, how will the strength in the legs of the three compare? [*The strength in Giant's legs will be 10 times that of Human's, but Sprout's will be only 1/10 Human's.*]
- Weight, however, is proportionate to volume. How will the weights of the three compare? [*Giant will weigh 1,000 times as much as Human; Sprout will weigh 1/1,000 Human's weight.*]

- What will be the ratio of weight to strength for each of the three beings? What is the likelihood that the Jolly Green Giant can stride across the valley? [*Giant's weight-to-strength ratio would be 10 times that of Human. In other words, every square inch of Giant bone needs to support 10 times the weight compared to 1 square inch of Human bone. Could your skeleton support 10 times your weight? Sprout, on the other hand, would have only 1/10 the weight for each square inch of bone.*]
- How does the surface area of Sprout's body compare with Human's? How do their weights compare? When an object falls, the resistance to falling caused by the air is proportional to the surface area of the falling body. How does this enable Sprout to jump freely from Giant's tall corn stalks? [*Sprout's weight is 1/1,000 of Human's, while his surface area is 1/100 of Human's, so his resistance to falling is 10 times greater than Human's. When Sprout falls from a tall stalk, he only experiences a small shock upon landing.*]

When students have finished these activities, gather them for a group discussion and summary of what they have learned. One possibility for assessment is to use question 6 on the activity sheet Perimeters and Areas of Similar Figures, question 5 on Surface Area and Volume of Similar Figures, and question 4 on Scale Models, or questions similar to those. They can give teachers a good summary of whether students are able to apply the relationships between corresponding perimeters, areas, and volumes of similar figures to solve problems.

SUMMARY

In this set of activities students have learned that applying a scale factor to length results in the scale factor multiplied by the length of the preimage; applying the scale factor to area or surface area results in the square of the scale factor multiplied by the area of the preimage; and applying the scale factor to volume results in the cube of the scale factor multiplied by the volume of the preimage. These activities help to solidify understanding of ratios, scales, scale factors, and similarity in two and three dimensions. Students are engaged with this exploration, especially when the tasks begin with stories. They are learning prealgebra as they work to summarize the patterns they find in the activities and as they learn to refine their statements of patterns that they observe. They are not only preparing for algebra later in middle school but for later study of advanced algebra in high school, where they will consider relationships such as the fact that two similar figures with scale factors of k have corresponding areas that are in a ratio of k^2 and corresponding volumes that are in a ratio of k^3.

Incorporating multiple strands of mathematics in this lesson allows not only teachers to address multiple standards and goals but also students to make valuable connections among concepts. In this investigation, students have engaged in the following concepts and strands:

- Similar figures (geometry)
- Perimeter, area, surface area, and volume (measurement)

- Ratio (number and operations)
- Pattern generalization (algebra)

To build on and complement the ideas in this investigation, consider the related investigation Block Buildings in *Navigating through Problem Solving and Reasoning in Grade 6*, pp. 18–29. In that set of activities, students continue to explore geometry and measurement from an algebraic point of view. Another investigation, Understanding Area Formulas, also in *Navigating through Problem Solving and Reasoning in Grade 6*, pp. 30–42, allows students to investigate area concepts and formulas for nonrectangular polygons. Both of these activities are available in the appendix as well as at this book's more4U site.

7

Three-Dimensional Shapes: Cross Sections and Constructions

OVERVIEW

Three-dimensional figures are complex shapes that may be examined from several points of view and in multiple ways. Much of students' experience with them in mathematics class and elsewhere will involve viewing two-dimensional drawings of three-dimensional shapes, and the ability to "see" with their mind's eyes the pertinent shape in three dimensions is an important skill. If students do not have previous experience with drawings on isometric paper, which is very helpful for such "seeing," you might consider preceding this activity with the Navigations activity Isometric Explorations from *Navigating through Geometry in Grades 6–8* (available in the appendix as well as at more4U).

Derived from "Cross Sections of Three-Dimensional Shapes" and "Constructing Three-Dimensional Figures" in *Navigating through Geometry in Grades 6–8* (NCTM 2002, pp. 67–68 and 71–72).

This current set of activities is intended for use over multiple days of class. It will concentrate on examining two-dimensional cross sections of three-dimensional shapes and proceed to creating models of three-dimensional shapes. There are three ways to create these models: (1) forming solid figures, (2) building shells of the shapes using only the faces, and (3) constructing skeletons of the figures using only the edges. In the course of these explorations, students will analyze the characteristics of the shapes using the solid and shell models. An excellent additional activity using skeletons is found in the article "Visualizing Three Dimensions by Constructing Polyhedra" by Victoria Pohl. It is included in the supplemental materials at more4U.

"Geometry is a skill of the eyes and the hands as well as of the mind." (Petersen 1983, in Del Grande 1990)

Throughout the activity, it will be most productive to use physical models. Each student should model the shapes and draw and describe the results. Working in pairs will yield maximum opportunities for communicating ideas, checking work, and clarifying thinking.

GOALS

- Describe the two-dimensional figures that result from slicing three-dimensional figures.
- Investigate characteristics of solids.
- Draw, construct, and describe geometric figures and relationships between them.
- Develop spatial visualization skills through constructing and disassembling shapes.
- Represent three-dimensional figures using nets.

MATERIALS NEEDED

- Rulers
- Paper
- Scissors
- For solids: modeling clay or Play-Doh with strong thread or dental floss
- For shells: Paper with tape or Polydrons
- For each student: copies of the activity sheets
  - Cross Sections of Three-Dimensional Shapes
  - Constructing Three-Dimensional Figures
  - The Platonic Solids
  - Nets of Polyhedra

"Students who learn to articulate and justify their own mathematical ideas, reason through their own and others' mathematical explanations, and provide a rationale for their answers develop a deep understanding that is critical to their future success in mathematics and related fields." (Carpenter, Franke, and Levi 2003, p. 6)

PART I CROSS SECTIONS

Engage

The importance of physical models when studying cross sections cannot be overemphasized. Students who have had little experience with spatial visualization activities will likely have difficulty visualizing these cross sections without a model because they cannot envision the unseen faces of the shapes (NCTM 2000, p. 237). Using modeling clay or Play-Doh and strong thread or dental floss, ask students to construct a cube with their clay. The more clearly defined the faces and edges are, the easier the activities will be. Then, using the thread or floss, ask them to slice their cube with a horizontal cut so that the cross section is a square. (See figure 7.1.) When everyone has completed this and had an opportunity to discuss their results, ask them to predict which other two-dimensional shapes could be made by a cut to a cube. If you judge that students need more initial group experience, do numbers 1–3 on the Cross Sections of Three-Dimensional Shapes sheets together, each time reforming the clay into a cube and each time predicting, modeling, drawing, and describing the cross sections. This time spent together with these cube cross sections will help all students as the problems become more difficult. Remember, however, that all students can become adept at this, especially using physical models, and differences among students are largely a result of previous classroom experience (or lack of it).

FIG. 7.1

Square cross section

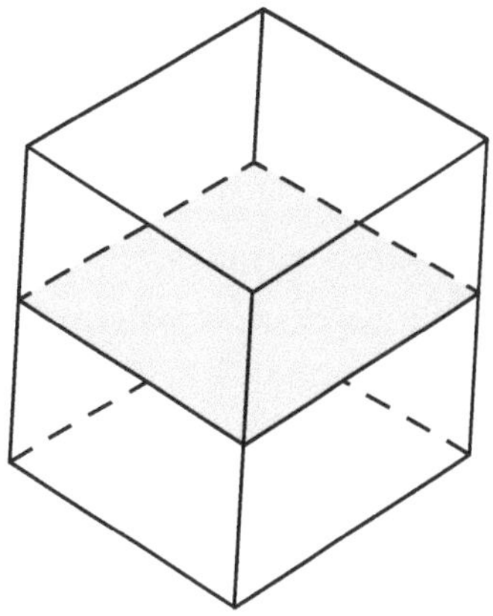

> *"In determining the level of task, it is important to consider the prior knowledge and experience of the students who will be engaged in the task. Tasks may begin as high-level tasks to students who are initially learning about the underlying mathematics. Eventually, as students solidify their understanding of the underlying mathematics, these tasks may become more routine experiences for them. Students then need tasks that further extend these mathematical ideas in ways that continue to deepen understanding and strengthen mathematical reasoning and problem solving."*
> (NCTM 2014, p. 22)

Explore

Continue the Cross Sections of Three-Dimensional Shapes activity sheet with students working independently, each time having them reform their clay into the specified shape and then predicting the shape of the cut. As students become more adept, some will be able to imagine the slices and picture the resulting cross sections without the modeling clay. When students have finished, ask them to share their results for the sheet (see figure 7.2 for solutions). If there is disagreement, ask students to demonstrate their result with their clay and

FIG. 7.2

Solutions for cross sections of three-dimensional shapes

The following answers represent the general shapes of the cross sections. In some cases, the ratios of the sides may vary depending on the placement of the "slice."

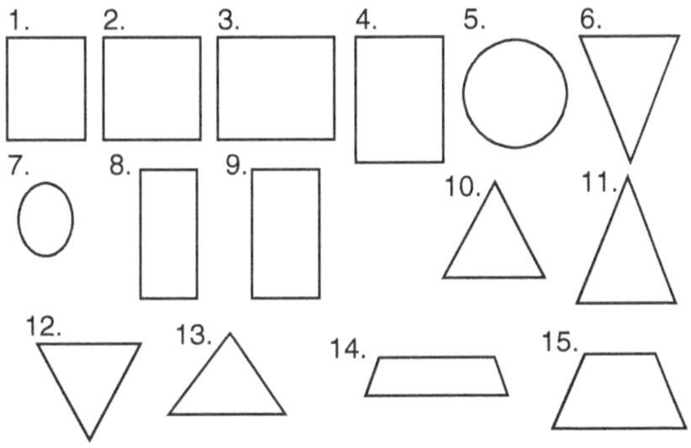

thread or floss. (Again, careful shaping of the clay helps accuracy of cuts.) End the discussion with a reflection question about each student's increasing ease at "seeing" three-dimensional shapes in the imagination.

Extend

Ask each student to find, describe, and list all the geometric figures that they can make by slicing a cube with a plane, that is, the shapes that can be a cross section of a cube. Point out that they have already found several. Are there others? [*The simplest figures, a point and a line, may not occur to many students, but will happen with a plane through a vertex or corner (a point) or through an edge (a line)*]. Most will be able to find a trapezoid (for example, from two adjacent midpoints on one face to the diagonally opposite vertices on the opposite face).

> *"Explicitly encourage students to persevere; find ways to support students without removing all the challenges in a task."* (NCTM 2014 p. 4)

FIG. 7.3

Hexagonal cross section of a cube

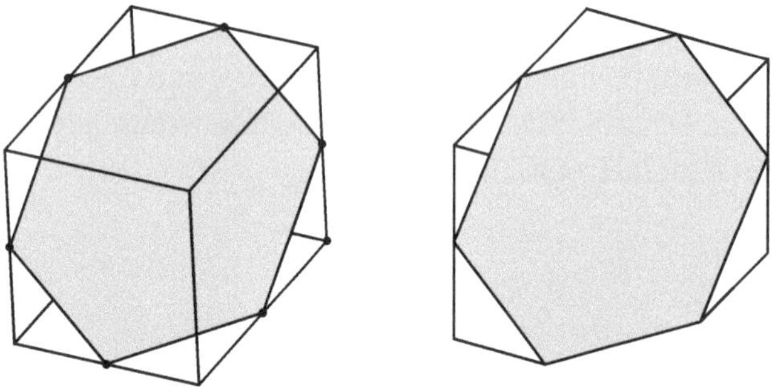

FIG. 7.4

Pentagonal cross section of a cube

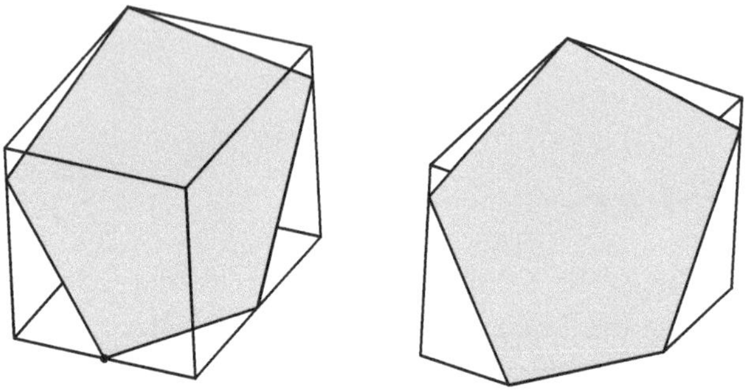

A pentagon and a hexagon are harder to "see" and therefore much harder to find, but some students may be able to find them. (For the pentagon, the plane must meet five faces of the cube; for the hexagon, it must meet all six.) Figures 7.3 and 7.4 show examples of these shapes.

PART II CONSTRUCTING THREE-DIMENSIONAL FIGURES

Engage

This part of the lesson is focused on polyhedra, those three-dimensional figures that have all flat polygon faces, straightedges, and sharp corners, called *vertices*. We will not consider such solid figures as cylinders, cones, or spheres at this time. Ask students to consider the different ways to make a three-dimensional shape. So far, students have been using clay to make solid models. What are some other examples of solid figures? [*Examples include pieces of wood, bricks, books, sugar cubes, etc.*] Ask them to think of other models of solid shapes.

If they have difficulty thinking of shells and skeletons, you could suggest that they think about construction toys that they used when younger. Once you have established these other models, ask for examples of each. [*Shells: empty boxes, the outsides of buildings, tubes. Skeletons: jungle gyms, frames of buildings, Tinkertoys®, or K'nex®.*] Begin this next part of the lesson using a shell model of three-dimensional figures by asking students to create a cube, using either paper with tape or Polydrons. Open it up into a net. Is there more than one way to do this? (Here is a diagram [figure 7.5] showing all 11 possible ways. Do not expect students to get all these. But they should at least recognize that there are many ways to do it!)

A Polydron piece

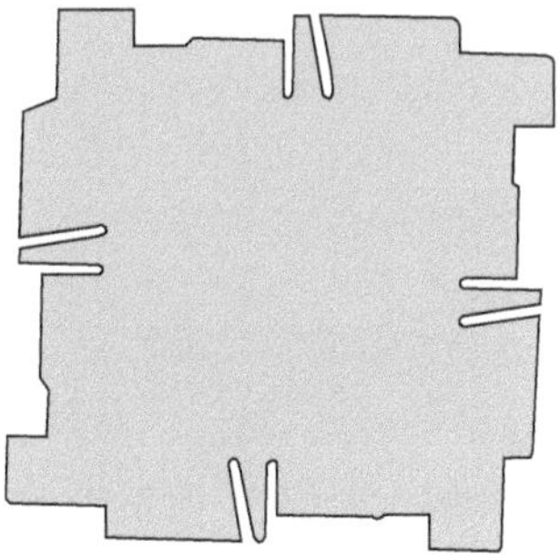

"The gathering of evidence should neither be left to chance nor occur sporadically. Preparation of each lesson needs to include intentional and systematic plans to elicit evidence that will provide a 'constant stream of information about how student learning is evolving toward the desired goal.'" (Heritage 2008, p. 6, quoted in NCTM 2014 p. 53)

FIG. 7.5

Nets for a cube

Explore

Continue using their shell models of solids and the sheet Constructing Three-Dimensional Figures. Ask students to build the two solids given in items 1 and 2 on the first page of their sheet (figure 7.6)

FIG. 7.6

Construct these shapes

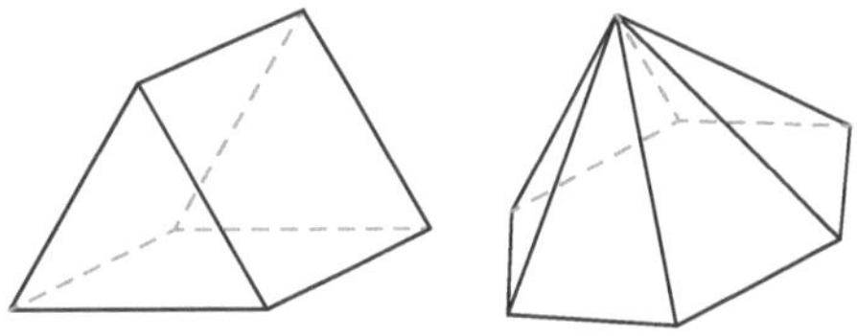

and complete the requested information (number of vertices, edges, and faces) for each of their figures.

Next, ask them in item 3 on their sheet to construct, draw, and describe some more solids of their own choosing. At least one should be a prism and one a pyramid.

As students complete their work, circulate around the room, monitoring students' progress on visualizing three-dimensional figures, and determining whether the students have noticed a pattern in the table of vertices, faces, and edges. At this time, it is not necessary to reveal a pattern for those who have not yet seen one. There will be a further chance later in the lesson. Again, students can work in pairs to encourage communication, with students building, drawing, and explaining on their own sheet.

Solutions for Constructing Three-Dimensional Figures

	V	*F*	*E*
1.	6	5	9
2.	7	7	12
3.	*Answers will vary*		

Extend

In item 3e on their sheets, students are asked to try to find a solid with exactly 8 faces. Some might have created an octahedron with 8 triangular faces. This is one of a very special set of polyhedra known as Platonic solids. We will build those solids with the shell model using nets. As students create these solids using the nets given, ask them to notice what is special about these figures, different from other figures they have made. [*All faces in each solid have the same shape (a regular polygon), and all edges are congruent or equal in length. Also, the same number of faces meet at each vertex.*] Because of these properties, these polyhedra are called *regular solids*. They occur often in nature, in the formation of many minerals, and even in viruses. Their names describe their shape. All are polyhedrons, from the Greek *poly-* (many) and *-hedron* (bases). Thus, they are called tetrahedron (4 faces), hexahedron or cube (6 faces), octahedron (8 faces), dodecahedron (do-, 2 + deca-, 10 = 12 faces), and icosahedrons (20 faces).

Give students a copy of the Platonic Solids activity sheet and have them complete the table for each of the Platonic solids (see figure 7.7).

Plato lived in Greece from about 428 to 348 BCE. He was a student of Socrates and the teacher of Aristotle. He was known as a philosopher and excellent teacher of mathematics.

FIG. 7.7

Solutions for Platonic solids

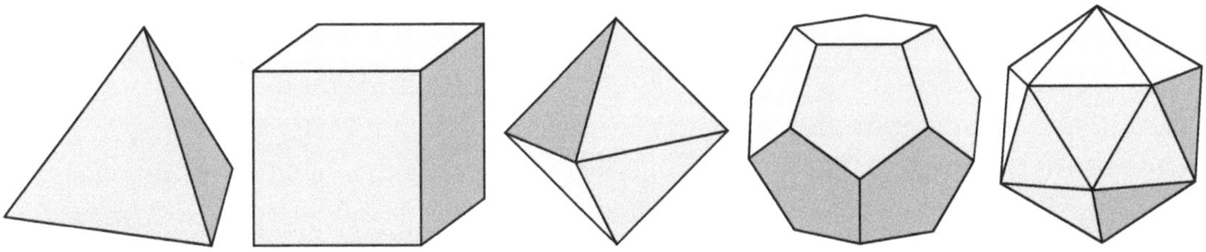

Shape of face	Angle measure of each angle of the face	Number of faces at each vertex	Total angle measure at each vertex	Name of polyhedron	Number of faces	Number of vertices	Number of edges
Equilateral triangle	60°	3	180°	Tetrahedron	4	4	6
Equilateral triangle	60°	4	240°	Octahedron	8	6	12
Equilateral triangle	60°	5	300°	Icosahedron	20	12	30
Square	90°	3	270°	Cube	6	8	12
Regular pentagon	108°	3	324°	Dodecahedron	12	20	30

Now, return to the tables that you made and consider the three columns titled "number of vertices," "number of edges," and "number of faces." What pattern is there among these parts of solid figures? Allow students plenty of time to find a pattern among the parts of the shapes and allow them to express the relationship in words. Some may use variable expressions. (If students seem unable to find anything, suggest actions like adding some of the columns, but try not to tell them a formula. This relationship is often expressed as $V + F = E + 2$, or $V + F - E = 2$.) This relationship was first stated by Leonard Euler, a Swiss mathematician, in 1758, and can be called Euler's formula for polyhedra.

Leonard Euler (pronounced like "oiler") (1707–1783) is considered to be the most prolific mathematician of all time. His extensive writing is all the more remarkable because he had 13 children and often wrote his mathematics papers with a child on his lap.

SUMMARY

In this set of activities, we explored several aspects of three-dimensional figures, always beginning with concrete representations and then moving on to other representations. We looked at cross sections, using solid models of the figures, cutting them with thread to assist reasoning about the shapes, and verifying our conjectures about what would happen when a cut was made. Next, we created various three-dimensional figures using a shell model, building only the faces. We did this first with Polydrons or other side models, then with nets of the figures, making the five Platonic solids. Another reasoning activity was a discovery of Euler's formula for polyhedra. Underlying all the activities is the goal of being able to understand and interpret two-dimensional representations of three-dimensional figures, a requirement of effective mathematics learning and advancement.

8

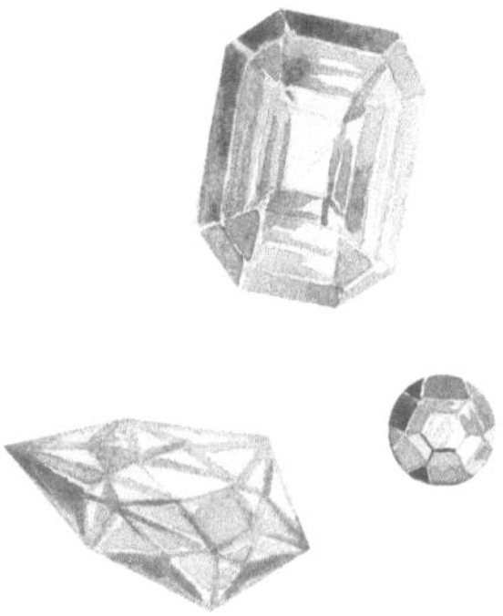

Transforming Shapes

OVERVIEW

Much of mathematics focuses on change and motion. Calculus, for instance, helps us describe and quantify instantaneous change. The mathematics of transformations provides ways to describe and carry out the movement of shapes and to characterize the results of the motion.

In this hands-on activity, students carry out transformations and study the characteristics of those actions, developing and extending their mathematical language to accurately capture their actions and their results.

Derived from "Translations, Reflections, and Rotations" in *Navigating through Geometry in Grades 6–8* (NCTM 2002, pp. 46–47).

GOALS

- Carry out rigid-motion transformations—translations, reflections, and rotations—using familiar geometric shapes.
- Describe transformations using appropriate mathematical language.
- Describe the characteristics of rigid-motion transformations.
- Connect transformations to aspects of congruence and symmetry.

MATERIALS NEEDED

- Translations, Reflections, and Rotations activity sheets for each student
- More Transformations activity sheets for each student
- For each student, several pieces of Patty Paper or another form of tracing paper that is easy to see through
- Ruler or other straightedge for each student

Engage

Arrange students in small groups so they can compare and discuss their work and help one another. Distribute a supply of Patty Paper or other tracing paper to each student, as well as a copy of the first page of the Translations, Reflections, and Rotations activity sheet. Model for your students what you intend for them to do, using the instructions from this activity sheet. Emphasize precision in their creations as well as the use and extension of appropriate language. Here is how this might unfold to create a translation.

> *"From a mathematical standpoint, the study of transformations is an important gateway to such concepts as function, ratio and proportions, symmetry, similarity, and congruence."* (Wiles, Lemon, and King 2019, p. 415)

Ms. M: OK, let's get started as we look at the activity sheet I just distributed. On one piece of Patty Paper, using just a corner of it, draw an arrow similar to what you see here (see figure 8.1). Be sure your arrow can be seen, so you can trace it when you place another sheet on top. (Emphasize the starting point and the tip of the arrow.)

FIG. 8.1

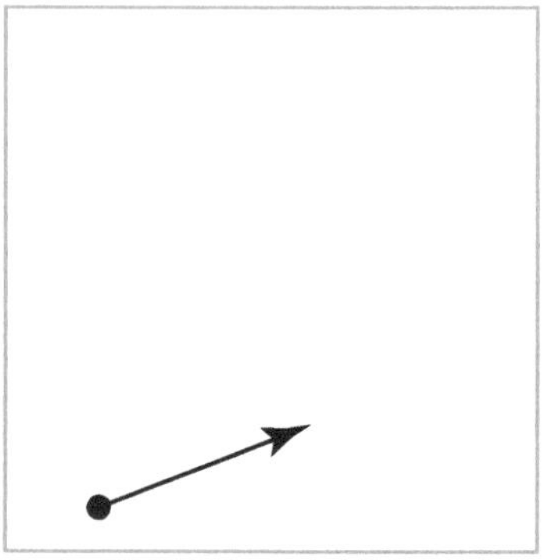

Ms. M: The arrow is called a *vector*. It has a *direction* and a *length*.

Ms. M: Now, on the same sheet as your vector, draw a unique triangle or quadrilateral. My example here shows a quadrilateral (see figure 8.2). The example on the activity sheet shows a pentagon. Draw your unique triangle or quadrilateral somewhere near the vector, as I've done.

FIG. 8.2

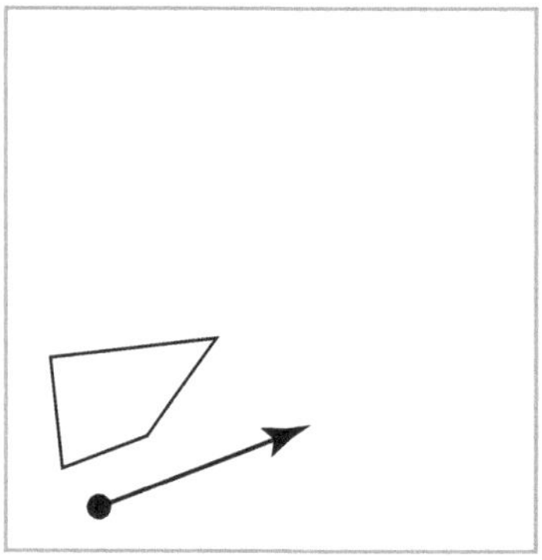

Ms. M: Your goal is to move your unique shape based on the length and direction of your vector. This movement is called a *translation*. You might think of it as sliding an object along a track. For this movement and other transformations we'll carry out, we call your unique shape the *preimage*.

Next, place a new piece of Patty Paper on top of the sheet that shows your preimage and vector. On this new blank sheet, do three things: (1) trace your vector, including its starting point and its tip; (2) draw a line that contains your vector; and (3) trace your preimage. Here is an example for you (see figure 8.3).

FIG. 8.3

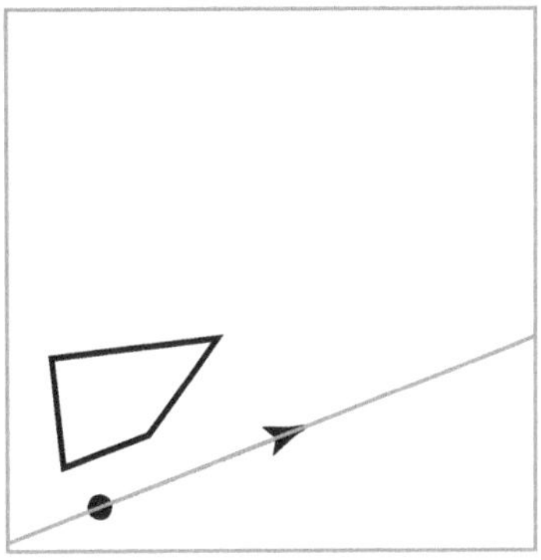

Ms. M: Now place your second sheet *under* your first one so that the vectors coincide. Then, slide the second sheet, still under the original, along the line, until the starting point on its vector matches the tip of the vector that's on the original top sheet (see figure 8.4).

FIG. 8.4

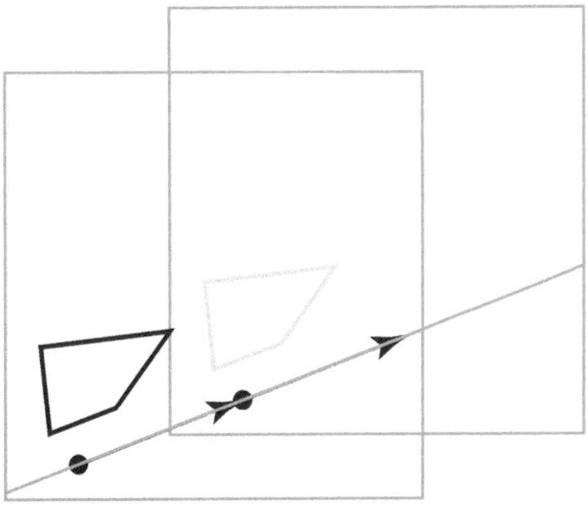

Ms. M: Finally, with your original sheet still on top, trace your unique shape from the second (bottom) sheet onto the top sheet (see figure 8.5).

Ms. M: You have just created a translation! Your unique shape—your preimage—has been translated along your vector to create another shape. We call the resulting shape the *image* of your translation.

FIG. 8.5

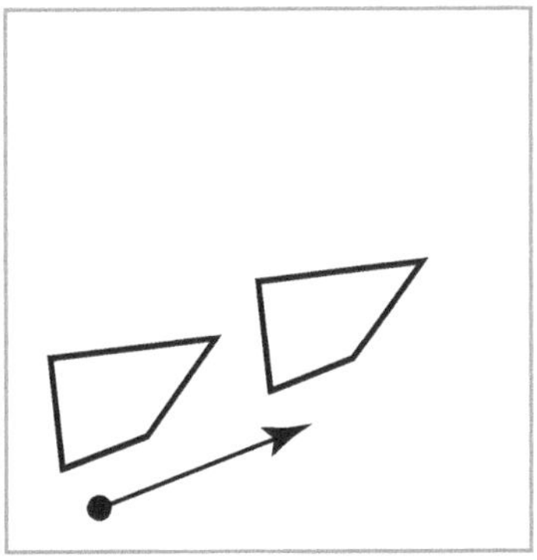

Together, you and your students have carried out your first *rigid-motion transformation*, in this case, a *translation*. In a rigid-motion transformation, the object moves, but its *size* and *shape* remain unchanged.

Two other rigid-motion transformations are the continued focus of this activity. One is called a *reflection*. Aptly named, a reflection involves flipping a preimage over a line rather than moving it with a sliding action. In a reflection, we call that line a *line of reflection* or the *mirror line*. The image of reflection will be the same distance from the mirror line as is the preimage.

The other rigid-motion transformation is called a *rotation*. Along with a preimage to be rotated, or turned, we designate a point as the *center of rotation*. We also need an *angle* that establishes the size of the rotation, and we must designate a *direction* for the rotation, either clockwise or counterclockwise.

You may choose to guide your students through a reflection and a rotation just as you did with a translation, serving to model with students the steps required, as described on each of the accompanying activity sheets. Alternatively, you may choose to pose the task to your students and direct them to follow the instructions on the activity sheets to complete these transformations at their own pace.

By this point, students will have carried out three rigid-motion transformations. Depending on your students, they will likely benefit by carrying out each transformation again, both to reinforce the process and as a way to observe what has happened with each transformation.

You can orchestrate that by asking each student to create a unique translation, reflection, and rotation on new sets of Patty Paper. Students can revisit each of the three activity sheets they have already completed to review the processes. Another option is to present the students with shapes and transformations that you have designated, such as the ones shown here and included on the activity sheet More Transformations. Figures 8.6, 8.7, and 8.8 show solutions for the tasks described on that sheet.

FIG. 8.6

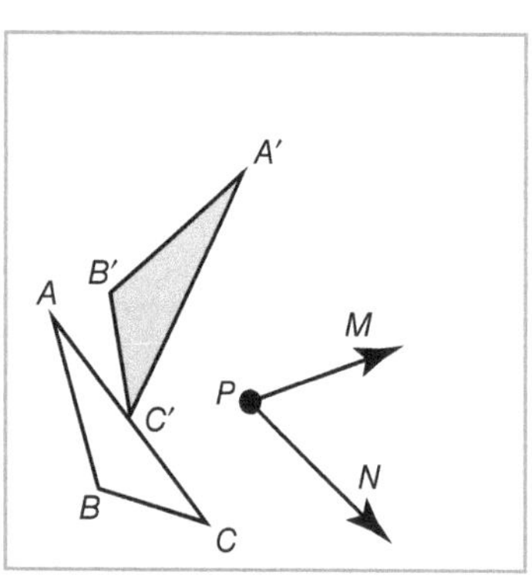

FIG. 8.7

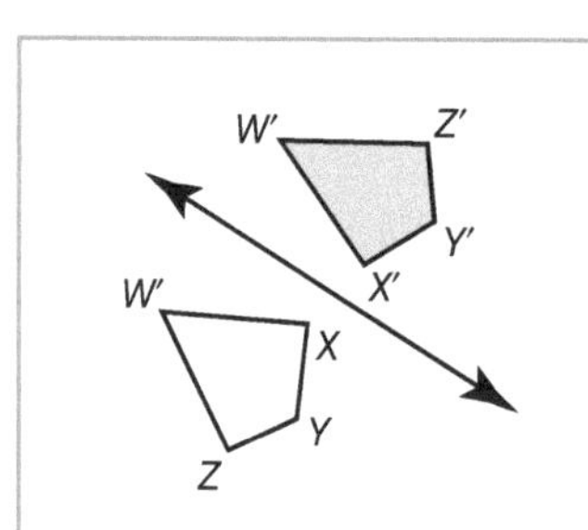

FIG. 8.8

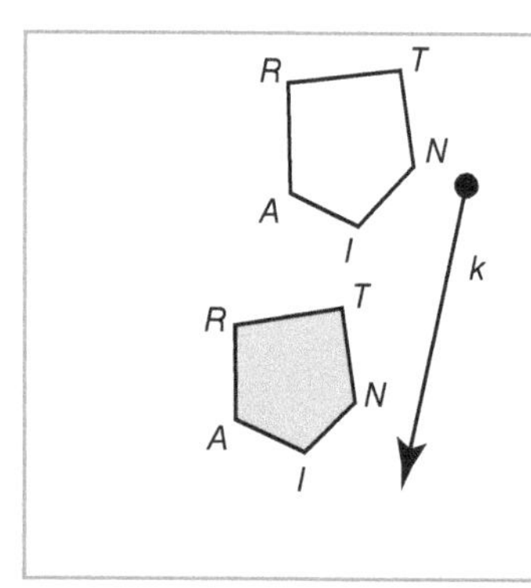

Explore

Whichever reinforcement option you choose—or none at all—it is important at this point that students reflect on the transformations they have carried out. As they study each preimage and image, and each transformation process, what might they observe?

- Ask your students to describe how the preimage moved to become the image. What path was followed?
- Challenge your students to identify what has changed and what has remained the same in each image, compared to its preimage.

> *"To support the study of geometry from the perspective of transformations, teachers should provide students with opportunities to examine the underlying properties of transformations."* (Wiles, Lemon, and King 2019, p. 417)

Discuss with your students their responses to these and similar prompts. This is an important second component of the activity. Not only does it involve communication of mathematical concepts and relationships but it is essential in helping reinforce for students the importance of analyzing the results of mathematical processes and procedures that they undertake. It's one thing to successfully complete a task and another thing to begin to understand, describe, and justify the task itself.

As mentioned earlier, a translation can be thought of as a slide, as the object moves in one direction along a straight line. The position of a translated image is different from the preimage, and the two objects are congruent.

Some students will describe a reflection as a flip across the mirror. Notice that the image and preimage of a reflection are congruent, but something has changed: the *orientation* of the object. If preimage quadrilateral $ABCD$ has named vertices that move clockwise from A to B to C to D, then the reflection image, call it $A'B'C'D'$, will have named vertices that move counterclockwise from A' to B' to C' to D'. This changing in the ordering of corresponding points is called a change in orientation.

The motion of a rotation is circular, moving or turning around some fixed center point. Again, we see that although a rotation image is in a different location from its preimage, the two objects remain congruent. In fact, that is a defining characteristic of rigid-motion transformations—size and shape remain unchanged, precisely the meaning of congruency!

> *"Effective teaching of mathematics uses purposeful questions to assess and advance students' reasoning and sense making about important mathematical ideas and relationships."* (NCTM 2014, p. 35)

Depending on your students' responses that focus on the basics of these rigid-motion transformations, here are some additional questions you can pose during this discussion session.

- What do you observe when you connect a preimage point of a reflection with its corresponding image point? [*The resulting segment is perpendicular to the mirror of reflection, and the mirror bisects that segment. In figure 8.9,* $\overline{AA'}$ *is perpendicular to mirror m, and P is the midpoint of* $\overline{AA'}$.]

FIG. 8.9

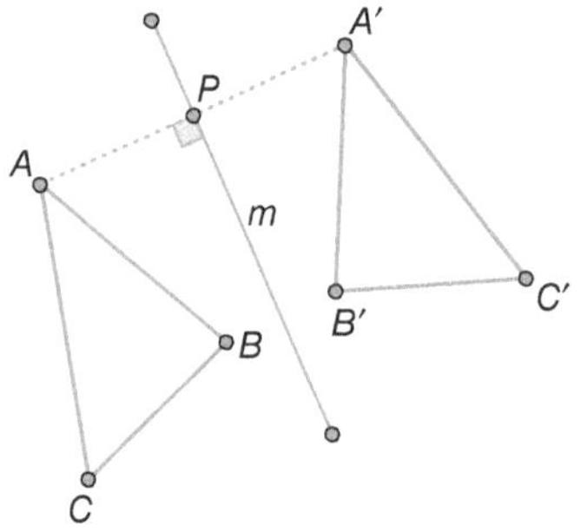

- When you create line segments with endpoints at corresponding preimage and image points of a translation, what do you notice? [*Those segments all have the same length—that of the translation vector—and those segments are parallel to each other and to the translation vector. In figure 8.10,* $\overline{AA'}$, $\overline{BB'}$, *and* $\overline{CC'}$ *are parallel to one another and all have the same length as translation vector j.*]

FIG. 8.10

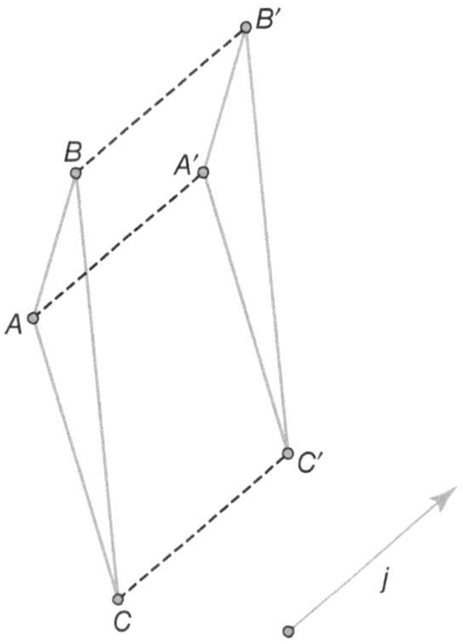

- Can the center of rotation be a point on the preimage? [*Yes, and, if so, that point will be both a preimage point of rotation and an image point. In figure 8.11, point B is the center of rotation, and* $\measuredangle DEF$ *is the rotation angle. Point B is both a preimage point and an image point.*]

FIG. 8.11

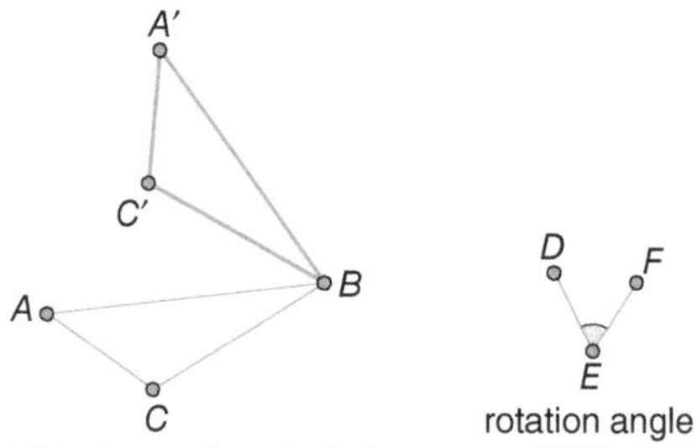

Point *B* is the center of rotation.

rotation angle $m\angle DEF = 60°$

- Can a preimage point of a reflection also be a corresponding image point? [*Yes, if the preimage point is on the mirror of reflection. In figure 8.12, point C is on the mirror of reflection, m, and point C is both a preimage point and an image point.*]
- When will a rotation result in the preimage and image being one unique object? [*This occurs when the angle of rotation is an integer multiple of 360°, including 0°. We typically use positive values to represent counterclockwise rotations and negative values to indicate a clockwise rotation.*]
- When we compose two reflections, are those reflections commutative? That is, does the order of reflection matter? [*Yes . . . and no. In figure 8.13(a), ABC is first reflected though mirror m and the resulting image, A′B′C′, is then reflected using mirror n, generating image A″B″C″. In figure 8.13(b), mirror n is used first, then mirror m. The final reflection image, A″B″C″, is* **not** *in the same position as in the first reflection composition. In figure 8.14, the relationship of m and n is changed so that the two mirrors form a 90° angle. Here, we see that the order of reflections (a) and (b) does not change the position of A″B″C″.*]

FIG. 8.12

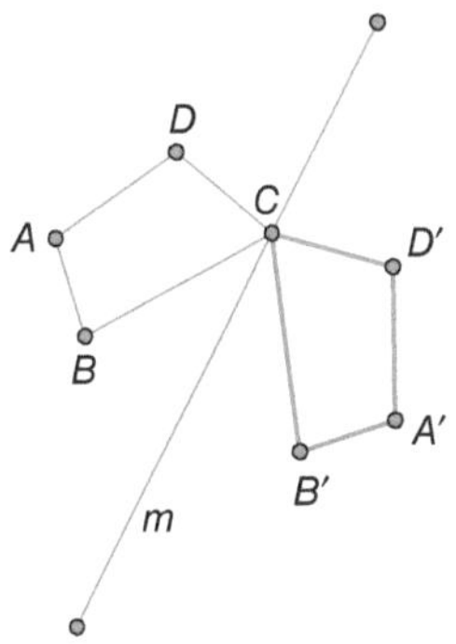

FIG. 8.13

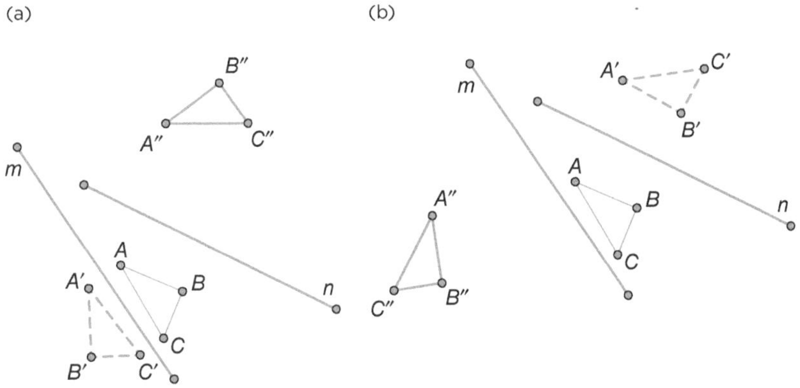

FIG. 8.14

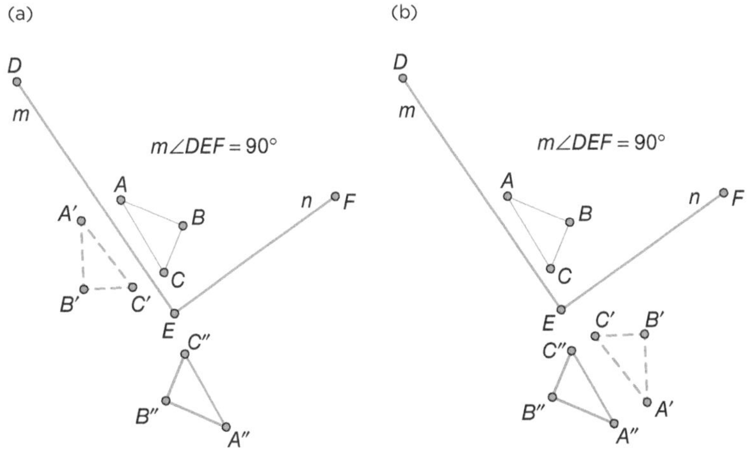

Extend

There are several ways to extend this activity in creating and analyzing rigid-motion transformations, including making connections to the concept of symmetry, as well as exploring transformations as functions.

Symmetry is a concept that students have likely encountered, both in and out of mathematics. Two fundamental forms of symmetry that connect with transformations include line symmetry and rotational symmetry.

An object has *line symmetry* when that object can be reflected through one or more lines of reflection and there is no change from the preimage to the image. The reflected image coincides precisely with the preimage. A nonsquare rectangle, for instance, has line symmetry because there are two mirrors of reflection within the rectangle, as illustrated in figure 8.15.

FIG. 8.15

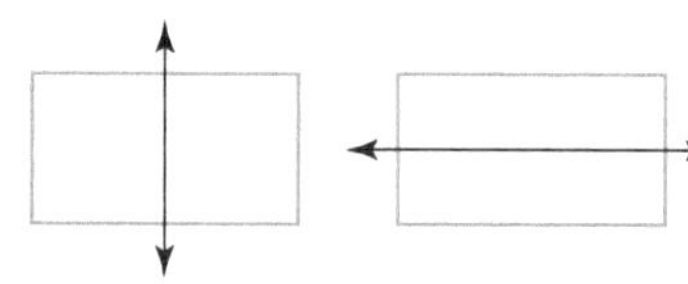

When you reflect the rectangle through either line of reflection, the rectangle falls back on itself, so the result is the same rectangle. Here, we call the reflection line a *line of symmetry*. Discuss with your students the concept of line symmetry and ask them to identify or create other geometric objects that have one or more lines of symmetry.

Another type of symmetry is rotational symmetry. An object has rotational symmetry when there exists a center of rotation and an angle of rotation such that when using those elements to rotate the indicated object, the preimage and image are the same. Once again, the object falls back on itself. A circle has rotational symmetry because you can rotate the circle around its center using any angle measure as the magnitude of rotation, and the same circle will result.

Figure 8.16 shows two objects that possess rotational symmetry about the indicated point. Can you determine the magnitude and direction of a rotation for each object that confirms the object's rotational symmetry? [*For the hexagon, a clockwise or counterclockwise rotation of 180° (or any integer multiple of that) demonstrates its rotational symmetry. For the equilateral triangle, a clockwise or counterclockwise rotation of 120° (or any integer multiple of that) demonstrates its rotational symmetry.*]

FIG. 8.16

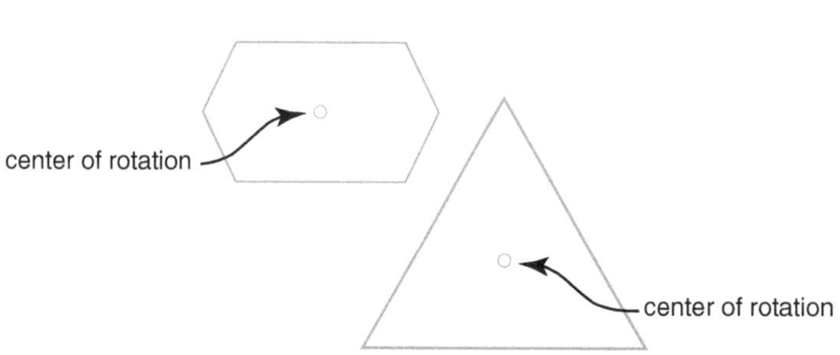

Discuss with your students the concept of rotational symmetry and ask them to identify or create other geometric objects that have rotational symmetry.

Your students may or may not have been introduced to the concept of a *function*, a mathematical operation that acts on some input to produce one unique output. Students might first encounter functions when arithmetic rules are applied to numbers. For instance, suppose the rule is "double the input." When we input 4, 8 is the output. For an input of –6, –12 is the output. This rule, double the input, is a function because each unique input results in one unique output. The rule "take the square root of the input" is *not* a function, because all positive real-number inputs result in two outputs, one positive and one negative. Consider the input 16, for instance.

We can extend the concept of function to the transformations your students have explored. Students who have explored functions as just described—knowing that a function rule generates exactly one unique output for each input—can be asked to determine whether any of the rigid-motion transformations are functions. For instance, does a translation vector—possessing direction and distance—assure that a translation is a function? Likewise for a center of rotation coupled with a rotation angle and direction of rotation and for a given mirror of reflection. You and your students can explore examples and eventually reach the conclusion that all three rigid-motion transformations are functions that act on objects.

SUMMARY

Transformations are an important topic for exploration in school mathematics. During the middle grades, students can create and study transformations to learn about mathematical tools used to move objects in the plane and in space.

Analyzing the process and the results of transformations illustrates a fundamental element of mathematical investigations: What has resulted from the actions that just took place? How do we describe them? What are the varying and invariant elements of those actions? This is a cornerstone of mathematical study, one that transcends transformations. Through such analysis, you can help your students see the interconnectedness of the processes and procedures they encounter.

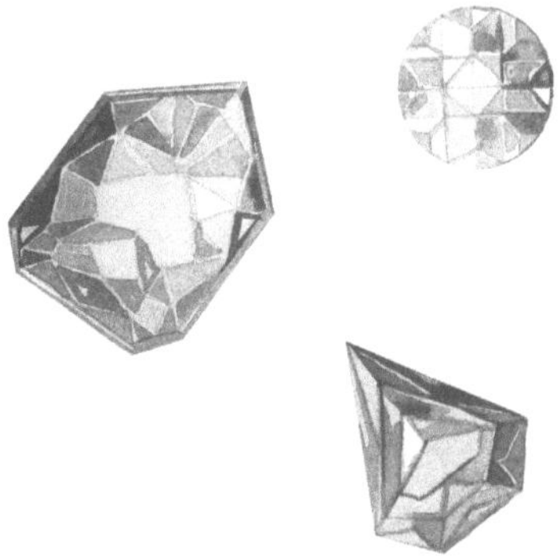

9

Reasoning about the Pythagorean Theorem

OVERVIEW

Ask someone you meet to explain the Pythagorean theorem and you are likely to hear the response "$a^2 + b^2 = c^2$." Ask them to explain what that means and you are likely to be greeted with a response that ranges from something like "multiply *a* times *a* . . ." to confused silence. The Pythagorean theorem is one of the first mathematical results that many people remember learning, and it is one that is used frequently both in and out of the classroom, yet far too often it is recalled only as an algebraic manipulation devoid of true understanding. In this investigation students will explore the Pythagorean theorem and begin to develop a conceptual understanding of what it says and why it is true.

Derived from "Reasoning about the Pythagorean Theorem" in *Navigating through Geometry in Grades 6–8* (NCTM 2002, pp. 28–30), and "Reasoning about the Pythagorean Theorem" in *Navigating through Problem Solving and Reasoning in Grades 6–8* (NCTM 2009c, pp. 113–122).

We do not know when the relationship that we attribute to Pythagoras was first discovered or by whom. We do know that the ancient Babylonians knew and applied the relationship more than a thousand years before Pythagoras, who lived in the sixth century BCE. We can also be sure that none of the ancient mathematicians would have written "$a^2 + b^2 = c^2$" because algebraic notation such as that did not emerge until well into the sixteenth century CE and did not come into common use until long after that. So, in this investigation we begin by exploring the Pythagorean relationship from its geometric roots.

GOALS

- Use an area model to develop an understanding of the Pythagorean theorem.
- Develop an understanding of the need to prove a mathematical conjecture.

- Recognize that finding a few (or even many) examples of a conjecture does not establish a proof.
- Explore a simple geometric proof of the Pythagorean theorem and explain its significance.

MATERIALS NEEDED

- Copies of the activity sheet Reasoning about the Pythagorean Relationship
- Copies of the activity sheet Take a Look at Those Squares
- Copies of the activity sheet Sets of Right Triangles
- Copies of the activity sheet Can You Prove It?
- Grid paper
- Rulers
- Scissors
- Index cards

Engage

Ask your students to explain what a right triangle is and to tell you what they know about right triangles. They should have familiarity with right triangles from elementary school, but their understanding may be sketchy and incomplete. Be sure that they recognize a right triangle as having one "square corner" even if they have not yet learned to measure angles in degrees. Before proceeding with the activity here, be sure that students know the following basic facts and vocabulary:

- A right triangle has one *right angle* which measures 90°. The other two angles are *acute angles*; each measures less than 90°.
- The two sides that form the right angle are called the *legs* of the triangle. The third side, opposite the right angle, is the *hypotenuse* of the right triangle.
- Students also need to know how to find the area of a square or rectangle and of a triangle.

Throughout this activity, in order to avoid confusing the students, we will consistently label the vertices of the right triangles A, B, and C, with C being the right angle. The sides will be labeled a (the leg across from angle A), b (the leg across from angle B), and c (the hypotenuse, across from right angle C) (see figure 9.1). Note that in this case the letters a, b, and c are used to designate both the *segments* that form the sides of the triangle and the *lengths* of the respective sides. Later in their mathematical studies, after the students exhibit understanding of the Pythagorean theorem, it will be important to expose them to triangles that are labeled differently, perhaps with other letters or with A, B, and C in some other permutation of the assigned vertices.

FIG. 9.1

A right triangle

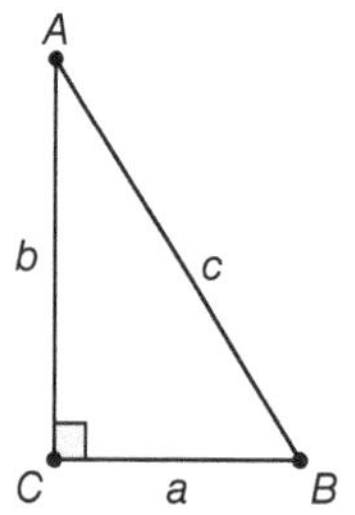

Launch the activity by giving the students grid paper and having them draw a right triangle with legs of three and four units lying along grid lines, as shown in figure 9.2a. Demonstrate what we mean when we say "draw the square on leg *a*" [a square with sides of length *a*] and have them draw the squares on the two legs of their triangles. Drawing the square on the hypotenuse may be a challenge for some students because the sides do not lie along grid lines. To help them complete that task, suggest that they measure the length of the hypotenuse with another piece of grid paper and cut out a square of the correct size that they can position on the hypotenuse (figure 9.2b).

FIG. 9.2

(a) (b)

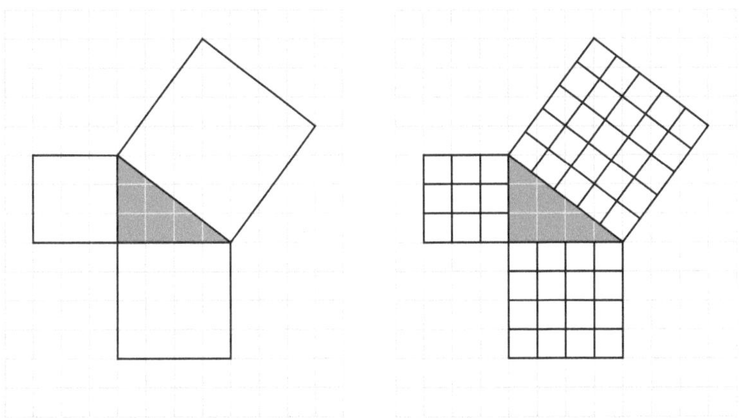

To provide a context for what follows, tell the students that sometime around 4,000 years ago ancient mathematicians discovered that right triangles have a very special property that sets them apart from all other triangles. They are going to try to discover what that property is and to prove that the ancient mathematicians were correct. They will begin by looking at the example in figure 9.2 and finding the area of the three squares drawn on the sides of the triangle. If necessary, remind them that the area of the square on the side of the triangle is given by the number of unit (small) squares needed to cover the larger square. For this triangle they can determine the area of the squares by counting.

Give each student a copy of the activity sheet Reasoning about the Pythagorean Relationship and additional grid paper, as needed. Have them record the area of the three squares in the first example (figure 9.2). Then, working individually or with a partner, direct them to repeat the process used earlier to construct three more examples of right triangles with the following legs:

- Triangle 2: legs of 5 units and 12 units. [*They should discover that the hypotenuse is 13 units.*]
- Triangle 3: legs of 6 units and 8 units. [*They should discover that the hypotenuse is 10 units.*]
- Triangle 4: legs of 8 units and 15 units. [*They should discover that the hypotenuse is 17 units.*]

Allow sufficient time to complete the triangles and the accompanying table, and then ask the students to describe any patterns that they observe and write their conclusions in the space provided in question 4 on the sheet. Call on students to share their observations and conclusions and to answer questions from other students. At this stage they should have noticed the relationship between the area of the square on the hypotenuse and the area of the squares on the legs.

What we have here is a *conjecture*: On the basis of what we observed in four examples of right triangles, it appears that the area of the square drawn on the hypotenuse is equal to the sum of the areas of the squares drawn on the two legs. We do not yet know if that is always true, but we have reason to believe that it might be, so in what follows we will see what more we can discover and prove.

In Proposition 47 of the Elements (fourth century BCE), Euclid states: In right-angled triangles the square on the side opposite the right angle equals the sum of the squares on the sides containing the right angle.

Explore

We have a *conjecture* about the Pythagorean relationship, but we cannot yet call it a *theorem*. To be accepted as a theorem, the relationship must be proven true for every right triangle without exception. We have drawn a tentative conclusion based on only four examples, and very special examples at that, for all four of the triangles so far had three sides with all integer lengths. We need to consider some more general cases.

The students are going to explore right triangles in which the sides do not necessarily have integer lengths, so the strategy of cutting squares from grid paper to measure area will not apply. But in the examples that they will explore, they can determine areas by decomposing the target square into smaller square and right-triangular regions that they can determine. Before proceeding with new examples, introduce the idea of decomposition by looking at the square on the hypotenuse of the 3–4–5 right triangle in a new way (see figure 9.3).

FIG. 9.3

Finding area by decomposition

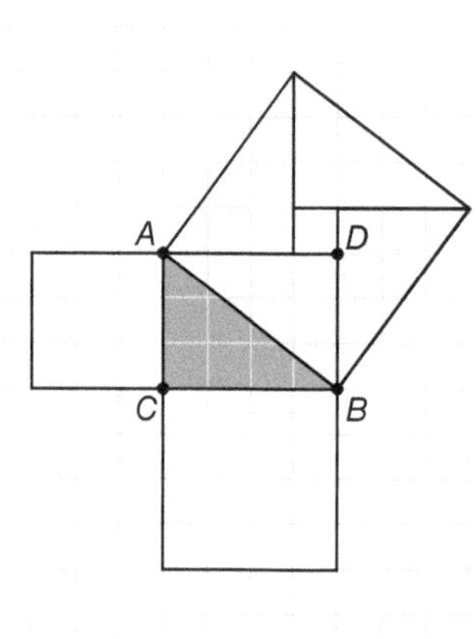

Note how the large square is partitioned, by drawing segments along grid lines, into four right triangles and a central square. The four gray triangles and the original green triangle are all identical (*congruent*). Further, ΔABC and ΔABD together form rectangle $ADBC$ with area 12 square units, and each of the triangles is half of that rectangle, or 6 square units. Now we can determine the area of the large square: area = 4(6) + 1 = 25 square units. The students will use that decomposition strategy throughout the rest of the activity, so to be sure they understand the procedure, you can ask them to demonstrate and explain how to decompose the square in the earlier example of a 5–12–13 right triangle. A solution is shown in figure 9.4.

FIG. 9.4

Area = 4(30) + 49 = 169 sq. units

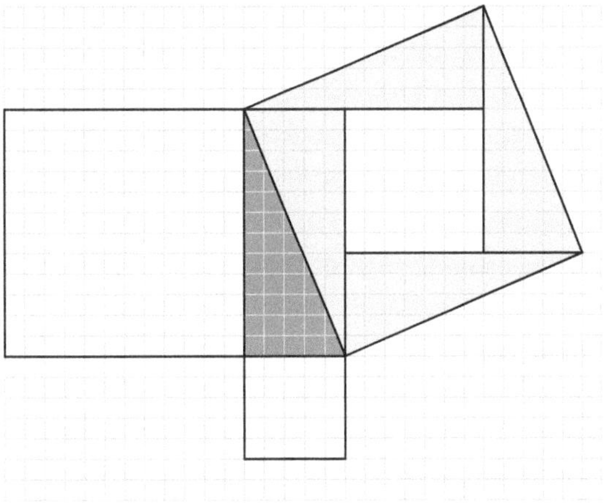

Remind the students that they have formed a conjecture based on four special examples and that now they need to check other, more general cases. As a next step they will examine some right triangles for which the sides are not necessarily whole numbers and the legs do not necessarily lie along grid lines; but in all of the cases, the triangles will have their three vertices at points of intersection of grid lines. (That will ensure that the decomposition strategy of drawing segments along grid lines will work nicely.) Give each student a copy of the activity Take a Look at Those Squares and let them work in twos or threes to complete problems 1 through 4 on the sheets. The triangles presented in those problems can be analyzed using the decomposition strategy on one or more of the squares. For example, the solution for problem 4 is shown here in figure 9.5.

FIG. 9.5

Problem 4 from Take a Look at Those Squares

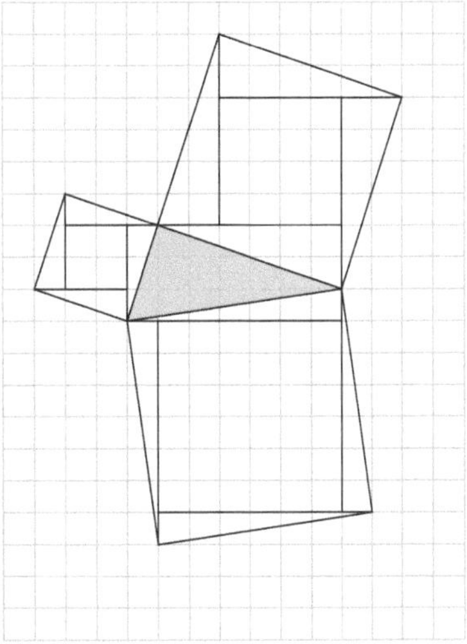

Square on short leg:

$$\text{Area} = 4\left(\frac{3 \times 1}{2}\right) + 4 = 6 + 4 = 10$$

Square on long leg:

$$\text{Area} = 4\left(\frac{6 \times 2}{2}\right) + 16 = 24 + 16 = 40$$

Square on hypotenuse:

$$\text{Area} = 4\left(\frac{7 \times 1}{2}\right) + 36 = 14 + 36 = 50$$

Bring the students together after they complete questions 1–4 and have them share their findings and conclusions. Does the Pythagorean conjecture still appear to be true? Did the new examples help to strengthen their opinions about the relationship? How? Why? [*The new examples were not limited to triangles with integer-length sides.*]

Challenge the students to each create one or two more examples of their own, different from those on the activity sheets. They should draw their triangles on grid paper, placing the vertices of the triangles at grid-line intersection points. But caution them that they must be sure the triangles they draw are right triangles. One way to do that is to use the corner of an index card to help locate a right (90°) angle (see figure 9.6). Also, students who are familiar with linear graphs can select a point for the vertex of the right angle and then apply their knowledge of the slopes of perpendicular lines to locate lattice points for the other two vertices. For example, in figure 9.6, if the point (1,2) is selected for vertex *C*, then side *CA* (leg *b*) has a slope of 3, while side *CB* (leg *a*) has a slope of –1/3, which guarantees that *ACB* is a right angle. Some students may struggle with the challenge of drawing right triangles like this, so allow ample time for them to work, and be prepared to assist them if needed.

FIG. 9.6

Make sure the triangle is a right triangle.

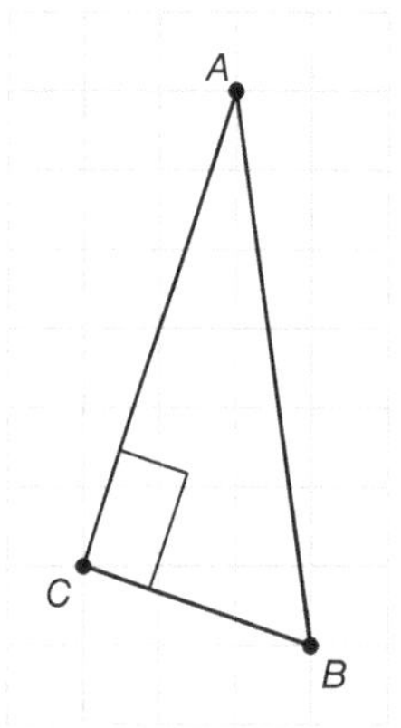

Once the students have drawn one or more right triangles, they should again construct the squares on the sides of their triangles, find the areas by decomposition, and record the results. Call on various individuals to demonstrate and explain their decompositions and the areas of their squares. Do their triangles support the conjecture?

For additional examples that do not require the decomposition procedure, you could use dynamic geometry software such as *Geometer's Sketchpad* or *Geogebra* to create right triangles and the squares on their sides. The software allows you to change lengths and shapes of the right triangles by dragging vertices and, as you do, to measure sides and areas, thereby generating as many examples as you like. You can also use an applet such as Squaring the Triangle that can be found at http://www.shodor.org/interactivate/activities/SquaringTheTriangle/. Figure 9.7 shows a screen shot from that applet. The lengths of the legs are changed by dragging the sliders that appear below the figure, while the length, angle, and area values appear on the left. Question 5 in the Take a Look at Those Squares activity asks students to use the applet (or you could use your dynamic geometry software) to generate additional triangles and record the data in the table given on the activity sheet.

Evidence in favor of our conjecture is mounting, and at this point some of the students may be content to accept it as "proof" that the relationship is true, especially when the examples set forth are more random and varied. But no finite set of examples will ever constitute a proof, for the possibility always remains that somewhere there may exist even one *counter-example*, one triangle that will disprove the conjecture. We need to prove, once and for all, that the conjecture is true.

"Part of the beauty of mathematics is that when interesting things happen, it is usually for good reason. Mathematics students should understand this." (NCTM 2000, p. 56)

FIG. 9.7

Squaring the Triangle applet screen

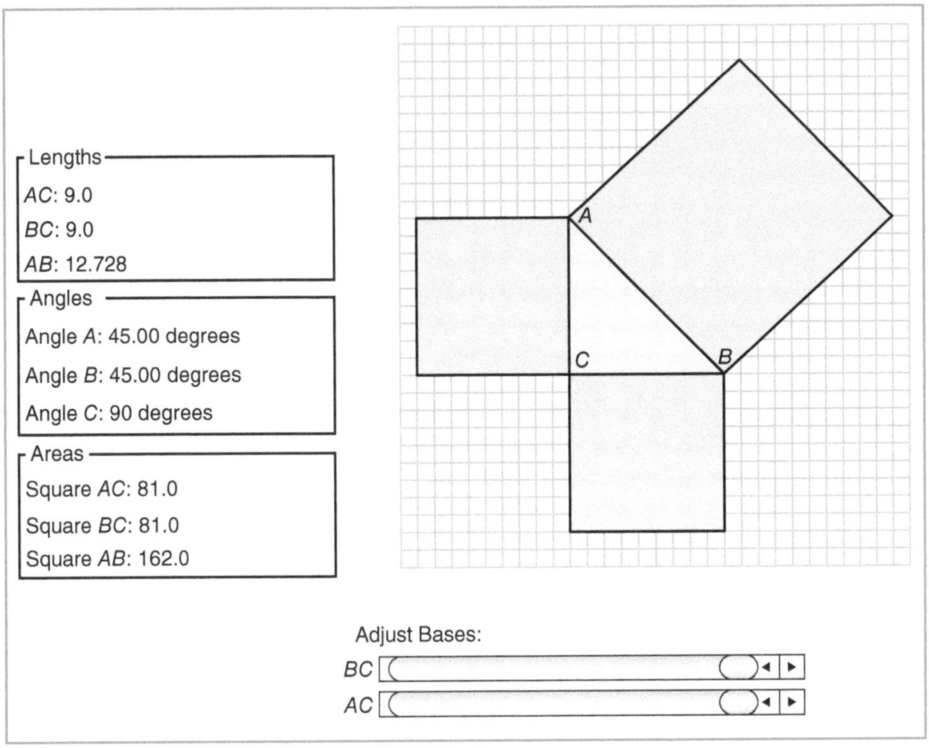

Over the centuries hundreds of proofs have been set forth for the Pythagorean theorem, and someday the students may be challenged to produce and explain a rigorous proof of their own. But we do not expect that at this stage of their mathematical development. Rather, they will examine a simple given proof and develop a rationale and explanation to support it. For this part of the activity, give the students copies of the activity sheets Sets of Right Triangles and Can You Prove It?

Have the students cut out the first set of four congruent triangles from the sheet and arrange them to form a square as shown in figure 9.8. How do we know that we have formed squares here? [*We know that both the outer and the inner figures have four right angles and four equal sides. We also know that the sides of the outer figure lie on a straight line because the three angles that meet at the vertices of the inner square—that is, one right angle and two complementary acute angles—always add up to 180°, a straight angle.*]

FIG. 9.8

Four copies of a right triangle arranged to form a square

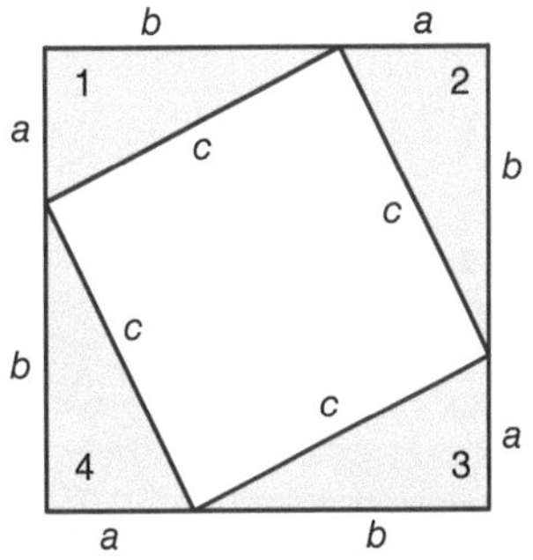

We need not know numerical values for the side lengths because this could be *any* right triangle; regardless of the lengths of the two legs, the four triangles form a square with sides of length $(a + b)$. Further, the outer *circumscribed* square encloses another *inscribed* square with sides of length c, as shown. Ask the students to describe the area of the outer square in terms of its five components:

$$\text{Area} = 4\left(\frac{a \times b}{2}\right) + c^2 = 2(ab) + c^2$$

Now outline the large square that you formed earlier, and then rearrange the four triangles by sliding triangle 3 to the upper-left corner and sliding triangle 2 down and triangle 4 to the right into the lower-right corner, as shown in figure 9.9.

FIG. 9.9

Four copies of the right triangle rearranged in the square

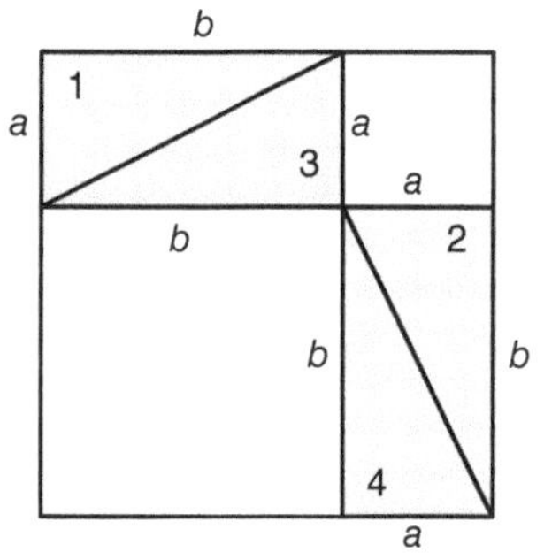

Repositioning the triangles does not alter the size of the original square, but it does provide a different way of describing the area of the large square in terms of two rectangles and two smaller squares:

$$\text{Area} = 2(ab) + a^2 + b^2$$

And now we have two different expressions describing the area of the same square, so the two expressions must be equal. The students should be able to show and explain the consequences:

$$2(ab) + c^2 = 2(ab) + a^2 + b^2$$

$$\therefore \quad c^2 = a^2 + b^2$$

Have the students repeat the previous steps using the other two sets of triangles cut from the activity sheet as they complete the Can You Prove It? activity. The three sets of four triangles represent three cases: (1) when $a < b$, (2) when $a = b$, and (3) when $a > b$. The results hold for all three, as shown in figure 9.10.

Discuss with the students the significance of what they have just done and why they are now justified in referring to the Pythagorean relationship as a *theorem* and not just a conjecture. They should recognize that the lengths of the two legs, a and b, can take on any values at all, and once those two lengths are fixed, the length of the hypotenuse, c, is uniquely determined. Thus, the general proof that they have just examined covers all possible right triangles.

Be aware, though, that some students may overgeneralize the result and attempt to apply it to non-right triangles. This is a good opportunity to introduce the concept of a *counterexample*. To do so, have each student draw on their grid paper a triangle with vertices at grid-line intersections, as before, but a triangle that is *not* a right triangle, then draw the squares on the three sides and determine their areas by the decomposition method used before. An example

FIG. 9.10

Three cases

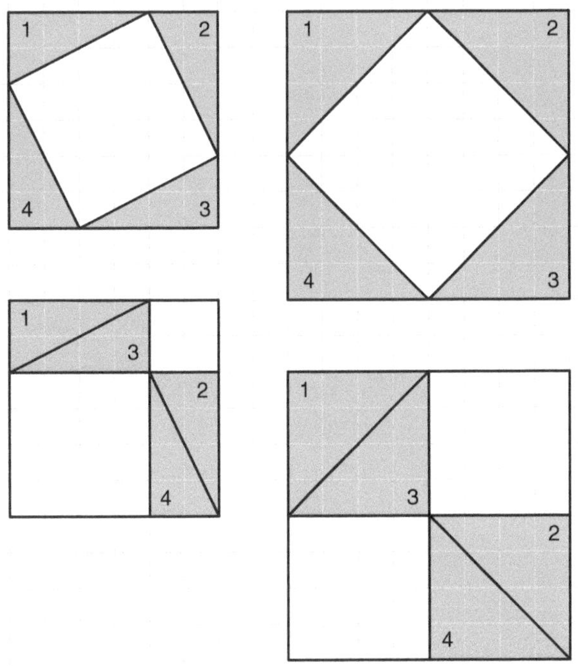

is shown in figure 9.11, where none of the areas of the squares equals the sum of the other two. This is only one example, but it is sufficient to demonstrate that the Pythagorean theorem cannot be applied to non-right triangles. Students will probably not fully appreciate the significance of counterexamples until later in their mathematical development, but this exposes them to the concept in a meaningful context.

FIG. 9.11

A counterexample

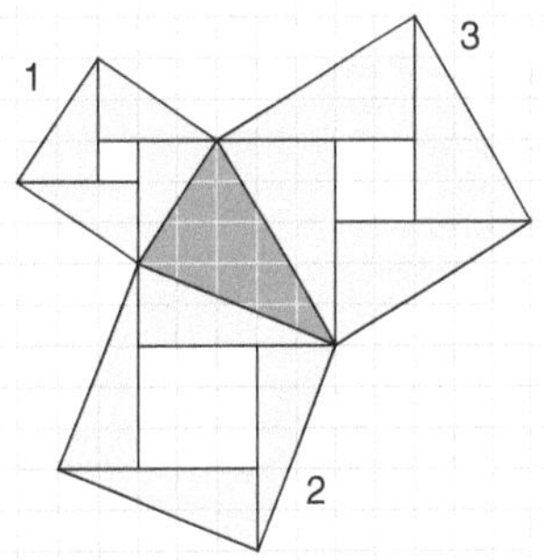

Area 1 = 4(3) + 1 = 13
Area 2 = 4(5) + 9 = 29
Area 3 = 4(7.5) + 4 = 34

Extend

To provide students with additional opportunities to analyze and explain a proof for the Pythagorean theorem, you can present them with the following two examples, each with an interesting history.

The first proof comes from Bhaskara, a 12th-century Hindu mathematician who presented the arrangement shown in figure 9.12. Note that this time four triangles are positioned so that the hypotenuse forms the side of the circumscribed square. The students can reproduce this arrangement using the sets of four triangles from the previous proof. By way of explanation, Bhaskara simply wrote: "Behold!" To him, the proof was clear. To the students, it merits additional scrutiny. A hint is provided in figure 9.13.

FIG. 9.12

Bhaskara: "Behold!"

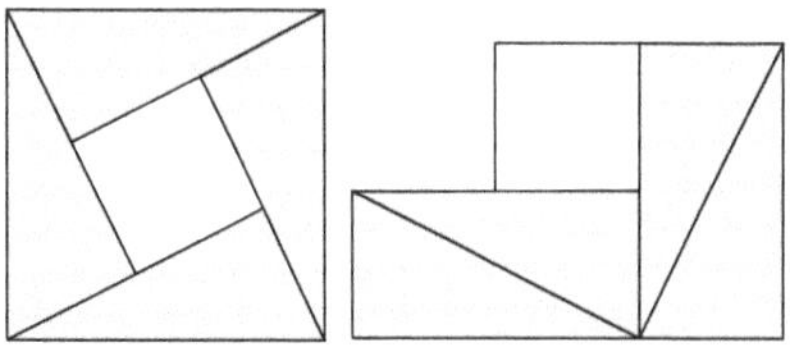

FIG. 9.13

Behold (again)

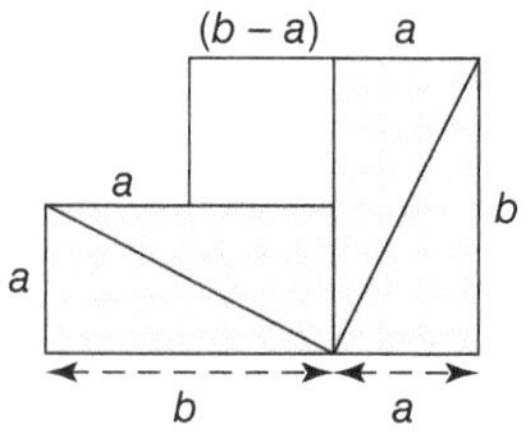

The second proof was discovered and published by US President James A. Garfield in 1876 while he was a congressman from Ohio, five years before becoming the 20th president of the United States in 1881. Garfield's proof is shown in figure 9.14. In this case we see a trapezoid, which may be unfamiliar to students at this grade level. But if the students do not notice it themselves, you can provide them with the following hint: Compare Garfield's figure to the figures you studied in the first proof of the theorem earlier. (Later in their study of geometry they can return to this and analyze it in terms of the area of a trapezoid.)

FIG. 9.14

President Garfield's proof

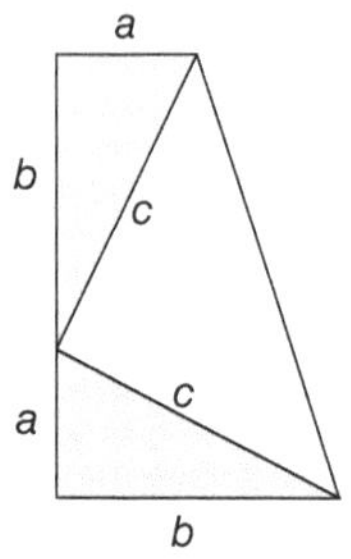

SUMMARY

The outcomes of this activity are twofold: developing a conceptual understanding of the Pythagorean relationship and laying a foundation for understanding and appreciating the nature of mathematical proof. The beauty of the activity lies in the use of a geometric model to focus on meaning rather than on calculations.

> *Instructional programs from prekindergarten through grade 12 should enable all students to—*
>
> - *Recognize reasoning and proof as fundamental aspects of mathematics*
> - *Make and investigate mathematical conjectures*
> - *Develop and evaluate mathematical arguments and proofs*
> - *Select and use various types of reasoning and methods of proof*
>
> (NCTM 2000, p. 56)

The initial cases presented in the Engage section were all built on Pythagorean triples—cases in which the side lengths of the triangles are all integers, as in (3, 4, 5) or (5, 12, 13). For those triangles students can use grid-paper squares to see and directly count the unit squares composing each of the three squares on the triangle's sides. For the more general examples shown in the Explore section, the grid paper and decomposition strategy demonstrates the relationship regardless of the side lengths. In those triangles the side lengths need not be integers, as is the case, for example, with problem 4 in Take a Look at Those Squares, where the triangle has sides of length $\sqrt{10}$, $2\sqrt{10}$, and $5\sqrt{2}$ (see figure 9.5 earlier). Without the decomposition strategy, students who are not proficient in calculating with radicals are faced with the need to approximate side lengths with decimals, thereby shifting the focus from meaning to calculation.

Neither complete understanding of the Pythagorean theorem nor proficiency with mathematical proofs will result from a single encounter such as this activity provides. But the activity lays an important foundation for both. Throughout their mathematical studies, students will encounter the theorem and its many applications, and as they mature mathematically, they will often be challenged to make conjectures and prove results, situations for which this activity begins to build readiness and appreciation.

10

Investigating Pick's Theorem

OVERVIEW

Formulas are essential in the study of mathematics, but too often students see formulas as isolated and confusing collections of symbols, presented to them in finished form without context or development, something to be remembered and manipulated but not necessarily understood. This activity, which will extend over several class periods, introduces students to Pick's formula for finding the area of polygons drawn on a lattice. The activity guides them through an investigation of how the formula is developed and why it makes sense. Because the formula will be new to most of the students, the investigation provides an opportunity to engage in a productive struggle and create new knowledge, first by exploring familiar figures and their areas and then by pushing forward into new territory. The investigation also highlights connections between geometry and algebra while allowing for differentiated levels of engagement, depending on the students' mathematical readiness.

Derived from "Pick's Theorem" in *Navigating through Measurement in Grades 6–8* (NCTM 2005, pp. 43–44).

Georg Alexander Pick (1859–1942) was an Austrian mathematician born in Vienna to a Jewish family. He spent his career teaching at the University of Prague until he retired in 1927. Pick died in the Theresienstadt concentration camp in 1942. He is best remembered for Pick's theorem, which he published in 1899.

GOALS

- Explore polygons drawn on geodot (lattice) paper and develop a formula for finding the area of any such polygon.
- Reason about special classes of polygons to develop an understanding of Pick's formula and its usefulness in solving area problems.
- Demonstrate how mathematical formulas are discovered, developed, and generalized.

MATERIALS NEEDED

- Pick's Theorem activity sheet for each student
- Exploring Pick's Rule activity sheets for each student
- What's the Area? activity sheet for each student
- Pick's Theorem—The Hole Truth activity sheets for each student
- Geoboards, if available
- Geodot paper
- Rulers or straightedge

Engage

Begin this activity with a brief discussion of area so you can assess your students' understanding of the topic. The problems that follow will all be concerned with polygons that can be made on a geoboard or drawn on geodot paper. Known as *lattice polygons*, these shapes have all their vertices at points of the lattice (geodot paper) or pegs of the geoboard. The first shapes will be relatively simple and familiar ones, but they will become more irregular as the activity progresses. Before beginning the activity, be sure your students can determine the area of simple, closed lattice polygons. Have them demonstrate their ability to determine areas using one of the following three ways, as appropriate for a given situation:

1. For rectangles, students may be able to count the unit squares directly. For rectangles or right triangles they can also apply area formulas that they have learned previously. (Area = length × width for rectangles; area = 1/2 base × height for triangles. Some students may also know area formulas for parallelograms or trapezoids.)

   A word of caution is in order here: Be sure the students understand the difference between determining the *length* of a line segment and the *number of lattice points* on the segment. For example, in polygon B pictured here the outer square has a side length of 2 units, but the side contains 3 lattice points.

2. Some areas can be determined by partitioning the shape. Polygon F from the first activity sheet is an example. The given shape, a kite, can be partitioned into four right triangles, as shown. We see that triangles 1 and 2 are each half of a 1-by-2 rectangle, so those triangles are each 1 square unit in area. Triangles 3 and 4 are each half of a unit square, so they each have an area of 1/2 square unit. The area of shape F is 1 + 1 + 1/2 + 1/2 = 3 square units. Caution: When students choose to find the area by partitioning, be sure that the smaller shapes into which they divide the original consist only of rectangles, squares, or right triangles.

FIG. 10.1

Two methods to determine area

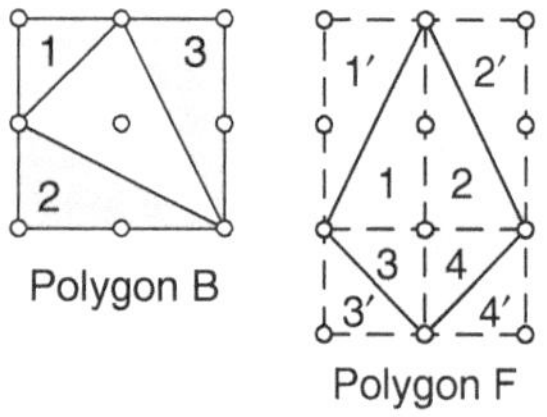

3. The third strategy for finding area is to inscribe the shape in a rectangle or square and subtract the area of

the outside regions. Polygon B from the first activity sheet is an example of this. The given triangle is inscribed in a 2-by-2 square from which we remove three triangles: triangle 1 with area 1/2 square unit and triangles 2 and 3 each with area 1 square unit. The area of shape B is then 4 – 1/2 – 1 – 1 = 1 1/2 square units.

When students have demonstrated their ability to find areas of simple shapes using one of these three strategies, distribute copies of the Pick's Theorem activity sheet and allow time for the students to find the areas of the given shapes. In addition to recording the areas in the table provided on the sheet, they will count and record two additional items for each shape: B, the number of *boundary points*, and I, the number of *interior points* for each polygon. Boundary points are lattice points that lie at a vertex or along a side of the polygon; interior points are lattice points that fall within the polygon. In the two examples shown earlier, polygon B has $B = 3$ and $I = 1$; polygon F has $B = 4$ and $I = 2$. The solutions for polygons A through L are shown in table 10.1.

Table 10.1. Solutions for Pick's Theorem Activity Sheet

Polygon	Boundary Points (B)	Interior Points (I)	Area Sq. Units
A	3	0	0.5
B	3	1	1.5
C	3	2	2.5
D	4	0	1
E	4	1	2
F	4	2	3
G	5	0	1.5
H	5	1	2.5
I	5	2	3.5
J	6	0	2
K	6	1	3
L	6	2	4

Referring to polygons A through L, the activity sheet poses three questions (questions 3–5):

- What patterns do you notice in the data in the chart?
- As the number of boundary points (B) increases, what happens to the value of the area? [*When B increases by 1, area increases by 1/2 square unit.*]
- As the number of interior points (I) increases, what happens to the value of the area? [*When I increases by 1, area increases by 1 square unit.*]

Ask the students to explain how they answered the questions on the basis of the 12 given figures. If you want them to gather more data, you can tell them to draw additional polygons on geodot paper and complete an expanded table such as table 10.2. (The information for shapes A through L on the activity sheet has been transferred into the upper-left section of this table. For example, table 10.1 shows that for shape F, $B = 4$ and $I = 2$. In table 10.2, at the intersection of the column $B = 4$ and the row $I = 2$, we enter the area for shape F, which is 3 square units.) Do their answers change? Or does the expanded table provide additional support for their observed patterns?

Table 10.2. Expanded Table for Pick's Theorem

		Number of Boundary Points (*B*)							
	Area ↘	3	4	5	6	7	8	9	10
Number of Interior Points (*I*)	0	0.5	1	1.5	2				
	1	1.5	2	2.5	3				
	2	2.5	3	3.5	4				
	3								
	4								
	5								
	6								
	7								
	8								

If nobody suggests a relationship between the area and the number of boundary and interior points, the activity sheet offers a hint in question 6: What is the relationship of $B/2$ and I to the area of each figure? The answer to that question leads us to the statement of Pick's theorem: For polygons drawn on a lattice, $area = \frac{B}{2} + I - 1$. Throughout the remainder of this activity we will investigate Pick's formula to gain insight into how it develops, why it makes sense, and how it applies in solving problems.

Pick's theorem: The area of a polygon drawn on a square lattice is given by

$$Area = \frac{B}{2} + I - 1,$$

where B is the number of lattice points on the edges of the polygon (including vertices) and I is the number of lattice points inside the polygon.

Explore

A complete and rigorous proof of Pick's theorem evolves through a number of steps. We do not expect middle school students to develop or even fully understand such a proof, but they can explore parts of it and at each stage understand the reasonableness of the process and the usefulness of the result. In the discussion that follows, the algebraic proof for each step will be shown separately so that you can decide whether and for which of your students it is appropriate to include. We begin by investigating several special cases of lattice polygons. You can use the activity sheet Exploring Pick's Rule to guide this inquiry.

"What are teachers doing? Motivating students' learning of mathematics through opportunities for exploring and solving problems that build on and extend their current mathematical understanding." (NCTM 2014, p. 24)

Step 1: Consider rectangles that have their sides aligned with the lattice.

Have the students use the first three rectangles on the Exploring Pick's Rule sheet to count points and complete the chart for lines a through f. Then, using the data for each rectangle, compute the area of the rectangle using Pick's formula and compare it with the area calculated with the familiar "area = $b \times h$" formula (line h). They will see that for rectangles aligned with the lattice, Pick's formula yields the correct value for the area of the rectangle. Distribute copies of geodot paper and invite the students to draw several more rectangles of their choosing, always making sure the sides are aligned with, and the vertices are on, lattice points. The students should verify the outcome for their examples as well.

The fourth rectangle on the activity sheet represents a generalized m-by-n rectangle. Refer to the first three examples on the activity sheet to develop three important generalizations here:

- First, a segment of length m contains $(m + 1)$ lattice points. (Relate this to a specific example, for instance, to the first rectangle on the sheet, where a side of length 6 units contains 7 lattice points, as shown in figure 10.2.)
- Second, a rectangle with sides of length m and n has $(2m + 2n)$ lattice points on the boundary. Again refer to examples from the sheet where, for instance, the rectangle shown in figure 10.3, with sides of length 6 and 4 units, has 20 boundary points $[20 = (2 \times 6) + (2 \times 4)]$.
- Third, a rectangle with sides of length m and n has $(m - 1)(n - 1)$ lattice points in the interior. Again, from the 6-by-4 example rectangle, there are $5 \times 3 = 15$ interior points $[15 = (6 - 1) \times (4 - 1)]$.

FIG. 10.2

Segment of length 6

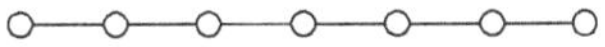

FIG. 10.3

A 6-by-4 rectangle

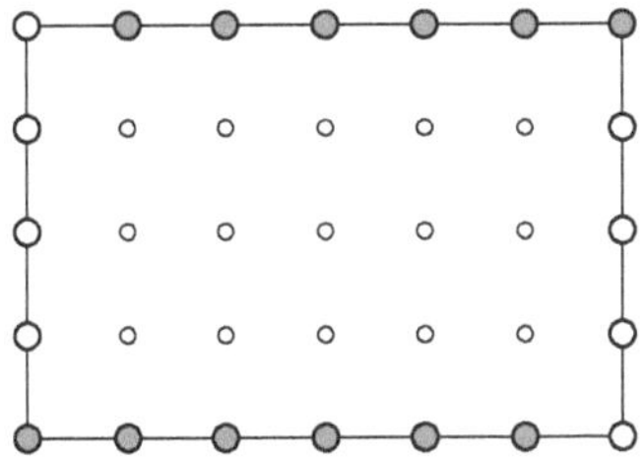

Not all middle-grades students are ready to deal with the general case, and you can skip this more abstract case for those students. But students with sufficient understanding of algebra can go on to apply Pick's formula to the generalized rectangle, as shown in figure 10.4. They will see that the formula yields the correct value for the area of any lattice-aligned rectangle.

FIG. 10.4

Pick's theorem for lattice-aligned rectangles

Consider a lattice-aligned rectangle with sides of length m and n (figure 10.5). Recall that a segment of length m contains $(m + 1)$ lattice points and that the rectangle has $(2m + 2n)$ lattice points on the boundary and $(m - 1)(n - 1)$ lattice points in the interior. Thus, Pick's rule applied to that rectangle gives this:

$$\begin{aligned} Area &= \frac{B}{2} + I - 1 \\ &= \frac{2m+2n}{2} + (m-1)(n-1) - 1 \\ &= (m+n) + (mn - m - n + 1) - 1 \\ Area &= mn \end{aligned}$$

FIG. 10.5

General m-by-n rectangle

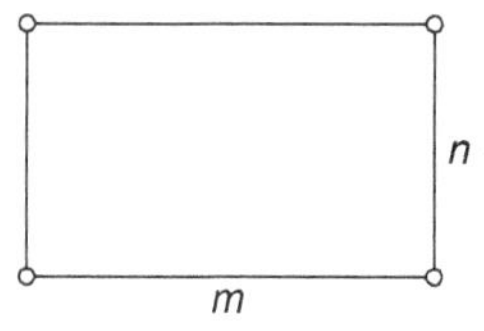

Step 2: Consider right triangles that have their legs aligned with the lattice.

As we move to the second case, right triangles with legs lying along lattice lines, we begin to see how each step toward a proof makes use of the results already proved. Again, the Exploring Pick's Rule sheet presents three examples of triangles with two sides aligned with the lattice. It should be obvious that the given condition is only possible for right triangles, and because they are right triangles, each one can be inscribed in a rectangle, as shown on the activity sheet. Have the students complete the chart for lines *a* through *g* for the first three triangles, and note that this time something has changed: The boundary points on the two legs of the triangle are similar to the case for rectangles, but now we must consider the third side of the triangle, the hypotenuse.

FIG. 10.6

Some triangles have lattice points on the hypotenuse

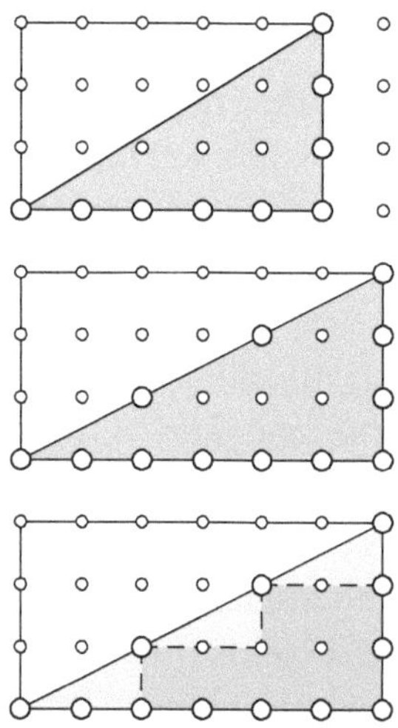

As the examples pictured here demonstrate (figure 10.6), some triangles have lattice points along the hypotenuse, and some do not. We will use h to denote the number of lattice points on the hypotenuse, not including the endpoints, since the endpoints are vertices of the triangle and have already been counted with the boundary points on the legs. Furthermore, the points on the hypotenuse are significant because they are now boundary points of the triangle whereas previously they were interior points of the rectangle.

The number of points on the hypotenuse, h, depends on the ratio of the lengths of the legs, m and n. In the first example shown here the legs have the ratio 3/5, a fraction in simplest form. In the second example, the ratio of the legs is 3/6, a fraction that can be simplified because the two values share a common factor of 3. (This is seen visually in the three small triangles, each similar to the original, with vertices on the hypotenuse.) Thus, points appear along the hypotenuse when the legs share a common factor >1. In fact, the number of points, h, is the greatest common factor of m and n, less 1. In the first example here, $h = \text{gcf}(5, 3) - 1 = 1 - 1 = 0$. In second example, $h = \text{gcf}(6, 3) - 1 = 3 - 1 = 2$.

For the first three triangles on the activity sheet, the students should again calculate the area of each triangle using Pick's formula and compare the result to the value of the area given by the formula "area = 1/2 base × height." As with the rectangles, they will see that Pick's formula yields the correct value for area. Once again, they can use geodot paper or geoboards to create additional examples of their own and further verify the outcome. Those students who have sufficient command of algebra can, if you choose, generalize the result as shown in figure 10.7.

FIG. 10.7

Pick's theorem for lattice-aligned right triangles

Consider a right triangle with horizontal and vertical legs of length m and n (figure 10.8). The number of **boundary points** is $\mathbf{m + n + 1 + h}$, where h is the number of lattice points on the hypotenuse, not including the hypotenuse endpoints ($m + n$ points on legs, plus 1 at the right angle, plus h on the hypotenuse).

For **interior points**: The number of interior points for the m-by-n rectangle is $I = (m - 1)(n - 1)$. When the rectangle is partitioned into two right triangles, interior points on the hypotenuse become boundary points of the triangle, and the number of interior points for one triangle is half of the remaining interior points of the rectangle:

$$I = \frac{(m-1)(n-1) - h}{2}$$

Use these values in Pick's theorem and, again, the formula yields the correct value for the area of the triangle.

$$\begin{aligned} Area &= \frac{B}{2} + I - 1 \\ &= \frac{m + n + 1 + h}{2} + \frac{(m-1)(n-1) - h}{2} - 1 \\ &= \frac{m}{2} + \frac{n}{2} + \frac{1}{2} + \frac{h}{2} + \frac{mn}{2} - \frac{m}{2} - \frac{n}{2} + \frac{1}{2} - \frac{h}{2} - 1 \\ Area &= \frac{mn}{2} = \frac{1}{2}mn \end{aligned}$$

FIG. 10.8

Lattice-aligned right triangle

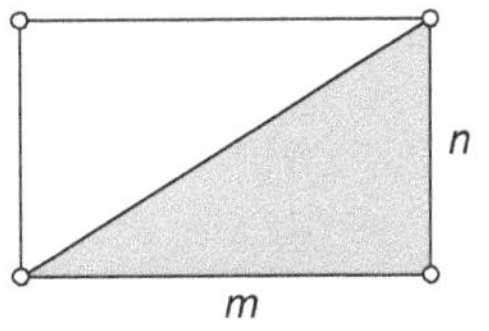

Step 3: Consider triangles that have one side aligned with the lattice.

We have just seen that Pick's formula is valid for lattice-aligned right triangles. For the third case, we consider triangles that have one side lying along a lattice line. These can be acute triangles (figure 10.9), obtuse triangles (figure 10.10), or right triangles (figure 10.11). The Exploring Pick's Rule activity sheet shows two examples each of acute and obtuse triangles. The students should complete the chart for lines a through d for the four triangles, then calculate the area of each triangle using Pick's formula and compare the result to the value of the area given by the formula "area = 1/2 base × height." Now we have evidence suggesting that Pick's formula also applies to acute and obtuse triangles—at least to those with one side aligned with the lattice. The students should draw examples of their own design on dot paper and replicate the steps they used on the activity sheet for additional verification.

FIG. 10.9

Acute triangle

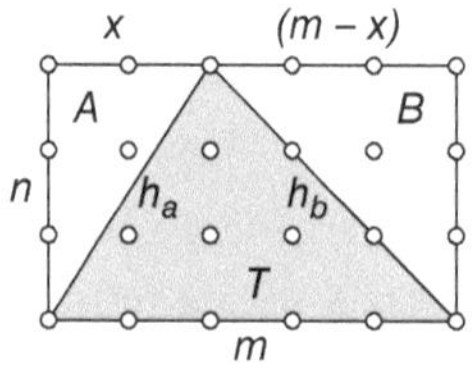

FIG. 10.10

Obtuse triangle

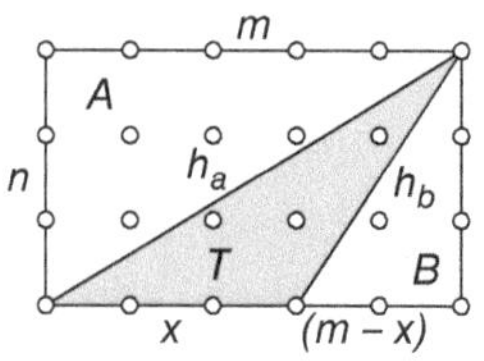

FIG. 10.11

Isosceles right triangle

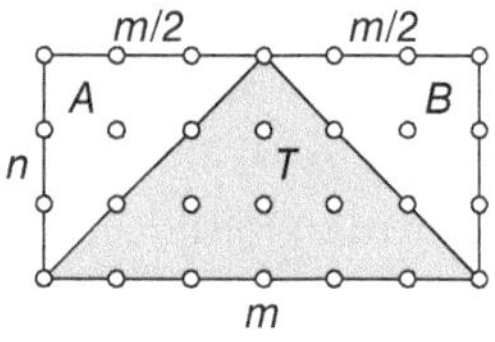

Note that it is also possible for a right triangle to be positioned with its hypotenuse aligned with the lattice. When that happens, the triangle will be an isosceles right triangle, as pictured here (figure 10.11). We will not treat it as a separate case because its proof will be exactly the same as for the acute triangle with the special circumstance that $x = (m - x) = m/2$.

For those who wish to generalize the result, the strategy for proof will take advantage of what we have already established, as follows:

- The triangle *T* has one side along a lattice line, so *T* can be inscribed in a rectangle. The rectangle, *R*, will be partitioned into three parts: the given triangle, *T*, and two right triangles, *A* and *B*.
- $\text{Area}_{\text{Rect.}} = \text{Area}_{\Delta A} + \text{Area}_{\Delta B} + \text{Area}_{\Delta T}$.
- Pick's formula is valid for *R*, *A*, and *B*.

An algebraic proof proceeds as demonstrated in figure 10.12.

FIG. 10.12

Pick's theorem for triangles with one lattice-aligned side

Step 3A: Consider an acute triangle, *T*, as shown:

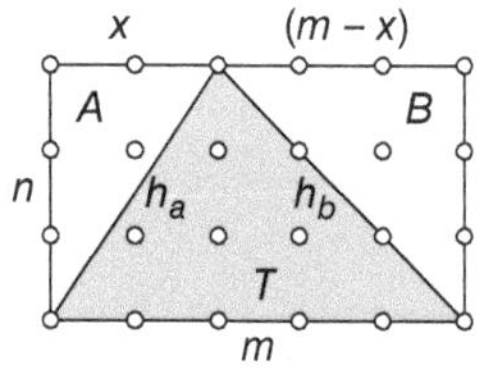

Boundary points of *T*: $B_T = h_a + h_b + (m+1) + 1 = h_a + h_b + m + 2$

Interior points of *T*:

$$I_T = I_R - I_A - I_B - (h_a + h_b)$$

$$= (m-1)(n-1) - \left[\frac{(n-1)(x-1) - h_a}{2}\right] - \left[\frac{(m-1-x)(n-1) - h_b}{2}\right] - (h_a + h_b)$$

$$= (m-1)(n-1) - \frac{(n-1)(x-1)}{2} + \frac{h_a}{2} - \left[\frac{((m-1)-x)(n-1) - h_b}{2}\right] - (h_a + h_b)$$

$$= (m-1)(n-1) - \frac{(n-1)(x-1)}{2} + \frac{h_a}{2} - \left[\frac{(m-1)(n-1) - x(n-1)}{2}\right] + \frac{h_b}{2} - (h_a + h_b)$$

$$= (m-1)(n-1) - \frac{(n-1)(x-1)}{2} + \frac{h_a + h_b}{2} - \frac{(m-1)(n-1)}{2} + \frac{x(n-1)}{2} - (h_a + h_b)$$

$$= \frac{(m-1)(n-1)}{2} - \frac{h_a + h_b}{2} - \frac{(n-1)(x-1)}{2} + \frac{x(n-1)}{2}$$

$$= \frac{(m-1)(n-1)}{2} - \frac{h_a + h_b}{2} + \frac{x(n-1) - (x-1)(n-1)}{2}$$

$$= \frac{(m-1)(n-1)}{2} - \frac{h_a + h_b}{2} + \frac{[x - (x-1)](n-1)}{2}$$

$$= \frac{(m-1)(n-1)}{2} - \frac{h_a + h_b}{2} + \frac{(n-1)}{2}$$

$$= \frac{[(m-1)+1](n-1)}{2} - \frac{h_a + h_b}{2}$$

$$I_T = \frac{m(n-1)}{2} - \frac{h_a + h_b}{2}$$

Apply Pick's theorem to T:

$$Area_T = \frac{B_T}{2} + I_T - 1$$

$$= \frac{h_a + h_b + m + 2}{2} + \frac{m(n-1)}{2} - \frac{h_a + h_b}{2} - 1$$

$$= \frac{m+2}{2} + \frac{mn - m}{2} - 1$$

$$= \frac{m}{2} + 1 + \frac{mn}{2} - \frac{m}{2} - 1$$

$$Area_T = \frac{mn}{2}$$

Step 3B: Consider an obtuse triangle, *T*, as shown:

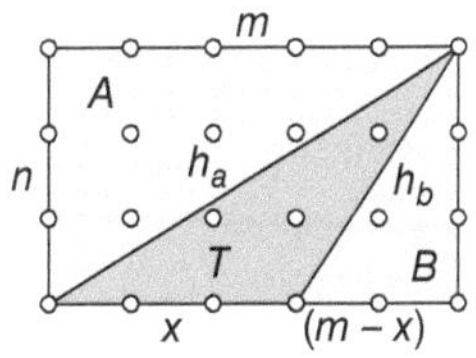

Boundary points of T: $B_T = h_a + h_b + (x+1) + 1 = h_a + h_b + x + 2$

Interior points of T:

$$I_T = I_R - I_A - I_B - (h_a + h_b)$$

$$= (m-1)(n-1) - \left[\frac{(m-1)(n-1) - h_a}{2}\right] - \left[\frac{(n-1)(m-x-1) - h_b}{2}\right] - (h_a + h_b)$$

$$= (m-1)(n-1) - \frac{(m-1)(n-1)}{2} + \frac{h_a}{2} - \frac{(n-1)(m-1-x)}{2} + \frac{h_b}{2} - (h_a + h_b)$$

$$= \frac{(m-1)(n-1)}{2} - \frac{h_a + h_b}{2} - \frac{(n-1)[(m-1)-x]}{2}$$

$$= \frac{(m-1)(n-1)}{2} - \frac{h_a + h_b}{2} + \frac{(n-1)(m-1)}{2} + \frac{(n-1)x}{2}$$

$$I_T = -\frac{h_a + h_b}{2} + \frac{nx}{2} - \frac{x}{2} = \frac{nx}{2} - \frac{x}{2} - \frac{h_a + h_b}{2}$$

Apply Pick's theorem to T:

$$Area_T = \frac{B_T}{2} + I_T - 1$$

$$= \frac{h_a + h_b + x + 2}{2} + \frac{nx}{2} - \frac{x}{2} - \frac{h_a + h_b}{2} - 1$$

$$= \frac{h_a + h_b}{2} + \frac{x}{2} + 1 + \frac{nx}{2} - \frac{x}{2} - \frac{h_a + h_b}{2} - 1$$

$$Area_T = \frac{nx}{2}$$

Step 4: Consider a general triangle that has no sides aligned with the lattice.

Finally, we can use what we know about rectangles and right triangles to show that Pick's theorem applies to all triangles, right (figure 10.13), acute (figure 10.14), or obtuse (figure 10.15), with no sides aligned with the lattice. The two examples shown in the Exploring Pick's Rule activity sheet illustrate how a general triangle can be inscribed in an outer rectangle and surrounded by right triangles and smaller rectangles. We can find the areas of those surrounding shapes and subtract them from the area of the outer rectangle to get the area of the triangle. The examples on the activity sheet, and other examples that you and the students can create on geodot paper, will demonstrate that for specific cases. For those who wish to generalize the result, proof is shown in figure 10.16.

FIG. 10.13

Right triangle

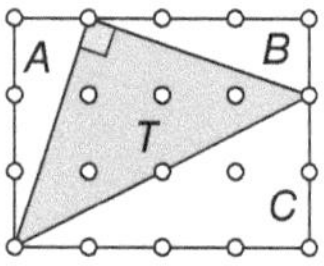

FIG. 10.14

Acute triangle

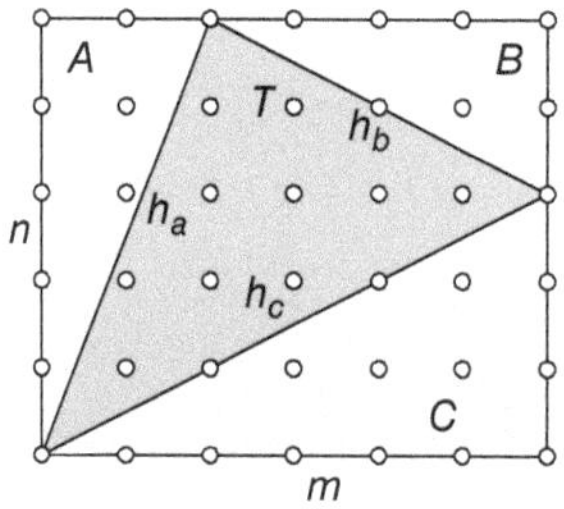

FIG. 10.15

Obtuse triangle

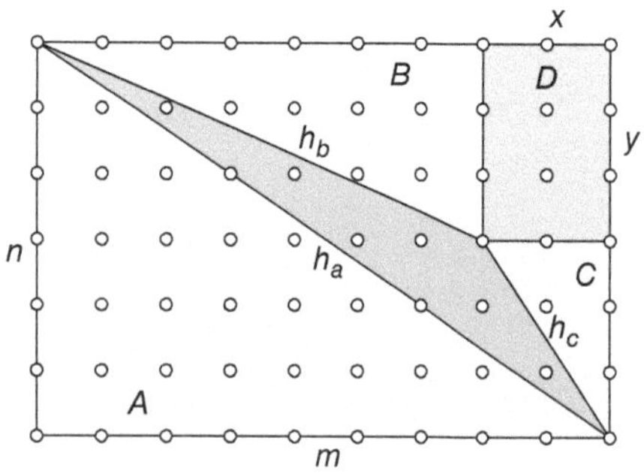

FIG. 10.16

Pick's theorem for triangles with no aligned sides

Step 4A: Consider a general acute triangle, *T*, as shown:

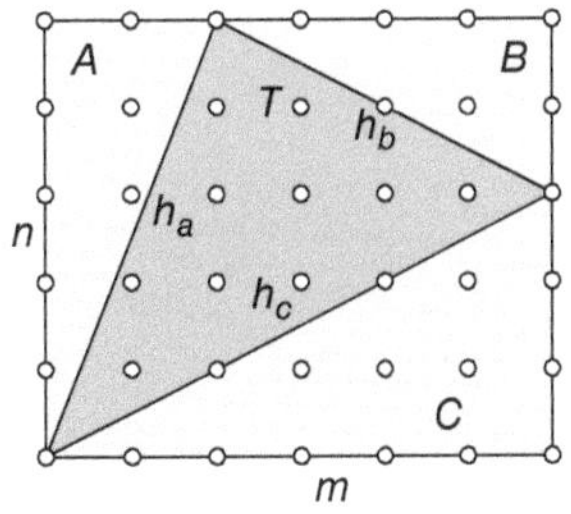

Boundary points of *T* are represented in two ways:

$$B_T = B_A + B_B + B_C - B_R$$

$$B_T = h_a + h_b + h_c + 3$$

Interior points of *T*: $I_T = I_R - I_A - I_B - I_C - (h_a + h_b + h_c)$

Area of *T*: $A_T = A_R - A_A - A_B - A_C$

Pick's theorem is valid for rectangle *R* and for right triangles *A*, *B*, and *C*, which leads to the following:

$$\begin{aligned}
A_T &= A_R - A_A - A_B - A_C \\
&= \left(\frac{B_R}{2} + I_R - 1\right) - \left(\frac{B_A}{2} + I_A - 1\right) - \left(\frac{B_B}{2} + I_B - 1\right) - \left(\frac{B_C}{2} + I_C - 1\right) \\
&= \frac{B_R - B_A - B_B - B_C}{2} + (I_R - I_A - I_B - I_C) - 1 + 3 \\
&= \frac{-B_T}{2} + I_T + (h_a + h_b + h_c) - 1 + 3 \\
&= \frac{-(h_a + h_b + h_c + 3)}{2} + I_T + (h_a + h_b + h_c) - 1 + 3 \\
&= \frac{(h_a + h_b + h_c)}{2} - \frac{3}{2} + 3 + I_T - 1 \\
&= \frac{(h_a + h_b + h_c + 3)}{2} + I_T - 1 \\
A_T &= \frac{B_T}{2} + I_T - 1
\end{aligned}$$

Step 4B: Consider a general obtuse triangle, *T*, as shown:

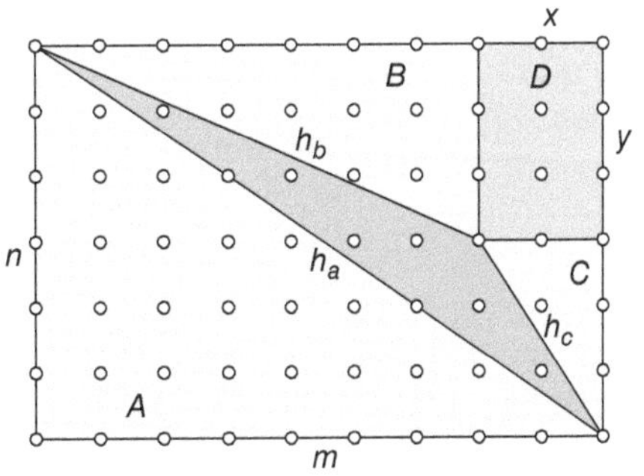

Boundary points of *T* are represented in two ways:

$$B_T = B_A + B_B + B_C - B_R$$

$$B_T = h_a + h_b + h_c + 3$$

Interior points of *T*: $I_T = I_R - I_A - I_B - I_C - I_D - (h_a + h_b + h_c) - (x + y - 1)$

Area of *T*: $A_T = A_R - A_A - A_B - A_C - A_D$

Pick's theorem is valid for rectangle R and for the surrounding shapes A, B, C, and D, leading to the following:

$$
\begin{aligned}
A_T &= A_R - A_A - A_B - A_C - A_D \\
&= \left(\frac{B_R}{2} + I_R - 1\right) - \left(\frac{B_A}{2} + I_A - 1\right) - \left(\frac{B_B}{2} + I_B - 1\right) - \left(\frac{B_C}{2} + I_C - 1\right) - \left(\frac{B_D}{2} + I_D - 1\right) \\
&= \frac{(B_R - B_A - B_B - B_C) - B_D}{2} + (I_R - I_A - I_B - I_C - I_D) - 1 + 4 \\
&= \frac{-B_T - B_D}{2} + I_T + (h_a + h_b + h_c) + (x + y - 1) - 1 + 4 \\
&= \frac{-(h_a + h_b + h_c + 3) - 2(x + y)}{2} + I_T + (h_a + h_b + h_c) + (x + y - 1) - 1 + 4 \\
&= \frac{(h_a + h_b + h_c)}{2} - \frac{3}{2} - (x + y) + I_T + (x + y) - 2 + 4 \\
&= \frac{(h_a + h_b + h_c)}{2} - \frac{3}{2} + 3 + I_T - 1 \\
&= \frac{(h_a + h_b + h_c + 3)}{2} + I_T - 1 \\
A_T &= \frac{B_T}{2} + I_T - 1
\end{aligned}
$$

Step 5: Apply to a lattice polygon.

Knowing that Pick's theorem applies to any triangle, we can now show that it applies to all other lattice polygons. We start by considering four-sided polygons that have their vertices on lattice points (figure 10.17).

FIG. 10.17

General four-sided polygon

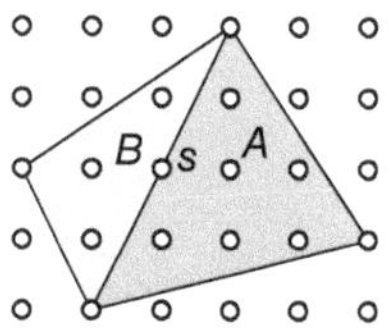

A diagonal of any given quadrilateral will partition it into two triangles, A and B, with Pick's formula applicable to both. For the polygon, P, the number of boundary points is given by

$$B_P = B_A + B_B - 2s - 2,$$

where s is the number of lattice points on the shared side of triangles A and B, excluding the endpoints. In adding $B_A + B_B$, those s points were counted twice, once with the boundary of A and once with the boundary of B; hence, the subtraction of $2s$ in the expression earlier. Also, the two vertices at the endpoints of the shared side were counted twice, once with B_A and once with B_B, and thus the −2 term to eliminate the double counting. For the interior points of P we see that

$$I_P = I_A + I_B + s.$$

Now we can invoke Pick's formula for the triangles to calculate the area of polygon P:

$$\begin{aligned}
Area_P &= Area_A + Area_B \\
&= \left(\frac{B_A}{2} + I_A - 1\right) + \left(\frac{B_B}{2} + I_B - 1\right) \\
&= \frac{B_A + B_B}{2} + (I_A + I_B) - 2 \\
&= \frac{B_P + 2s + 2}{2} + (I_P - s) - 2 \\
&= \frac{B_P}{2} + s + 1 + I_P - s - 2 \\
Area_P &= \frac{B_P}{2} + I_P - 1
\end{aligned}$$

And we find that Pick's theorem applies to four-sided polygons.

The rest of the proof develops by repeating the previous steps for the cases of five-sided, six-sided, and so on polygons (figure 10.18). For example, a five-sided polygon can be partitioned into a four-sided polygon, P, and a triangle, T, both of which are covered by Pick's theorem, and the previous calculations repeated for these new shapes P and T establish the theorem for all five-sided polygons. Next, a six-sided polygon is partitioned into a five-sided polygon, P, and a triangle, T, and the process repeats. This extension can continue to cover polygons with any number of sides, all of which can be partitioned into nonoverlapping triangles that will combine to extend Pick's result. This is what mathematicians call proof by mathematical induction: We have shown the theorem to be true for polygons with three, four, five, . . . n sides, and, by the same procedure as earlier, it will also be true for polygons with $(n + 1)$ sides, so it holds for all lattice polygons.

FIG. 10.18

Five-sided and six-sided polygons

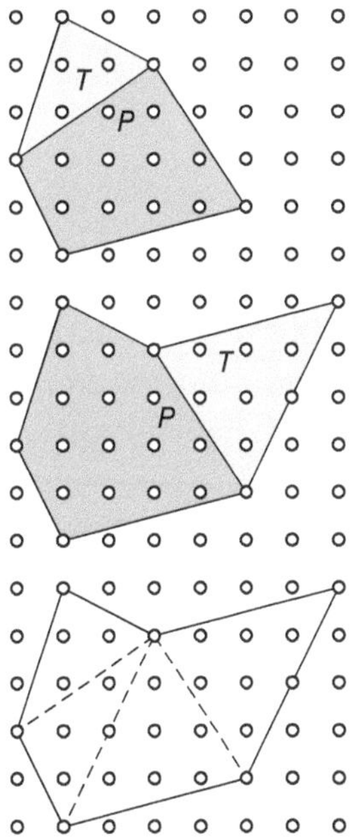

Pick's theorem is a beautiful mathematical relationship that allows us to determine the area of any polygon constructed on a lattice (or on a geoboard), including odd-shaped figures whose area would be very hard to determine in any other way.

Figure 10.19 shows some examples of polygons that you might choose to present to your students for practice (found in the appendix and at more4U).

FIG. 10.19

Use Pick's formula to find the area of odd shapes

The theorem also reveals an unexpected result: No matter the size or the shape of the lattice polygon, its area will be either an integer or a half-integer value. (Since the number of boundary and interior points are both integers, $A = B/2 + I - 1$ will yield either integer solutions when B is even or half-integer solutions when B is odd.)

So far we have worked in one direction only: Given a lattice polygon, we have used Pick's rule to determine its area. But let's reverse the process and pose problems that ask the students to create the polygons given certain parameters. For these problems we recommend that the students use geoboards, if they are available, because students can easily reposition the rubber band as they try various shapes. When they find a polygon that satisfies the specified conditions, they can then draw the shape on dot paper. Here are three sample problems:

1. Create two or more polygons with area of 9 square units and 6 boundary points. [*Since the values of A = 9 and B = 6 are given, we can deduce that I = 7. Three examples are shown in figure 10.20.*]

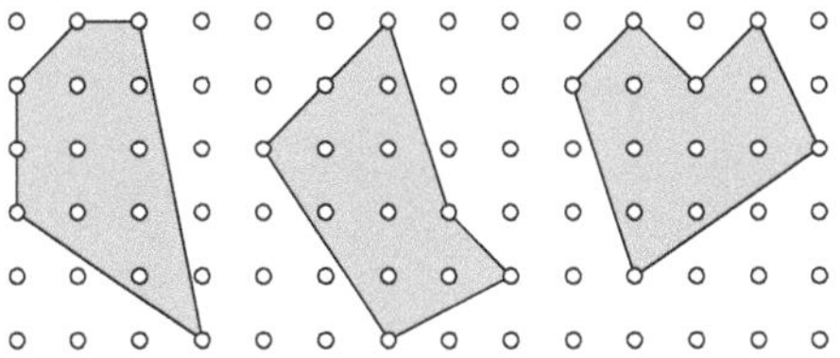

FIG. 10.20

Some solutions, problem 1

2. Create two or more polygons with area of 12.5 square units and 9 interior points. [*Since the area is not an integer value, we know that the number of boundary points must be odd. Given that A = 12.5 and I = 9, we can deduce that B = 9. Three examples are shown in figure 10.21.*]

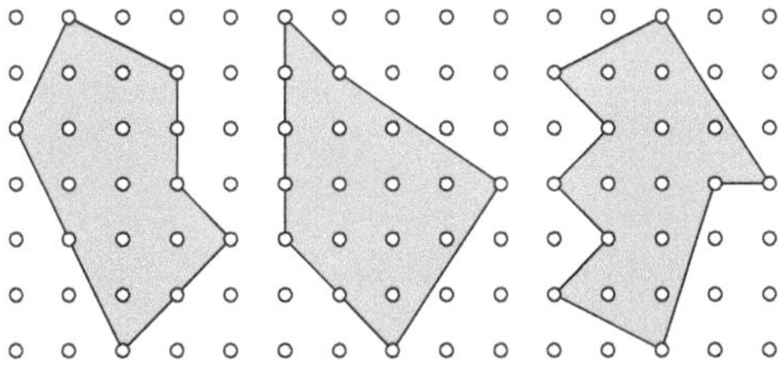

FIG. 10.21

Some solutions, problem 2

3. Create at least three polygons that all have an area of 10 square units but with different numbers of boundary points for each shape. [*Since the area, 10 square units, is an integer value, we know that the number of boundary points must be even and ≥4. Figure 10.22 shows four examples with boundary-point values of 4, 6, 8, and 10.*]

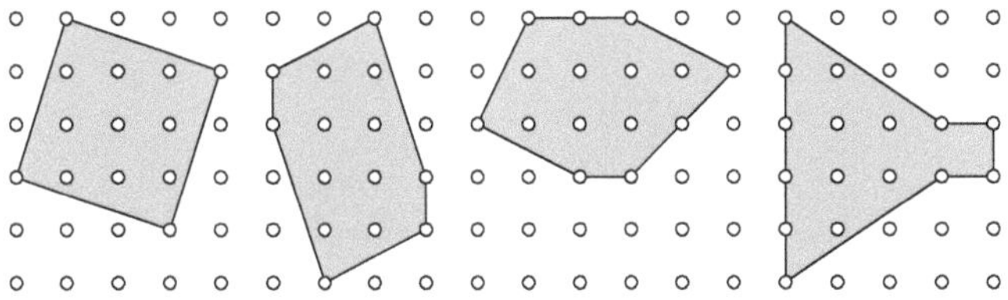

FIG. 10.22

Some solutions, problem 3

You can create additional problems of this type, or the students can create their own problems and give them to one another to solve.

Extend

All of the polygons considered so far have been simple closed figures. But what if some of the polygons contained "holes"? Figure 10.23 gives examples of polygons with one, two, or three holes. Will Pick's theorem apply in cases like these?

FIG. 10.23

Polygons with holes

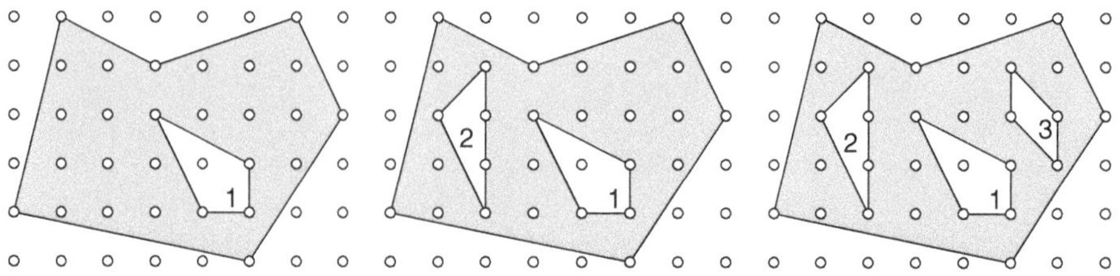

The students can explore this situation with the help of the activity sheet Pick's Theorem—The Hole Truth.

The Hole Truth activity presents simple shapes where the "outer" polygon is either a rectangle or a right triangle, and the "holes" are simple shapes whose area can be readily determined. It should be obvious that the area of the "holey" polygon equals the area of the outer shape (without holes) minus the area of the holes, and for the figures in the activity, the areas can easily be calculated. Then the students count the number of boundary points (B) and interior points (I) and calculate the area of the polygons using Pick's formula. Table 10.3 summarizes the answers for questions 1 through 3 of the Hole Truth activity. (Note that in these cases the points on the boundary of the holes are now boundary points of the holey polygon.) When they enter the values for B and I into Pick's formula, they will discover that the area calculated falls short of the true area by an amount that varies with the number of holes: a polygon with one hole falls short by 1 square unit, a polygon with two holes falls short by 2 square units, and a polygon with three holes falls short by 3 square units. This suggests a needed modification of the formula for Pick's theorem:

$$A = \frac{B}{2} + I + H - 1,$$

where H is the number of holes.

Does this mean that there was something wrong with the formula we have been using throughout this activity until now? No! Until now, all of the polygons under consideration were closed figures without holes, so $H = 0$, and the formula we started with is just a special case of the more general formula for polygons with holes.

Table 10.3. Solutions for the Hole Truth Activity Sheet							
Polygon	**Area Outer**	**Area Holes**	**Outer Minus Holes**	**B**	**I**	**Area by Pick**	**Error**
1	9	1	8	16	0	7	1
2	12	1	11	18	2	10	1
3	16	2	14	20	4	13	1
4	8	0.5	7.5	15	0	6.5	1
5	16	1) 0.5 2) 1	14.5	23	2	12.5	2
6	24	1) 3 2) 1	20	30	4	18	2
7	24	1) 5 2) 1	18	32	1	16	2
8	30	1) 1 2) 2 3) 3	24	40	2	21	3
9	21	1) 0.5 2) 0.5 3) 1	19	24	5	16	3
10	37.5	1) 4.5 2) 2 3) 3	28	48	2	25	3

As with all of the previous steps in this activity, you can offer your students a chance to generalize and prove this final result if they have facility with algebra. Here is how a proof might proceed:

Consider a polygon (*P*) with one hole. We know that Pick's formula applies to the outer polygon (P_O) and to the hole (*H*). We also know that $area_P = area_O - area_H$, and we can see that $B_P = B_O + B_H$ and $I_P = I_O - I_H - B_H$. Therefore,

$$Area_P = \left(\frac{B_O}{2} + I_O - 1\right) - \left(\frac{B_H}{2} + I_H - 1\right)$$

$$= \frac{B_O - B_H}{2} + (I_O - I_H) - 1 + 1$$

$$= \frac{B_O - B_H}{2} + (I_P + B_H)$$

$$= \frac{B_O + B_H}{2} + I_P$$

$$Area_P = \frac{B_P}{2} + I_P$$

FIG. 10.24

Polygon with one hole

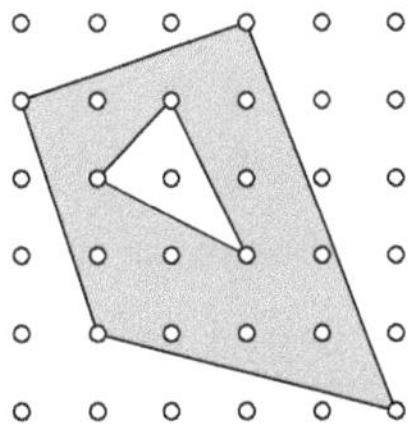

This is exactly what we are trying to show: When there is one hole, $(H = 1)$, $A = B/2 + I + H - 1$ becomes $A = B/2 + I$. For additional holes, the proof is similar. We will look at one more example, the case for $H = 2$. Now $area_P = area_O - area_{H1} - area_{H2}$; $B_P = B_O + B_{H1} + B_{H2}$; and $I_P = I_O - I_{H1} - I_{H2} - B_{H1} - B_{H2}$. This time we get the following:

$$\begin{aligned}
Area_P &= \left(\frac{B_O}{2} + I_O - 1\right) - \left(\frac{B_{H1}}{2} + I_{H1} - 1\right) - \left(\frac{B_{H2}}{2} + I_{H2} - 1\right) \\
&= \frac{B_O - B_{H1} - B_{H2}}{2} + (I_O - I_{H1} - I_{H2}) - 1 + 2 \\
&= \frac{B_O - B_{H1} - B_{H2}}{2} + (I_P + B_{H1} + B_{H2}) + 1 \\
&= \frac{B_O + B_{H1} + B_{H2}}{2} + I_P + 1 \\
Area_P &= \frac{B_P}{2} + I_P + 1
\end{aligned}$$

FIG. 10.25

Polygon with two holes

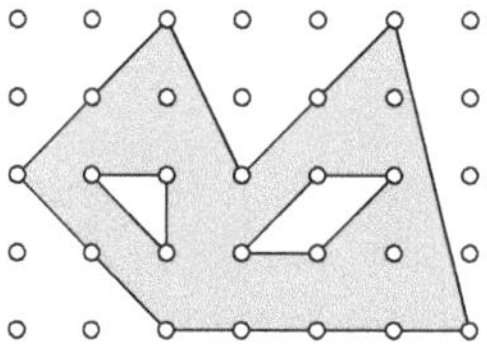

Now, with two holes $(H = 2)$, $A = B/2 + I + H - 1$ becomes $A = B/2 + I + 1$, as we just saw. Repeating the process for $H = 3, 4, \ldots$ will confirm the truth of the generalized Pick's formula $A = \frac{B}{2} + I + H - 1$.

One more intriguing extension of Pick's theorem, perhaps a subject for an individual or class project for interested students, is to ask whether Pick's theorem also applies to polygons drawn on an isometric lattice or isodot paper. But that is a subject for another day.

SUMMARY

This activity offers a guided tour through the development of a beautiful, surprising, and useful mathematical formula, showing how the initial observation of a pattern begins with a property of rectangles and then expands to apply to more and more polygons, resulting in a simple formula that enables us to find the area of even very irregular shapes whose area calculation would otherwise be extremely difficult or impossible. The investigation can proceed at an inductive level appropriate for middle-grades students, or it can proceed in a more formal, deductive manner by students who have a background in algebra. Because the formula will be new to almost all the students, it presents an opportunity for engaging in productive struggle while creating new knowledge and understanding.

> *"Effective teaching of mathematics consistently provides students, individually and collectively, with opportunities and supports to engage in productive struggle as they grapple with mathematical ideas and relationships."* (NCTM 2014, p. 10)

11

Dice and Coins: Empirical and Theoretical Probability

OVERVIEW

Perhaps the most prevalent applications of mathematics to our daily lives—our personal lives, our working lives, our civic and commercial lives—involve probability. We decide whether to purchase an extended warranty for a product, in part on the basis of our assessment of the probability that the product will need repairs. As drivers, we look left into the oncoming traffic lane and assess the probability that we can safely pass the vehicle in front of us. We ***ought*** to decide whether to play the state lottery on the basis of the probability that we will win!

Derived from "Empirical Probabilities," "Test Guessing," "First Head," and "String of Heads" in *Navigating through Probability in Grades 6–8* (NCTM 2003b, pp. 26–28, 43–44, 47–48, and 49–50, respectively).

Take just a minute and reflect on your life situations that in some way involve probability and ask your students the same question: "What decisions have you recently made for which the chance or likelihood of something has influenced your decision?" Use a think-pair-share approach to generate and discuss students' ideas. Consider the probabilistic elements of their replies.

- Should I try out for the jazz band? (*What's the **chance** I'll be selected?*)
- I wonder if I'll like this new spaghetti sauce? (*Is there **likely** to be garlic in it? I usually don't like garlic.*)
- Is now a good time for me to text Jeremy? (*He **probably** is at work this time on a Saturday.*)

And then consider the flip side. In the first sentence of his introduction to the article, "Why Do People Find Probability Unintuitive and Difficult?," David Spiegelhalter answered, "This is quite an easy question to answer: because ***it is*** unintuitive and difficult" (emphasis his) (Spiegelhalter 2010). Through the activities in this Gem, you can help your students address their intuitions and suppositions about probabilities and help them begin to see that many events are based on chance and can be explored and quantified using mathematics.

> *"Misconceptions about probability have been held not only by many students but also by many adults."* (NCTM 2000, p. 254)

This Gem supports you with hands-on activities followed by discussion and reflection. The activities are designed to be carried out over several days, and you will find it a must to work through the data-collection activities in advance as you revisit your own understanding of probability. In so doing, you can anticipate challenges you and your students may encounter and the potential modifications you might consider for your students.

GOALS

- Create and use relative-frequency ratios to represent empirical probabilities.
- Explore the results when a relative-frequency experiment is carried out over and over.
- Transition from empirical probabilities to theoretical probabilities by generating lists of possible outcomes.
- Calculate theoretical probabilities.

MATERIALS NEEDED

- Copies of the following activity sheets for each student:
  - Ratios
  - Test Guessing
  - First Head (page 1)
  - Strings of Heads
- Standard six-sided dice (two colors, such as red and green)
- Coins

Engage

Arrange your students in pairs or in small groups and give every student the Ratios activity sheets. Distribute a pair of dice to each group, preferably two dice of different colors. For our discussion here we will assume each pair includes one red die and one green die. Discuss with students the task at hand: Generate and record some data (in this case, the sums of the two numbers rolled) and use them to determine the likelihood of an event (whether or not the sum is a prime number). In other words, you and your students will be determining *empirical probabilities*: ratios that represent the likelihood of an event occurring, based on experimental data.

Empirical probability: a ratio that represents the likelihood of some event occurring, based on data from an experiment, simulation, or other source.

Ms. G: In your small group, roll two dice and record the information in the table shown on the first page of the activity sheet. Let's all agree to record the number on the red die first and the number on the green die second.

Here's an example. Suppose we roll a 3 on the red die and a 5 on the green die. We record both numbers and their sum in the first column for roll number 1. We then answer the two yes-no questions (Prime sum? Not a prime sum?) in the next two columns and, finally, calculate the ratio of "number of prime sums" to "cumulative number of rolls" and enter that in the last column. How would you answer the yes-no questions for a roll of a red 3 and a green 5?

Leona: The answers are *no* and *yes*, in that order.

Ms. G: How did Leona decide that?

Susie: Well, the sum of 3 and 5 is 8, and 8 is not a prime number.

Ms. G: Is that correct? What is a prime number?

Elmo: Prime numbers are values with exactly two different factors, 1 and the number itself. So, 8 isn't prime because 8 has more than two factors: 1, 2, 4, 8.

Ms. G: And what value do we enter into the last column?

Jane: It would just be 0, because the ratio of prime sums to total number of sums after one roll is 0/1 or just 0.

Ms. G: Let's try another example. Suppose the red die shows a 1 and the green die shows a 4. Discuss with your group the entries we would have for roll number 2, assuming the results of roll number 1 are just as we discussed.

"Effective teaching of mathematics uses evidence of student thinking to assess progress toward mathematical understanding and to adjust instruction continually in ways that support and extend learning." (NCTM 2014, p. 53)

Give your students a few minutes to determine the entries for this new sample roll.

Ms. G: Simon, what did your group come up with?

Simon: We would record 1 and 4 and the sum, 5, in the first column, for roll number 2. We would answer *yes* and *no* to the prime sums questions in the next two columns, because 5 is a prime number. If this example is roll number 2, we'd enter 0.50 as the cumulative ratio—one of our two rolls has resulted in a prime sum.

Ms. G: That's it! Now, every group, carry out 20 actual rolls; and everyone, record the information on your activity sheet. Let me know if you have questions.

As you move around your room observing and helping students, check students' work, especially the calculations in the last column—emphasize that the denominator in each ratio is increasing with each row. As they complete page 1, instruct students to move on to page 2 of the Ratios activity. Here, students will create a scatter plot of their prime-sums ratios from page 1 and then respond to questions about their results. Figure 11.1 shows a sample response from one hypothetical group. Your students' responses will vary from group to group.

FIG. 11.1

Sample solutions for Ratios activity sheet pp. 1–2

Solutions for "Ratios"

1. Answers will vary. See the sample answers in the chart.

Roll	Numbers Rolled and Sum	Prime Sum?	Not a Prime Sum?	Ratio of "Number of Prime Sums" to "Cumulative Number of Rolls"
1	2 + 6 = 8		X	.00
2	4 + 3 = 7	X		.50
3	3 + 4 = 7	X		.67
4	6 + 3 = 9		X	.50
5	3 + 3 = 6		X	.40
6	5 + 6 = 11	X		.50
7	5 + 5 = 10		X	.43
8	3 + 2 = 5	X		.50
9	3 + 6 = 9		X	.44
10	1 + 3 = 4		X	.40
11	3 + 6 = 9		X	.36
12	2 + 2 = 4		X	.33
13	5 + 4 = 9		X	.31
14	4 + 1 = 5	X		.36
15	5 + 2 = 7	X		.40
16	3 + 1 = 4		X	.38
17	4 + 1 = 5	X		.41
18	3 + 1 = 4		X	.39
19	6 + 2 = 8		X	.37
20	6 + 1 = 7	X		.40

2. Graphs will vary. See the graph of the sample data for task 1.

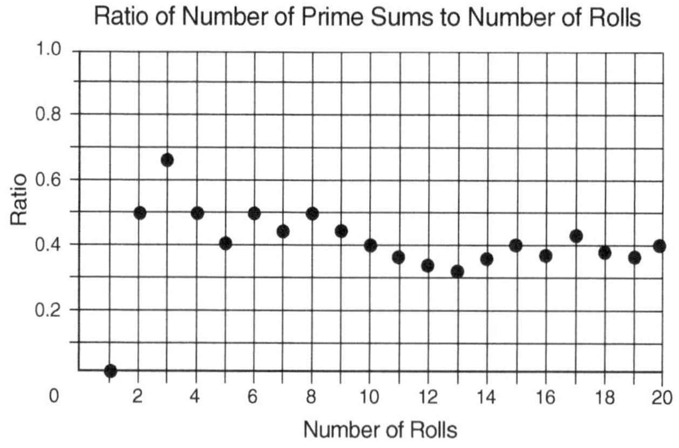

Focus on these three important considerations at this point. One focal point emerges from your students' responses to the last question (no. 4) on page 2 of the Ratios activity:

> If you rolled the dice many times, about what ratio of sums do you think would be prime? Explain your answer.

On the basis of their observations of their graphs, we ought to see the ratio begin to stabilize as the number of rolls increases. This might not be apparent to the same degree on each group's graph; you can help students see this by pooling the results for your class. Table 11.1 shows an example of pooled data for 10 student groups, each group having generated 20 sums.

Table 11.1. Pooled Data for Prime Sums Activity

Number of Rolls	Number of Prime Sums	Relative Frequency of Prime Sums
20	11	0.55
40	21	0.525
60	30	0.5
80	39	0.4875
100	46	0.46
120	53	0.4417
140	60	0.4286
160	67	0.4188
180	77	0.4278
200	86	0.43

This stabilization in the long run gives us a better and better measure of probability.

> **Point 1**: The more times we carry out an experiment, the more reliable the relative frequency becomes as a probability representation.

"Although the computation of probabilities can appear to be simple work with fractions, students must grapple with many conceptual challenges in order to understand probability." (NCTM 2000, p. 254)

This ties into the second important focal point that ought to emerge from this data-generating activity: Could we have determined a probability *without* generating all these data and carrying out the related calculations? The answer, of course, is YES! Such a probability is called *theoretical probability*. For our prime-sums experiment, we can determine the theoretical probability that a prime sum will occur on a roll by creating another ratio. In this case, we count the number of ways that a prime sum could occur and compare that to the total number of ways to get any sum with two dice.

Theoretical probability: the determination of the likelihood of an event expressed as a ratio comparing the number of ways that event can occur to the number of all possible outcomes.

The prime sums possible for a roll of two dice are 2, 3, 5, 7, and 11, and the nonprime sums are 4, 6, 8, 9, 10, and 12. But we also need to determine *how many ways* each of those sums could occur.

A helpful representation for making this determination is a two-way table. Table 11.2 shows the possible rolls for a red die in the left margin and the possible rolls for a green die in the top margin. Dice sums are shown where each row and column intersect.

Table 11.2. Possible Dice Sums

All Possible Sums When Two Dice Are Rolled							
	Green Die: Possible Rolls						
		1	2	3	4	5	6
Red Die: Possible Rolls	1	2	3	4	5	6	7
	2	3	4	5	6	7	8
	3	4	5	6	7	8	9
	4	5	6	7	8	9	10
	5	6	7	8	9	10	11
	6	7	8	9	10	11	12

Table 11.3 summarizes the 36 ways to generate a sum with two dice. We see that there are 15 ways to get a prime sum. Notice that 1 + 2 and 2 + 1 are both shown as ways to get a sum of 3. Assuming red and green dice, 1 + 2 represents a red 1 and a green 2, whereas 2 + 1 represents a red 2 and a green 1. Helping students see this distinction is important.

The desired probability ratio is $15/36 \approx 0.4167$. This is the theoretical probability of generating a prime sum on any roll of two dice.

Table 11.3. All Possible Sums Using Two Dice

Possible Sums	Ways to Generate a Sum	Total Number of Ways
2	1 + 1	1
3	1 + 2, 2 + 1	2
4	1 + 3, 2 + 2, 3 + 1	3
5	1 + 4, 2 + 3, 3 + 2, 4 + 1	4
6	1 + 5, 2 + 4, 3 + 3, 4 + 2, 5 + 1	5
7	1 + 6, 2 + 5, 3 + 4, 4 + 3, 5 + 2, 6 + 1	6
8	2 + 6, 3 + 5, 4 + 4, 5 + 3, 6 + 2	5
9	3 + 6, 4 + 5, 5 + 4, 6 + 3	4
10	4 + 6, 5 + 5, 6 + 4	3
11	5 + 6, 6 + 5	2
12	6 + 6	1

Point 2: Theoretical probability can be determined by comparing the number of ways a particular *event* occurs to the total number of *outcomes* that can occur.

Outcomes: All the possibilities that could occur. Table 11.2 shows there are 36 outcomes for the dice-roll sums activity.

Events: Collections of one or more outcomes. In the dice-roll sums activity, our event is "generating a prime sum."

Finally, when we consider these two fundamental ideas together, a third focal point emerges: When we carry out an experiment many, many times, not only does the empirical probability stabilize, it stabilizes toward the associated theoretical probability. Thus, as we generate more experimental data and use those data to calculate an empirical probability, that empirical probability approaches the theoretical probability. This phenomenon is called the *Law of Large Numbers*.

Point 3: When we carry out an experiment many times, the empirical probability stabilizes toward the associated theoretical probability (Law of Large Numbers).

The third and fourth pages of the Ratios activity offer students another dice-roll setting to reinforce determination of empirical probabilities, this time involving the *product* of the values showing on two rolled dice. In the dice-roll products activity, our event is "generating a two-digit product." The process is precisely the same as used earlier, including the use of red and green dice. Students work in pairs to generate the dice-roll data and complete the requested information in the table. Students then use these data to create a scatter plot of their data, plotting the ordered pairs (dice roll, ratio of two-digit products to total number of rolls). Finally, all the information is used to respond to reflection questions. See figure 11.2 for sample solutions.

In asking students to explore this setting, you can require them to determine the theoretical probability as well, mimicking the process we outlined for the prime-sums question. The task of determining all possible outcomes is a bit more complex for this setting. Again, emphasize the importance of die color: a red 3 and a green 4 generate a product of 12; a red 4 and a green 3 is a different way to get a product of 12. We again use a two-way table to help see all the possibilities (table 11.4) and a summary in table 11.5.

"Effective teaching of mathematics facilitates discourse among students to build shared understanding of mathematical ideas by analyzing and comparing student approaches and arguments." (NCTM 2014, p. 29)

FIG. 11.2

Sample solutions for Ratios activity sheet pp. 3–4

Roll	Numbers Rolled and Product	Two-Digit Product?	Not a Two-Digit Product?	Ratio of "Number of Two-Digit Products" to "Cumulative Number of Rolls"
1	5 × 1 = 5		X	.00
2	2 × 4 = 8		X	.00
3	5 × 2 = 10	X		.33
4	2 × 6 = 12	X		.50
5	4 × 6 = 24	X		.60
6	5 × 4 = 20	X		.67
7	3 × 5 = 15	X		.71
8	2 × 1 = 2		X	.63
9	1 × 1 = 1		X	.56
10	5 × 2 = 10	X		.60
11	1 × 3 = 3		X	.55
12	2 × 2 = 4		X	.50
13	4 × 3 = 12	X		.54
14	6 × 2 = 12	X		.57
15	3 × 6 = 18	X		.60
16	6 × 6 = 36	X		.63
17	1 × 1 = 1		X	.59
18	1 × 3 = 3		X	.56
19	6 × 6 = 36	X		.58
20	2 × 5 = 10	X		.60

6. Graphs will vary. See the graph of the sample data for task 5.

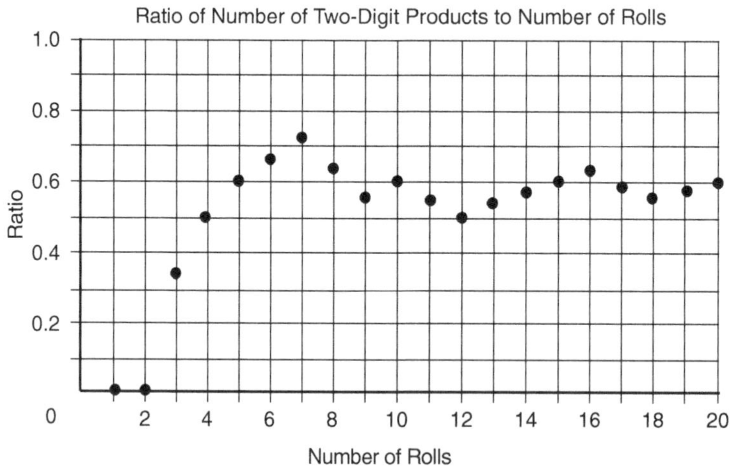

Table 11.4. Possible Dice Products

All Possible Products When Two Dice Are Rolled							
		Green Die: Possible Rolls					
		1	2	3	4	5	6
Red Die: Possible Rolls	1	1	2	3	4	5	6
	2	2	4	6	8	10	12
	3	3	6	9	12	15	18
	4	4	8	12	16	20	24
	5	5	10	15	20	25	30
	6	6	12	18	24	30	36

Table 11.5. All Possible Products Using Two Dice

Possible Products	Ways to Generate a Product	Total Number of Ways
1	1 × 1	1
2	1 × 2, 2 × 1	2
3	1 × 3, 3 × 1	2
4	1 × 4, 2 × 2, 4 × 1	3
5	1 × 5, 5 × 1	2
6	1 × 6, 2 × 3, 3 × 2, 6 × 1	4
8	2 × 4, 4 × 2	2
9	3 × 3	1
10	2 × 5, 5 × 2	2
12	2 × 6, 3 × 4, 4 × 3, 6 × 2	4
15	3 × 5, 5 × 3	2
16	4 × 4	1
18	3 × 6, 6 × 3	2
20	4 × 5, 5 × 4	2
24	4 × 6, 6 × 4	2
25	5 × 5	1
30	5 × 6, 6 × 5	2
36	6 × 6	1

Explore

The Ratios activity is designed to help students learn how to generate empirical and theoretical probabilities and to distinguish between empirical probabilities and theoretical probabilities. Students also should recognize that as we carry out an experiment more and more times, the empirical probability approaches the theoretical probability. This is especially useful and important when we have access to technology that can model or simulate experiments. The earlier dice activities can be modeled with tech tools that generate random outcomes. A spreadsheet, for instance, includes a random number generator, and additional columns in the spreadsheet can be used to organize the data, carry out necessary calculations, and report the results.

In the next activity, we focus on probabilities associated with guessing strategies. The setting will likely be familiar to students—guessing responses in a true/false or multiple-choice assessment. The activity sheet Test Guessing provides a recording sheet for information generated and space for students to explain their responses.

Begin by posing a three-question true/false assessment to your students with questions for which the students will need to guess. These should include questions for which students will almost certainly ***not*** know the answer. Table 11.6 shows two sample assessments. Try using one of these with your students.

Table 11.6. Sample True/False Assessments

True/False Assessment Sample A
1) ***Fromatte*** is the name for a French bread. [*False. John Fromatte is a name found in the 1940 US Census. https://www.archives.com/1940-census/john-fromatte-ny-56139654*]
2) ***Khoubz*** is the name for a Lebanese bread. [*True.*]
3) ***Saimin*** is the name for a Hawaiian bread. [*False. Saimin is a Hawaiian noodle-soup dish. https://en.wikipedia.org/wiki/Saimin*]
True/False Assessment Sample B
1) ***Guar gum*** is sold in the candy department of most grocery stores. [*False. Guar gum is a food additive. https://www.healthline.com/nutrition/guar-gum*]
2) ***Fattoush*** is a weight-loss diet plan. [*False. Fattoush is a Lebanese salad.*]
3) ***Sheepshead*** is the name for a saltwater fish. [*True.*]

This introduction can be used to discuss the nature of guessing on such questions, a technique students will have used here and will likely be familiar with from previous experiences. Here is a slice of such a class discussion.

Ms. G: Ben said he guessed his response to each question. What does that mean, to guess, and what chance is there Ben will be correct?

Leona: One way of guessing is to just choose the same response for each question. I just wrote True for all three questions.

Fritz: I used a pattern, guessing True, False, True.

Susie: I did something like that, except I wrote False, True, False.

Linn: As long as you have no idea what the correct answer is to one question, you have a 50-50 chance of getting it correct, right?

Ms. G: What do you think about what Linn just said?

Henry: Well, if there are two response options for a question and we have no idea what the answer is, then, yes, Linn is correct.

Ms. G: So, do you think we can begin to quantify—use mathematics to describe—what's going on when we guess?

Inga: We talked about probabilities last time; seems like the probability of getting one question correct by guessing is 1/2, right? One correct choice compared to two choices in all?

Tasha: I know, we could try an experiment. Take the three-question quiz over and over and record our results. What portion of time did we get none correct? One? Two? All three?

At this point in the discussion, you can introduce or solicit ideas for ways to generate lots of data to address Tasha's suggestion. Among other options, your students can use the results of a coin toss to represent a guess for one assessment question and use the result of three ordered coin tosses to simulate a response to the set of three assessment questions.

Direct each small group to carry out 20 trials—generate 20 sets of three ordered coin tosses. Consider heads to be a response of true (T) and let tails be a response of false (F). For example, if a small group tossed heads, heads, tails, the three-question assessment response would be true, true, false. If true, true, false is a simulated guess to Sample Assessment B, that guess would result in no correct answers, because the correct responses for Assessment B are false, false, true. After your students have recorded 20 trials, reveal the correct responses to Assessment B and ask them to determine how many of the 20 trials resulted in no correct responses, one correct response, two correct responses, and all three correct. Table 11.7 shows a recording sheet to use with your student groups.

Figure 11.3 shows the entry for trial 1 that was discussed in the previous paragraph for Sample Assessment B.

Now pool the groups' results to generate data for your entire class. Table 11.8 shows pooled data for a class that carried out this activity, with 10 groups each carrying out 20 trials. The rightmost column shows the empirical probabilities that Tasha alluded to earlier.

***Outcomes:** There are eight outcomes to the test-guessing activity.*

***Events:** For the test-guessing activity, the events describe the number of correct responses: all three correct, two correct, one correct, and none correct.*

Table 11.7. Coin Toss Recording Sheet

	First Coin Toss	Second Coin Toss	Third Coin Toss	Associated Assessment Response	Number Correct on Assessment
Trial 1					
Trial 2					
Trial 3					
Trial 4					
Trial 5					
Trial 6					
Trial 7					
Trial 8					
Trial 9					
Trial 10					
Trial 11					
Trial 12					
Trial 13					
Trial 14					
Trial 15					
Trial 16					
Trial 17					
Trial 18					
Trial 19					
Trial 20					

FIG. 11.3

Sample entry for trial 1

	First coin toss	Second coin toss	Third coin toss	Associated Assessment Response	Number Correct on Assessment
Trial #1	*head*	*head*	*tail*	*True True False*	*0*

Table 11.8. Pooled Results

0 Correct Responses	20	10%
1 Correct Responses	68	34%
2 Correct Responses	86	43%
3 Correct Responses	26	13%

In completing this portion of the activity, you have helped your students reinforce the use of experiments in calculating empirical probabilities. This also provides you a transition to a theoretical-probability approach to this problem. Announce to your students that they will now explore another way to determine a guesser's probability of success on a three-question true/false assessment.

Arrange your students into small groups and distribute a Test Guessing activity sheet to each student. Having been led through the coin-toss discussion and activity just described, your students will be able to complete this activity in small groups. Move around among groups to observe their interactions and address student questions.

Here are a few comments related to the responses students will generate.

> Question 2: Using *C* for a correct guess and *W* for a wrong guess, list all the possible outcomes of answering the three questions on the test. For example, you would record *CCC* to indicate the possibility of getting all three questions correct. (*Hint*: Eight outcomes are possible.)

Notice that we are focusing on a guess being correct (*C*) or wrong (*W*), *not* whether the assessment statement itself is true or false. Some students will be thinking about the assessment statements being true or false, but our focus is on whether a guess to one question is correct or wrong.

> Question 3: If you are truly guessing, what is the probability associated with each of the eight outcomes? Describe two ways to explain your answer.

Students often consider a ratio approach, as we used in determining theoretical probabilities with the dice activities earlier. We have eight unique outcomes [*CCC, CCW, CWC, WCC, WWC, WCW, CWW, WWW*] and when it is a guess, each outcome is equally likely to occur. The probability of each outcome is 1/8.

You and your students may be familiar with tree diagrams as another way to generate the outcomes. If not, here is a good opportunity to introduce tree diagrams. Figure 11.4 shows possible results for each assessment question, starting at the left and branching to the right.

FIG. 11.4

Tree diagram for test guessing

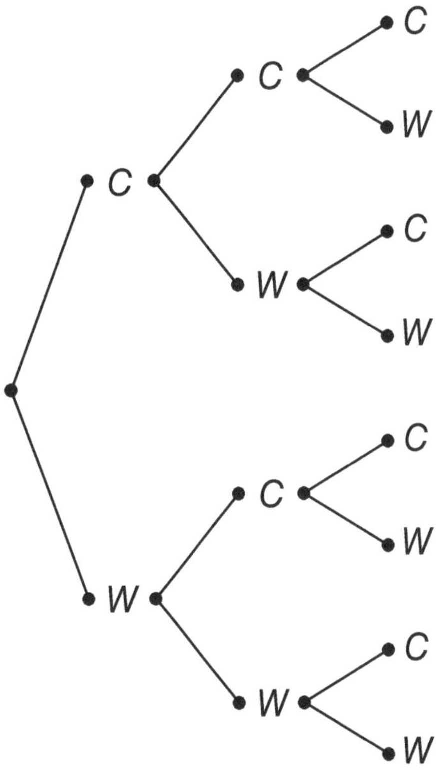

Following the top branch at each decision point, for instance, gives us the *CCC* result mentioned earlier. Each unique path from left to right generates a unique outcome. Figure 11.5 shows all those outcomes, with indication of the number of correct assessment responses associated with each outcome.

FIG. 11.5

Tree diagram with eight outcomes identified

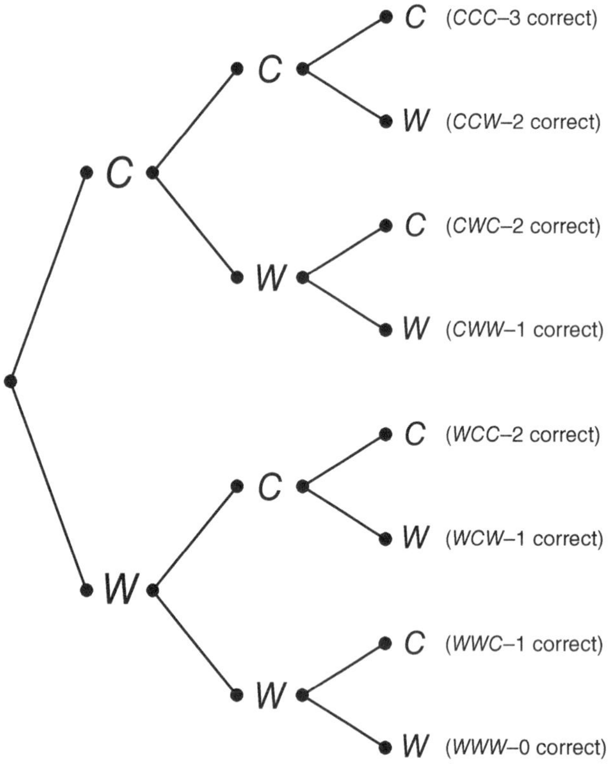

> Question 4: If 70 percent is the lowest passing grade, what is the probability you will pass the test by guessing?

Only one outcome, *CCC* (100 percent correct), gives us a better than 70 percent grade. The other seven outcomes give us scores below 70 percent: 67 percent (two of three correct: *CCW, CWC, WCC*), 33 percent (one of three correct: *CWW, WCW, WWC*), and 0 percent (none of three correct: *WWW*). This shows that if guessing, the probability of passing—earning 70 percent or better—is 1/8, or 12.5 percent.

> Questions 5 and 6: (5) Repeat the analysis (questions 1–4) for a true-or-false test of five questions. (6) If time permits, repeat the analysis (questions 1–4) for a three-question multiple-choice test with three options for each answer.

These questions offer you and your students the opportunity to reinforce the processes used in questions 1–4.

Extend

You can reinforce the concepts of empirical probability through the activities described in the handouts First Heads and String of Heads.

In First Heads we encounter an experiment that requires an unknown number of coin flips in each trial. The students flip a fair coin repeatedly and record the results until a heads first appears. A sample is shown on the activity sheet (see figure 11.6) followed by space for recording 20 trials, with additional space to record probability estimates based on those results. There is a concluding reflection question.

FIG. 11.6

Sample trial for First Heads

Exploration 1

1. Use any fair coin. Toss it repeatedly, recording the outcome of each toss as H or T, until the first heads appears. Then record the number of the toss on which the first H appears. Repeat this process 20 times.

Trial	String of Hs and Ts	Number of Tosses to Get First Heads
Sample	T T T H	4
1	____________	____
2	____________	____

Begin the activity by first discussing with students what they think will happen and why: How many coin flips are required to get the first heads? Then, after generating data, compare their results with their predictions. Extreme cases do emerge. Some of your students will likely have trials that required many flips before a heads appeared. Is that surprising to your students?

In the activity String of Heads students complete several explorations for which they focus on repeated consecutive occurrences of an outcome. They first record the string of heads/tails results when tossing a coin 10 times (see figure 11.7 for sample data). Students then analyze the data to determine strings of heads that occur and empirical probabilities for each string length. After repeating that same exploration for a 20-toss string, students look at data from a professional sports team and consider strings of wins for that team.

FIG. 11.7

Sample trial for String of Heads

Exploration 1

1. Use any fair coin. Toss it 10 times. Record the longest string of heads in the 10 tosses. For example, if the tosses are H H T H H H T T T T, the longest string of heads is 3. Repeat this process 20 times, making 10 tosses each time.

Trial	Tosses	Longest String of Heads
Sample	H H T H H H H T T T T	3
1	____________	________
2	____________	________

A common misconception here is that the more tosses we consider—or games played, for the last setting—the longer we expect consecutive strings to be. The data that students generate—or, even more powerful, pooled data for the class—will contradict that misconception. As for a sports team, its probability of winning changes throughout a season, and a team chosen by your students is unlikely to have a season for which they won exactly half their games. Discuss with your students how a team's ongoing success will have an impact on the lengths of their strings of wins or losses.

> *Many of us have a "(wrong) intuition that randomness should be somehow regular and balanced, and so we think it unlikely that a coin will flip 4 heads or tails in a row. And yet with 20 flips there is a 77% chance of getting such a sequence, which generally enables a real random sequence to be distinguished from a fake."* (Spiegelhalter 2010)

SUMMARY

The activities in this Gem require students to calculate empirical probabilities using data they generate and to determine theoretical probabilities by identifying all possible outcomes to an experiment or other setting. Important discussions ought to emerge in comparing these two methods for determining numerical measures for the likelihood of an event. Students' distinction between empirical probability and theoretical probability is a cornerstone of these activities.

Access to user-friendly technology has made data-driven empirical probabilities easier and more efficient to generate for large samples. The formal study and determination of theoretical probabilities—delineating what could happen—sets the stage for students' development and expansion of probability concepts that they will explore in subsequent courses and apply in science fields and other disciplines.

12

Histograms and Box Plots: Same Data, Different Views

OVERVIEW

Histograms and box plots provide two essential visualization tools for data analysis. In this activity, students create and use these tools to assess the effectiveness of two different drugs used for migraine headaches. They use numerical test results for each drug and transform these data into numerical summaries and visual representations. Students make observations and draw conclusions based on their representations, and they compare and contrast histograms and box plots for the same data set in order to identify key characteristics of each data representation.

Derived from "Migraines: Histograms" and "Migraines: Box Plots" in *Navigating through Data Analysis in Grades 6–8* (NCTM 2003a, pp. 60–65).

GOALS

- Create and use histograms, relative-frequency histograms, and box plots to analyze data and make decisions.
- Describe key characteristics of a data set based on information extracted from histograms, relative-frequency histograms, and box plots.
- Compare and contrast histograms and box plots and reflect on their usefulness.

MATERIALS NEEDED

Copies of activity sheets Migraines: Histograms and Migraines: Box Plots for each student.

Engage

Set the stage for this activity by sharing with students these two data sets (table 12.1). A copy of these two data sets suitable for projection is available at more4U.

Table 12.1. Two Sets of Data

Set A	16, 18, 18, 20, 22, 22, 24, 24, 26, 26, 28, 28, 30, 30, 32, 32, 34, 36, 36, 36, 38, 38, 40, 42, 44, 44, 46, 46, 48, 50, 54, 56, 56, 58, 58, 58, 62, 62, 64, 64, 66, 68, 68, 70, 70, 70, 72, 72, 74, 76, 76, 76, 78, 78, 80, 80, 80, 82, 82, 84, 84, 84, 86, 86, 88, 88, 88, 88, 90, 90, 90, 90, 90, 92, 92, 92, 92, 94, 94, 94, 96, 96, 98, 98, 98, 98, 100, 100, 100, 100, 102, 102, 102, 104, 104, 106, 106, 108, 108, 108, 110, 110, 112, 114, 118, 120
Set B	18, 20, 20, 22, 24, 24, 24, 26, 26, 30, 30, 30, 34, 34, 34, 36, 36, 36, 38, 38, 40, 40, 44, 44, 46, 50, 52, 52, 56, 56, 58, 62, 62, 66, 74, 74, 78, 88, 94, 98, 98, 100, 104, 106, 110, 116, 120

"Effective teaching of mathematics engages students in solving problems and discussing tasks that promote mathematical reasoning and problem solving and allow multiple entry points and varied solution strategies." (NCTM 2014, p. 10)

These data are identical to those shown on the activity sheets for this exercise, with the exception that no labels, units, or other contextual information is given here. *This is intentional.* Ask your students their initial reaction to seeing these data sets and prompt them to ask questions about these data. Discuss with students the necessity for contextual information because, without it, data are essentially meaningless. Perhaps more important for middle-grades students, data without contexts offer little motivation to move forward with any sort of meaningful representations or analyses.

At this point, ask students to suggest what these data might represent. Are they test scores? Ages? Some sort of length or height measures? Speed? Eventually, tell them that the units of measure are minutes and ask for further suggestions. Race times? Prep times? Times to complete some task?

Describe the context from which these data have emerged, that of drug testing. Specifically, for sufferers of migraine headaches, these data represent the elapsed times medicine users reported until a migraine medication gave relief after taking that medication at the onset of the headache. So, for instance, the value 44 represents that one migraine sufferer reported that 44 minutes passed from the time the medicine was taken until migraine relief was recognized. Time values are self-reported—directly from the migraine sufferers—and are rounded to the nearest two minutes.

Each time value represents one unique migraine sufferer, and the data are from two different migraine medications. Set A times are from 106 users of a traditional migraine medication, and set B times are from 47 users of a new, experimental medication. We will refer to Medication A and Medication B related to these data sets.

Now ask your students for ideas about why such data are collected. This discussion should eventually turn to the reason for these data: **Which medication is more effective?**

Ask your students their ideas and suggestions for addressing this question. There are many appropriate responses, and your students should be commended as they share their ideas. Students might suggest determining some sort of numerical average, such as the mean or the median. Such a value is called a *measure of central tendency*, or simply a measure of *center*. Measures of center provide one of three critical elements used in describing and comparing data sets, that of *location*. Given a number line, a measure of center fixes or anchors the data set. From that location, that measure of center, we can move in either direction to further describe and represent a data set.

> The mean *of a data set is its arithmetic average, determined by summing the data values and dividing that sum by the number of values in the set.*
>
> The median *of a data set is the middle value of the ordered data set. If the set has an even number of values, the median is the mean of the two middle values.*

For the elapsed-times data sets, the mean elapsed times are 71.49 minutes (Medication A) and 54.64 minutes (Medication B). The median elapsed times are 78 minutes (A) and 44 minutes (B).

Do these numerical values provide enough information so you would conclude that Medication B is more effective? You might think so, noting that the means and medians differ so much between the two data sets.

The story of a data set has more to it than its location, however. Two other characteristics of a data set include its *spread* and its *shape*. The spread of a data set helps us see how far from the center the data values are, and the shape of a distribution helps us know how the data are dispersed within the span of the data values.

Neither spread nor shape is revealed if we know only a data set's location. Spread and shape help provide a more comprehensive picture of a data set and, consequently, offer more ways to compare data sets.

> *"Effective teaching of mathematics engages students in making connections among mathematical representations to deepen understanding of mathematical concepts and procedures as tools for problem solving."* (NCTM 2014, p. 24)

Histograms, box plots, and other visual representations provide insight into both spread and shape. The two activity sheets that accompany this exercise help your students create and use those two visual representations. The notes, comments, and instructions here are intended to support you and your students as they complete these activities.

Use the Migraines: Histograms sheet to help students construct histograms and relative-frequency histograms for Medication A and Medication B. To complete this activity sheet, we assume students know how to construct a histogram and a relative-frequency histogram. Your students, however, may need instruction to create one or both of these visual representations.

Here are instructions for the histograms. Move to the next section if your students need no instruction.

CREATING HISTOGRAMS

To create a histogram, first create a *frequency distribution* of the data. This is a table that shows intervals of data values (also called *bins*) and the number of data values in each interval. Table 12.2 shows frequency distributions for Medication A and Medication B.

Table 12.2. Frequency Distributions

Frequency Distributions for Migraine Medications

Time Interval (Minutes)	Medication A	Medication B
10-19	3	1
20-29	9	8
30-39	10	11
40-49	7	5
50-59	7	6
60-69	7	3
70-79	11	3
80-89	14	1
90-99	18	3
100-109	5	3
110-119	1	2
120-129	1	1

Note that the interval sizes (also known as *bin widths*) are somewhat arbitrary. An informal guide is to use from 5 to 20 bins, all with the same width. Here, the table has 12 bins with a consistent bin width of 10 minutes. The first bin collects data showing 10–19 minutes and the last bin collects data showing 120–129 minutes.

To transform the frequency-table information into a histogram, we need a horizontal scale and a vertical scale. Typically, the horizontal scale shows the interval measures and the vertical scale shows the frequency values. The vertical scale—the frequency—has been included on the activity sheet. Students should determine a horizontal scale to represent the intervals in their frequency distributions.

Once we have scaled axes, we can build the histogram. We create rectangular bars over each interval or bin, with the height of each bar representing the frequency for that bin. Finish the histogram by including descriptive labels for each axis and for the entire histogram. Figure 12.1 shows the histograms for Medication A and Medication B.

FIG. 12.1

Histograms for medications A and B

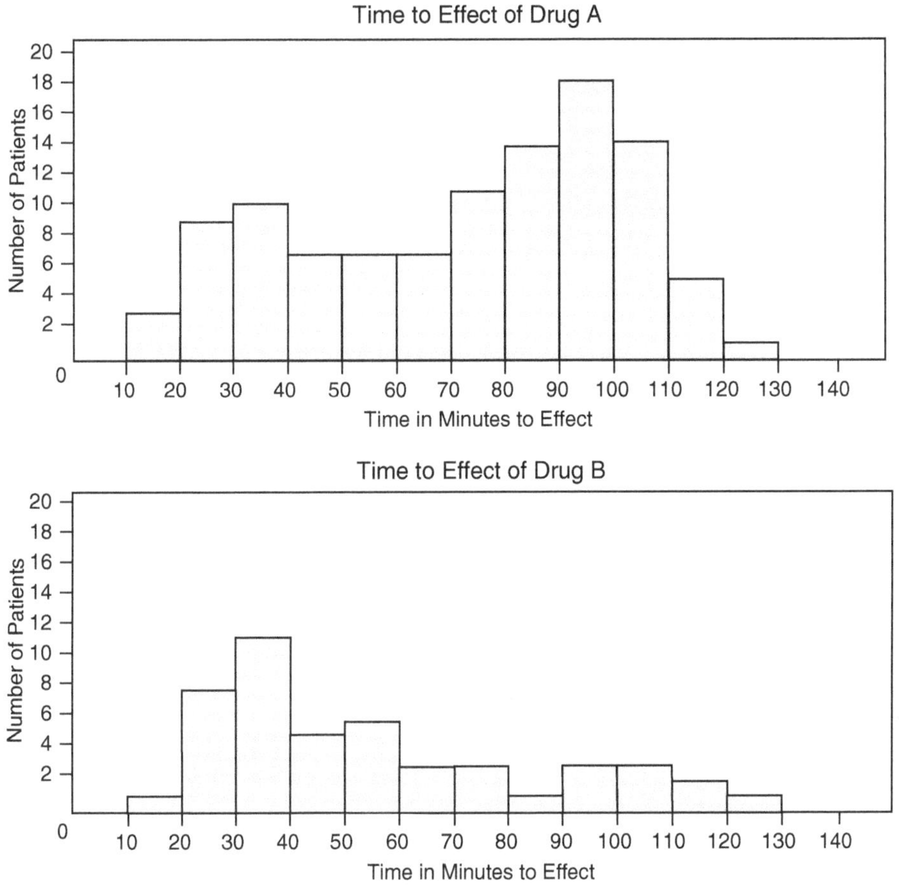

USING HISTOGRAMS

Show students the histograms pictured earlier or refer them to the histograms they have created. Revisit the question posed at the start: Which medication is more effective?

Discuss with students the information the histograms—and their accompanying frequency distributions—reveal, above and beyond the location information provided with the means and medians.

- We readily see the *range* of each data set, that is, the number of units—minutes, here—from the smallest value to the largest. The range for Medication A is 104 minutes, and for Medication B the range is 102 minutes.
- We see a *cluster* of data for Medication A, from 70 minutes to 109 minutes (57 of the 106 data values), and from 20 minutes to 39 minutes for Medication B (19 of 47 data values). Data clusters represent concentrations of data values.
- For these data sets, no apparent *outliers* can be seen. Outliers are data values that are somehow separated from the rest of the data values, most frequently at the upper or lower end of a data distribution. Outliers should be investigated as possible recording errors or values that may indicate that other anomalies occurred during data collection.
- The shape of each distribution is revealed in the histogram. Neither data set is *uniformly* distributed, that is, has approximately the same number of data values in each bin. The shape of the distribution for Medication A shows more values at the upper end with a tail of values at the lower end. With the tail at the lower end, it is called a *negative skew* or a *left skew*. A left-skewed distribution has the mean to the left of the median, as is true for Medication A. The shape of the distribution for Medication B shows more values at the lower end with a tail of values at the upper end. With the tail at the upper end, it is called a *positive skew* or a *right skew*. A right-skewed distribution has the mean to the right of the median, as is true for Medication B.

Medication A:

Mean: 71.49 minutes

Median: 78 minutes

Medication B

Mean: 54.64 minutes

Median: 44 minutes

All of these characteristics are above and beyond what can be determined by knowing only the measures of center. For comparison purposes, Medication B shows a cluster of values at the lower end, consistent with the positively skewed shape. We see that relatively more data values are shorter elapsed times, which indicates for this context that Medication B brought migraine relief sooner than Medication A.

Looking only at the frequency values for the two data sets—either from the frequency distribution tables or reading the vertical scale of the histograms—may lead your students to conclude that Medication A is more effective. After all, 29 users of Medication A got relief in less than 50 minutes, whereas only 25 users of Medication B did. Further, 68 Medication A users got relief in less than 80 minutes, and only 38 users of Medication B got such relief.

This provides you with a perfect transition to an alternative type of histogram, called a *relative-frequency histogram*. Relative-frequency histograms are especially useful for comparisons when the data sets being compared have distinctly unequal total numbers of data values. Here, there were 106 users of Medication A and 47 users of Medication B. Absolute comparisons, such as those described in the previous paragraph, are not useful when the numbers of data values differ significantly.

Here are instructions for relative-frequency histograms. As before, move to the next section if your students need no instruction.

CREATING RELATIVE-FREQUENCY HISTOGRAMS

A relative-frequency histogram will have the same shape as its histogram counterpart, assuming the same number of bins and that the bin widths are the same. The only additional requirement, or difference between the two plots, is to alter the scale to represent relative frequencies rather than absolute frequencies.

We can show this in a modified frequency distribution table by including an additional column that contains the relative portion of the data contained in that bin. Table 12.3 is a relative-frequency distribution table for the medications.

Table 12.3. Relative-Frequency Distributions

Relative-Frequency Distributions for Migraine Medications				
	Medication A		Medication B	
Time Interval (Minutes)	Absolute Frequency	Relative Frequency	Absolute Frequency	Relative Frequency
10–19	3	2.8%	1	2.1%
20–29	9	8.5%	8	17.0%
30–39	10	9.4%	11	23.4%
40–49	7	6.6%	5	10.6%
50–59	7	6.6%	6	12.8%
60–69	7	6.6%	3	6.4%
70–79	11	10.4%	3	6.4%
80–89	14	13.2%	1	2.1%
90–99	18	17.0%	3	6.4%
100–109	14	13.2%	3	6.4%
110–119	5	4.7%	2	4.3%
120–129	1	0.9%	1	2.1%

The entries in the relative-frequency columns are created by dividing the frequency for that bin by the total number of values in the data set. For instance, for Medication A, the 14 values that are in the 80–89 minutes bin represent approximately 13.2 percent of the entire set of values.

Because a distribution's shape has not changed, the only remaining task is to modify the vertical scale. The relative-frequency histograms shown in figure 12.2 have identical vertical scales, from 0 percent to 25 percent, in order to facilitate comparison. What does change is what those percentages represent for each data set. For medication A, 25 percent is about 26 data values, whereas 25 percent of the data for Medication B is about 12 data values.

FIG. 12.2

Relative-frequency histograms for Medications A and B

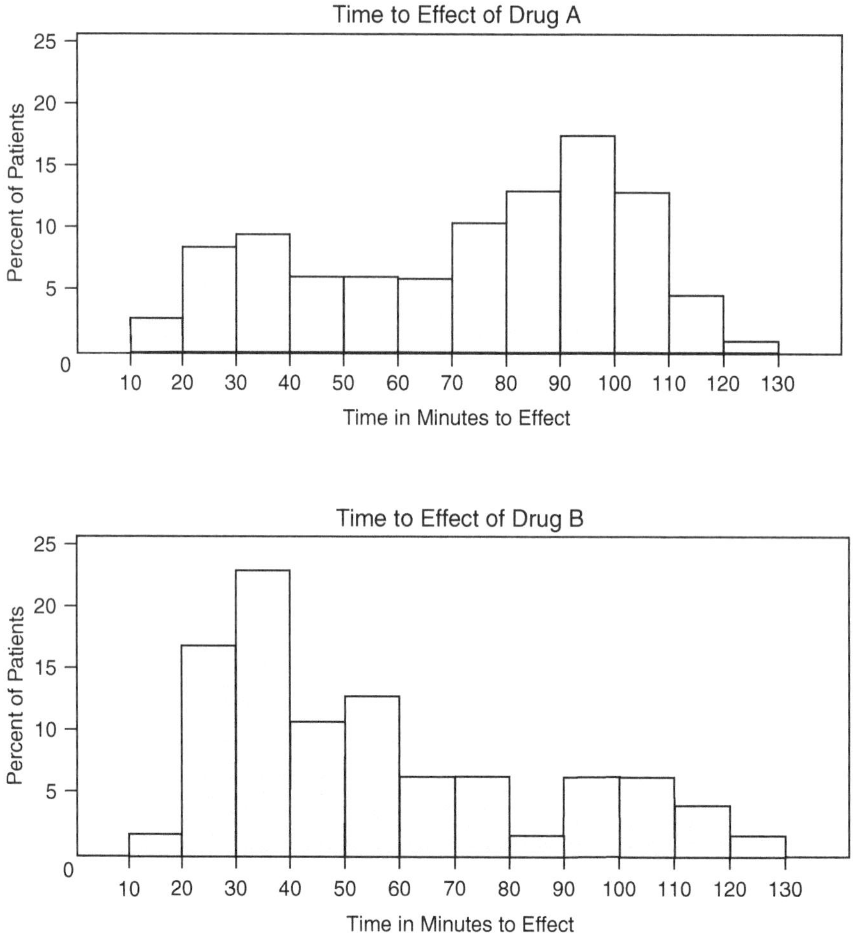

USING RELATIVE-FREQUENCY HISTOGRAMS

Show students the relative-frequency histograms pictured earlier or refer them to those they have created and once again revisit the question posed at the start: Which medication is more effective?

Now we can compare relatively similar components of each data set. For instance, about 27 percent of users of Medication A got relief in 49 minutes or less, whereas about 53 percent of those using Medication B got relief in that same span of time. This is further evidence that Medication B seems to be more effective—in less than 50 minutes, only about one-fourth of Medication A users got relief, whereas more than half the users of Medication B were relieved in that time span.

The use of relative frequencies offers opportunity for another transition in students' exposure to visual representations. Histograms provide a way to compare data sets when bin widths are the same—in the same 90- to 99-minute interval, 17 percent of Medication A users got relief, whereas just more than 6 percent of Medication B users took that long to get relief—however, another visual representation called a *box-and-whisker plot*, more commonly referred to as a *box plot*, offers another way to see important characteristics of a data set.

Next, we describe how to create and use box plots. The activity sheet Migraines: Box Plots includes instruction to help students create a box plot. Instructions are also provided here. Move to the next section if your students know how to construct a box plot.

CREATING BOX PLOTS

The histograms your students created are characterized by fixed-width intervals and varying frequencies within those intervals. Box plots reverse those characteristics by fixing the frequencies and varying interval widths. This makes histograms and box plots useful and complementary visual representations for comparing data sets.

With box plots, frequencies are fixed as *quartiles* of data. We create boundary lines that separate the data into four quartiles, and each quartile contains approximately the same number of data values. The width of each quartile, then, is determined by its data values. This is precisely complementary to histograms, for which the frequency of each interval is determined by the data values.

> *"Although the box plot is a relatively simple graph to construct, Bakker, Biehler, and Konold (2004) point out that middle-grades students generally have difficulties interpreting box plots. One explanation is that the four groups of data formed from the five-number summary are based on percentages and that their interpretation requires proportional reasoning. Guidance and practice are required for middle-grades students to understand the five-number summary and be able to interpret and compare box plots. Middle school is an appropriate place for this effort to begin, because developing proportional reasoning skills is a goal for the middle and junior high grades."* (Kader and Mamer 2008, p. 43)

To determine the quartile boundary lines, first determine the median of each data set. This positions a boundary line with half the data values below it and half above it. We previously determined the median elapsed times to be 78 minutes (Medication A) and 44 minutes (Medication B).

We carry out this same process within each half of the data set. That is, determine the median of the lower half of the data values and the median of the upper half of the data values. Together with the median, the *lower-quartile* boundary and the *upper-quartile* boundary tell us the three boundary points that separate the data into four quartiles, each quartile containing an approximately equal number of data values.

We include two more values with this set of three boundary locations. The *lower extreme* is the smallest value in a data set, and the *upper extreme* is the largest value in a data set. We now have five values that span a data set from smallest value to largest value. We refer to this set of five values as a data set's *five-number summary*. Table 12.4 gives the five-number summaries for Medication A and Medication B.

Table 12.4. Five-Point Summary for Drug Data

	Least Value	First Quartile	Median	Third Quartile	Greatest Value
Drug A	16 min.	46 min.	78 min.	94 min.	120 min.
Drug B	18 min.	30 min.	44 min.	74 min.	120 min.

We now use each five-number summary to create a box plot, illustrated here using the information for Medication A. Begin at the lower-quartile and upper-quartile values from the five-number summary. Over or beside a scale that shows the range of elapsed times from smallest to largest, create a box that captures the middle two quartiles (figure 12.3).

FIG. 12.3

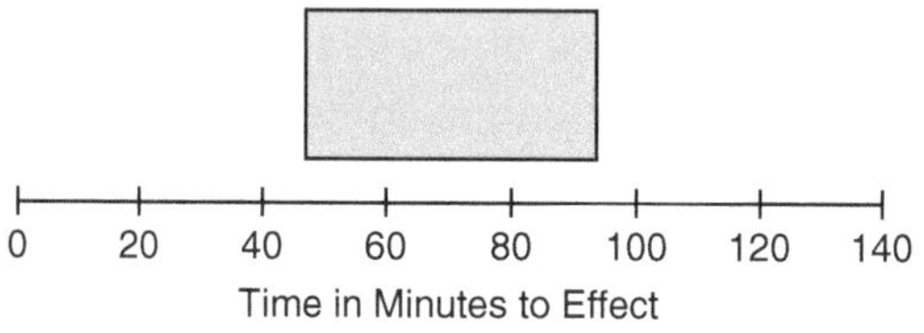

Next, include a segment within the box that identifies the location of the median (figure 12.4).

FIG. 12.4

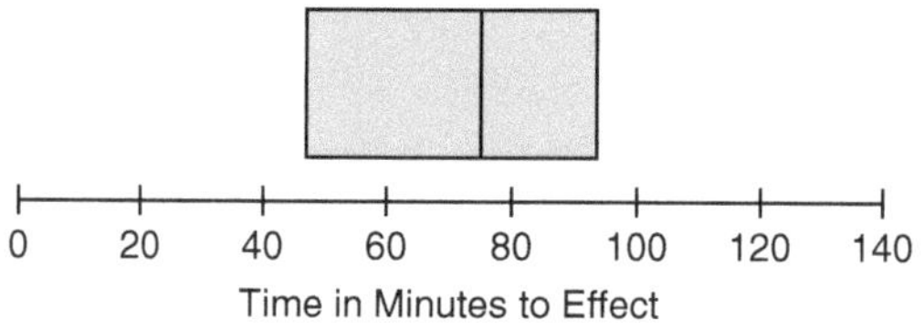

Now, extend a segment, called a whisker, from the quartile boundaries out to each extreme. That is, a segment from the lower-quartile boundary line to the lower extreme and a segment from the upper-quartile boundary line to the upper extreme (figure 12.5).

FIG. 12.5

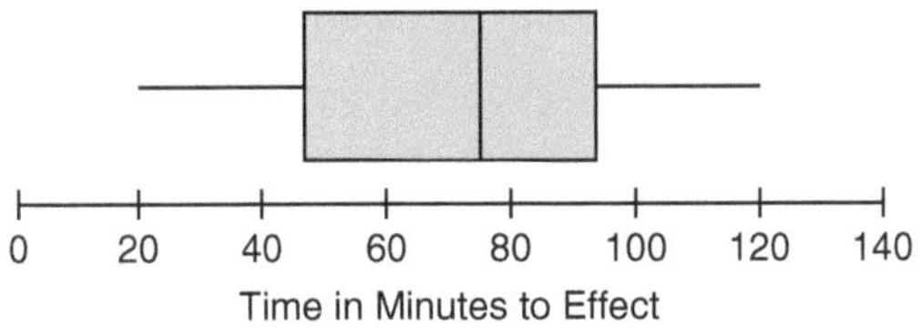

Finally, include labels to provide a context for the plot. Shown here (figure 12.6), using the same time-span scale so the data sets can be more effectively compared, are the two box plots for the medications data.

FIG. 12.6

Box plots for Medications A and B

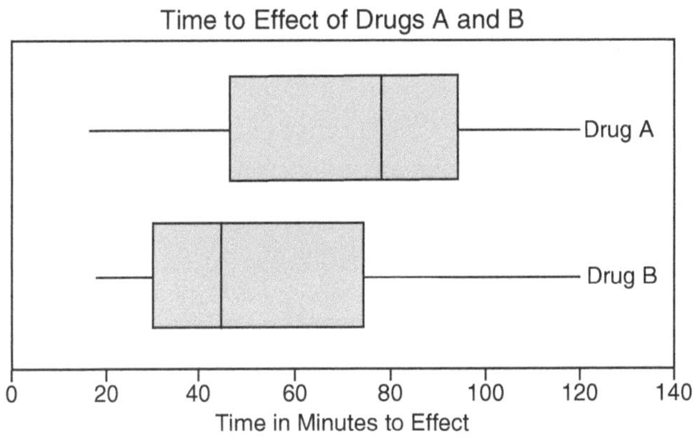

USING BOX PLOTS

Show students the box plots pictured earlier or refer them to the box plots they have created using the activity handout. Revisit once again the question posed at the start: Which medication is more effective?

Discuss with students information the box plots—and their accompanying five-number summaries—reveal above and beyond the location information provided with the means and medians.

- The box plots emphasize visually how different the median values are. Although 50 percent of those using Medication A required 78 minutes or less to achieve migraine relief, 50 percent of those using Medication B required no more than 44 minutes for relief.
- The whiskers show that these data span almost exactly the same range of times because the whiskers' endpoints are at approximately the same locations at the lower extreme and at the upper extreme. Comparing extreme values is a common practice when comparing two data sets.
- The middle 50 percent of the data—from the lower-quartile boundary to the upper-quartile boundary—spans approximately the same elapsed times, 48 minutes for Medication A and 44 minutes for Medication B. Each of these values is called the *interquartile range*. When comparing two data sets, the middle 50 percent of the data is a good place to look for similarities and differences.
- The smaller the time span for any one quartile, the more compressed or clustered the data are relative to the entire data set. For Medication B, we see the first and second quartiles (shorter time spans to migraine relief) are the most compressed, whereas for Medication A, the most compressed quartile is the third quartile, with time spans to relief longer than the median time span.
- Compare the median of each data set to its location in the other data set. The median for Medication B—the location at which half the elapsed times are below it—is at the same time when less than 25 percent of Medication A users have achieved migraine relief. In other words, by the time 25 percent of Medication A users reported relief, half the Medication B users had already experienced relief. Likewise, the median for Medication A is at an elapsed time for which more than 75 percent of Medication B users have already reported migraine relief.

These and other comparisons, made more apparent through the box plot visualization and its accompanying five-number summary, add more evidence to our claim that Medication B was more effective than Medication A in offering migraine headache relief to its users. Armed with evidence of this type—both numerical and visual—you and your students can engage in a meaningful discussion of what it means to be "more effective" and how that can be justified. Let your students know that the practices you are engaging in are precisely what professionals do in beginning efforts to explore data.

Extend

As already mentioned, histograms are characterized by fixed-width intervals and varying frequencies within those intervals. Box plots reverse those characteristics, with fixed frequencies and varying interval widths. A natural extension to this activity is to have students use a common scale and create both a box plot and a histogram for the same data set. Here (figure 12.7) are such plots for the migraine medication data.

FIG. 12.7

Box plots and histograms for each medication

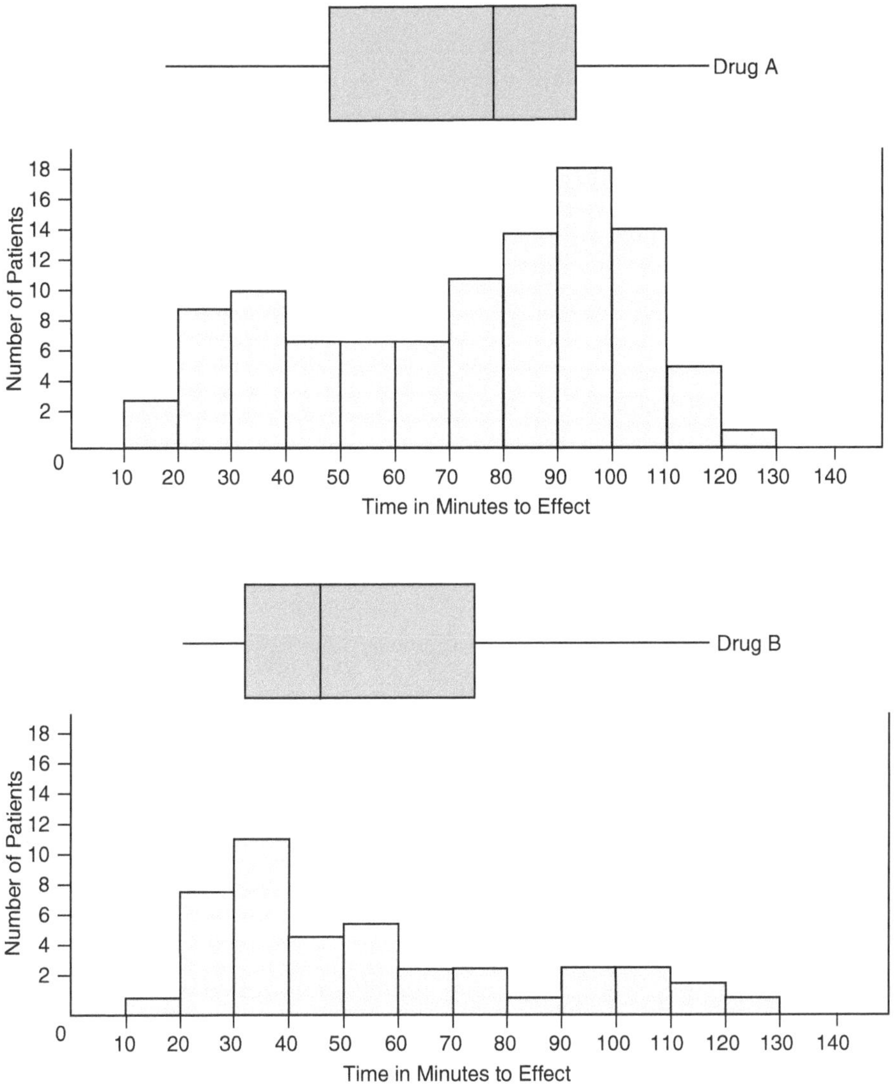

Discuss with your students the similarities and differences revealed by the types of plots on each scale. This discussion will likely review and emphasize many of the characteristics already mentioned earlier in the bulleted lists. It is important to help students realize that neither plot type—histogram nor box plot—is better or worse than the other. Rather, each type has useful characteristics that can help us analyze a data set or compare two or more data sets.

To offer your students more practice in creating and interpreting visual representations, use the battery-life data shown in the activity sheet Batteries (available in the appendix and at more4U). You can tailor specific data-representation tasks around these two data sets, based on your students' strengths and needs, or you can simply use the activity as shown, complete with the questions indicated.

The data sets used in the activities here are called *single-variable data sets*, as each set identifies a single characteristic, in this case, elapsed time. Often, situations reveal two or more variables that are related. Examples include number of minutes a cell phone is used and the cost of those minutes, hours worked and pay received for a job, and height of a burning candle as time passes. Data sets from such situations are called *multivariable data sets*. As an extension to the activities here, with single-variable data, you might consider students' exploration of two-variable, or bivariate, data sets. The original Navigations Data Analysis activities include an entire chapter focused on representing and analyzing bivariate data sets.

> *"Statistical literacy is essential in our personal lives as consumers, citizens and professionals. Statistics plays a role in our health and happiness. Sound statistical reasoning skills take a long time to develop. They cannot be honed to the level needed in the modern world through one high school course. The surest way to reach the necessary skill level is to begin the educational process in the elementary grades and keep strengthening and developing these skills throughout the middle and high school years. A statistically literate high school graduate will know how to interpret the data in the morning newspaper and will ask the right questions about statistical claims. He or she will be comfortable handling quantitative decisions that occur on the job, and will be able to make informed decisions about the quality of life issues."* (Kader and Perry 2006, p. 1)

SUMMARY

In this activity, we have explored two common and useful tools for visualizing single-variable data sets, including histograms and box plots. Students have created these plots and used them for analysis and comparison of data sets, a common and significant aspect of exploratory data analysis. We have also determined and described numerical representations that are used for both creating the visual representations and as data-analysis tools in and of themselves.

From a broader perspective, we have identified and described three essential characteristics of a single-variable data set, including its center, its spread, and its shape. As students continue exploring data and statistics, these three characteristics play a significant role as tools for analysis and comparison.

Next Steps

Imagine a classroom, a school, or a school district where all students have access to high-quality, engaging mathematics instruction . . .

We opened this collection of Gems with a scenario describing an ideal classroom, a scene that some view as utopian. Today we do stand closer to this reality than we did in 2000, when the scenario was published in *Principles and Standards for School Mathematics* (NCTM 2000). In some cases, we have taken only small steps; in others, we have made great strides. Our Introduction offers many sources that give guidance to teachers, curriculum planners, and others on how to teach rich and important mathematics effectively and to have it "stick" with students.

The NCTM *Navigations* books were published soon after *PSSM* was released, intended to offer examples and resources for teachers by illustrating classroom tasks that can be used to implement the ideas in *PSSM*. The *Navigations* "gems" in this document are a small subset of those original Navigations activities, updated and enhanced, and offered in the spirit of moving closer to an ideal classroom.

To support teachers and others as they move beyond the activities highlighted here, as well as activities in the original *Navigations* books, let's look to two particularly useful resources. One was mentioned in our Introduction and another highlights next steps you might take.

The Preface to *Principles to Actions* states that the volume was intended to "articulate a unified vision of what is needed to realize the potential of educating all students," and it "describes the actions required to ensure that all students learn to become mathematical thinkers and are prepared for any . . . path they choose" (NCTM 2014, p vii). These principles are most helpful as individual and collaborative groups of teachers develop a research-based framework for planning mathematics lessons, thinking carefully about each one of the principles as they develop plans for instruction.

FIG. NEXT.1

Mathematics teaching practices (*Principles to Actions*, NCTM 2014)

P to A Teaching Practices	
1	**Establish mathematics goals to focus learning.** Effective teaching of mathematics establishes clear goals for the mathematics that students are learning, situates goals within learning progressions, and uses the goals to guide instructional decisions.
2	**Implement tasks that promote reasoning and problem solving.** Effective teaching of mathematics engages students in solving and discussing tasks that promote mathematical reasoning and problem solving and allow multiple entry points and varied solution strategies.
3	**Use and connect mathematical representations.** Effective teaching of mathematics engages students in making connections among mathematical representations to deepen understanding of mathematics concepts and procedures and as tools for problem solving.
4	**Facilitate meaningful mathematical discourse.** Effective teaching of mathematics facilitates discourse among students to build shared understanding of mathematical ideas by analyzing and comparing student approaches and arguments.
5	**Pose purposeful questions.** Effective teaching of mathematics uses purposeful questions to assess and advance students' reasoning and sense making about important mathematical ideas and relationships.
6	**Build procedural fluency from conceptual understanding.** Effective teaching of mathematics builds fluency with procedures on a foundation of conceptual understanding so that students, over time, become skillful in using procedures flexibly as they solve contextual and mathematical problems.
7	**Support productive struggle in learning mathematics.** Effective teaching of mathematics consistently provides students, individually and collectively, with opportunities and supports to engage in productive struggle as they grapple with mathematical ideas and relationships.
8	**Elicit and use evidence of student thinking.** Effective teaching of mathematics uses evidence of student thinking to assess progress toward mathematical understanding and to adjust instruction continually in ways that support and extend learning.

Another resource that can be extremely helpful in planning, offering extensive examples and guidance, is *5 Practices for Orchestrating Productive Mathematics Discussion* (Smith and Stein 2018). The content in this resource connects with *Principles to Actions*, getting more specific about using those ideas in planning mathematics lessons. The five practices are as follows:

1. ***Anticipating*** likely student responses to challenging mathematical tasks and questions to ask to students who produce them;
2. ***Monitoring*** students' actual responses to the tasks (while students work on the tasks in pairs or small groups);
3. ***Selecting*** particular students to present their mathematical work during the whole-class discussion;

4. ***Sequencing*** the student responses that will be displayed in a specific order;
5. ***Connecting*** different student responses and connecting the responses to key mathematical ideas. (Smith and Stein 2018, p. 9)

Let's look at one of these practices. How do you begin to think about ***anticipating*** student responses? What if you have never taught this lesson before, or you are teaching at a new grade level or course this year and are unsure what students already know? What if in the past you primarily thought about the right answer and not what might be a good follow-up question for an individual student, whether the student's answer showed understanding or misunderstanding? Chapter 4 in *5 Practices* deals with this practice, anticipating student responses. The authors offer abundant support, examples, and possible responses to student ideas and approaches, and they invite teachers to carefully listen to students' responses.

Such lesson planning is an opportunity for collaborative planning with fellow teachers. If a colleague is able to observe a lesson you have coplanned and can monitor student responses to the lesson, your colleague could note especially unanticipated student responses as well as questions from you that elicited student responses illustrating active engagement. If you do not have a partner for observation, it is especially important that you allow time for analysis after your lesson, making notes on successes as well as generating ideas to make the lesson better next time.

Each of the other practices has a specific chapter in *5 Practices*, together with a separate chapter focused on setting clear goals and identifying tasks consistent with those goals. Other chapters focus on planning structure and on collaboration.

The result of a focus on effective practices and principles is "that the identification and use of a codified set of practices can make student-centered approaches to mathematics instruction accessible to and manageable for more teachers. By giving teachers a road map of things that they can do in advance and during whole-class discussions," teachers can maintain their focus on student thinking and the use of important mathematics (Smith and Stein 2018, p. xi).

Our hope and intent is that the Gems we have collected here, and in the other grade-band volumes, will help us all inch closer to our ideal classroom, thereby helping to engage our students in meaningful tasks that prepare them for a future that may currently be unknown but without a doubt will feature meaningful mathematics.

Appendix

MATERIALS AVAILABLE AT MORE4U

The following list includes all the activity sheets, classroom materials, book pages, and other resources from the Navigations series that are available to be downloaded at this book's page on NCTM's more4U website. To access these materials, go to **https://www.nctm.org/more4u/** and enter the code found on the title page of this book.

Activity sheets and classroom materials with a page number indicated are included in the appendix pages that follow the list. These materials can either be printed from the more4U site or copied directly from the book. Enlarging a book page to approximately 115 percent of its original size should fill a standard 8 1/2-by-11-inch sheet of paper.

1 Reasoning about Sums of Consecutive Numbers

"Reasoning about Sums of Consecutive Numbers" from *Problem Solving and Reasoning in Grades 6–8*

Sum-thing about Consecutive Numbers activity sheets (pp. 159–162)

Recording Sheet for Sum-thing about Consecutive Numbers activity sheets (pp. 163–164)

2 Squaring Off with Rational Numbers

"Representing Shaded Areas of Rectangular Grids" from *Number and Operations in Grades 6–8*

"Shading Areas of Rectangular Grids" from *Number and Operations in Grades 6–8*

Representing Shaded Areas of Rectangular Grids activity sheets (pp. 165–166)

Shading Areas of Rectangular Grids activity sheet (p. 167)

"Presenting and Representing: From Fractions to Rational Numbers" by Susan Lamon, from NCTM Yearbook 2001

3 Rates and Unit Rates

"Using a Unit Rate to Solve Problems" from *Number and Operations in Grades 6–8*

Using a Unit Rate to Solve Problems activity sheets (pp. 168–170)

4 From Stories to Graphs and Graphs to Stories

"From Stories to Graphs" from *Algebra in Grades 6–8*

"From Graphs to Stories" from *Algebra in Grades 6–8*

From Stories to Graphs activity sheet (p. 171)

From Graphs to Stories activity sheet (p. 172)

5 Tiling Tubs and Plotting Land

"Tiling Tubs" from *Algebra in Grades 6–8*

"Plotting Land" from *Algebra in Grades 6–8*

Tiling Tubs activity sheet (p. 173)

Plotting Land activity sheets (pp. 174–176)

"Teaching Algebra in the Middle Grades Using Mathmagic" by Hari P. Koirala and Phillip M. Goodwin, from *Mathematics Teaching in the Middle School* (May 2000)

"Uncovering the Magic" by Peggy O'Connor, from *Teaching Children Mathematics* (September 2000)

6 Scale Factors and Measurement Relationships

"Scale Factors and Measurement Relationships" from *Problem Solving and Reasoning in Grade 6*

Scale It Up, Scale It Down activity sheet (p. 177)

Perimeters and Areas of Similar Figures activity sheets (pp. 178–180)

Surface Areas and Volumes of Similar Figures activity sheets (pp. 181–182)

Scale Models activity sheets (pp. 183–185)

"Block Buildings" from *Problem Solving and Reasoning in Grade 6*

Block Buildings activity sheet, Set 1—A Constant Footprint (pp. 186–187)

Block Buildings activity sheet, Set 2—A Constant Height (pp. 188–189)

Block Buildings activity sheet, Set 1—Constantly Cubes (pp. 190–191)

"Understanding Area Formulas" from *Problem Solving and Reasoning in Grade 6*

Measuring Shapes activity sheets (pp. 192–193)

Make a Rectangle from That Parallelogram activity sheets (pp. 194–195)

Compare That Triangle with That Rectangle activity sheets (pp. 196–197)

Compare That Trapezoid with That Parallelogram activity sheets (pp. 198–199)

7 Three-Dimensional Shapes: Cross Sections and Constructions

"Cross Sections of Three-Dimensional Shapes" from *Geometry in Grades 6–8*

"Constructing Three-Dimensional Figures" from *Geometry in Grades 6–8*

"Isometric Explorations" from *Geometry in Grades 6–8*

Cross Sections of Three-Dimensional Shapes activity sheet (p. 200)

Constructing Three-Dimensional Figures activity sheets (pp. 201–202)

The Platonic Solids activity sheet (p. 203)

Nets of Polyhedra activity sheets (pp. 204–205)

Isometric Explorations activity sheets (pp. 206–207)

"Visualizing Three Dimensions by Constructing Polyhedra" by Victoria Pohl, from NCTM Yearbook 1987

8 Transforming Shapes

"Translations, Reflections, and Rotations" from *Geometry in Grades 6–8*

Translations, Reflections, and Rotations activity sheets (pp. 208–210)

More Transformations activity sheet (p. 211)

9 Reasoning about the Pythagorean Theorem

"Reasoning about the Pythagorean Theorem" from *Geometry in Grades 6–8*

"Reasoning about the Pythagorean Theorem" from *Problem Solving and Reasoning in Grades 6–8*

Reasoning about the Pythagorean Relationship activity sheet (p. 212)

Take a Look at Those Squares activity sheets (pp. 213–219)

Can You Prove It? activity sheets (pp. 220–221)

Sets of Right Triangles for Can You Prove It? activity sheets (p. 222)

10 Investigating Pick's Theorem

"Pick's Theorem" from *Measurement in Grades 6–8*

Pick's Theorem activity sheets (pp. 223–224)

Exploring Pick's Rule activity sheets (pp. 225–228)

What's the Area? activity sheet (p. 229)

Pick's Theorem—The Hole Truth activity sheets (pp. 230–231)

11 Dice and Coins: Empirical and Theoretical Probability

"Empirical Probabilities" from *Probability in Grades 6–8*

"Test Guessing" from *Probability in Grades 6–8*

"First Head" from *Probability in Grades 6–8*

"String of Heads" from *Probability in Grades 6–8*

Ratios activity sheets (pp. 232–235)

Test Guessing activity sheet (p. 236)

First Head activity sheets (pp. 237–238)

Strings of Heads activity sheets (pp. 239–242)

12 Histograms and Box Plots: Same Data, Different Views

"Migraines: Histograms" from *Data Analysis in Grades 6–8*

"Migraines: Box Plots" from *Data Analysis in Grades 6–8*

Migraines: Histograms activity sheets (pp. 243–245)

Migraines: Box Plots activity sheets (pp. 246–248)

Two Data Sets (table 12.1, for projecting) (p. 249)

Batteries activity sheet (p. 250)

Multiuse Grid and Dot Papers

Sum-thing about Consecutive Numbers

Examine the three sums of consecutive integers below:

$$3 + 4 = 7 \qquad 2 + 3 + 4 = 9 \qquad 4 + 5 + 6 + 7 = 22$$

Note that 7 appears as the sum of two consecutive numbers, 9 appears as the sum of three consecutive numbers, and 22 appears as the sum of four consecutive numbers. Which counting numbers (1, 2, 3, ...) from 1 to 35 can be the sums of consecutive counting numbers? Which cannot?

1. Find all the ways in which you can write the counting numbers from 1 to 35 as sums of two or more consecutive counting numbers.

1		2	
3		4	
5		6	
7		8	
9		10	
11		12	

(continued)

This activity is adapted from Mark Driscoll, *Fostering Algebraic Thinking: A Guide for Teachers, Grades 6–10*, Education Development Center (Portsmouth, NH: Heinemann, 1999), p. 79.

Sum-thing about Consecutive Numbers

13		14	
15		16	
17		18	
19		20	
21		22	
23		24	
25		26	
27		28	
29		30	

(continued)

Sum-thing about Consecutive Numbers

31		32	
33		34	
35			

2. Have you discovered any patterns in sums of the consecutive addends? On "Recording Sheet for 'Sum-thing about Consecutive Numbering'" organize your data according to the number of addends in each sum. Write out your findings on a sheet of chart paper, and be prepared to share your ideas.
3. Without doing any calculations, predict whether each of the following numbers is the sum of two, three, four, or more consecutive counting numbers. Explain your predictions in each case.

45

57

62

75

80

Sum-thing about Consecutive Numbers

4. Do your discoveries in step 2 suggest any shortcuts that you could use for determining which of the following numbers are the sums of two or more consecutive addends? Explain your shortcuts and tell how to use them to write each number below as the sum or sums of consecutive numbers.

45

57

62

75

80

Recording Sheet for Sum-thing about Consecutive Numbers

In step 1 of "Sum-thing about Consecutive Numbers," you discovered which numbers from 1 to 35 are the sums of consecutive counting numbers. Below, display your strings of addends again, this time sorting them according to how many consecutive addends are in a string for a particular sum.

	Number of Consecutive Addends					
Sum	2 Addends	3 Addends	4 Addends	5 Addends	6 Addends	7 Addends
1						
2						
3						
4						
5						
6						
7						
8						
9						
10						
11						
12						
13						
14						

Recording Sheet for Sum-thing about Consecutive Numbers

Sum	2 Addends	3 Addends	4 Addends	5 Addends	6 Addends	7 Addends
15						
16						
17						
18						
19						
20						
21						
22						
23						
24						
25						
26						
27						
28						
29						
30						
31						
32						
33						
34						
35						

Representing Shaded Areas of Rectangular Grids

For each of the rectangular grids below, express the shaded region as a fraction, a decimal, and a percentage of the total area. Explain your reasoning in the space below each grid.

1.

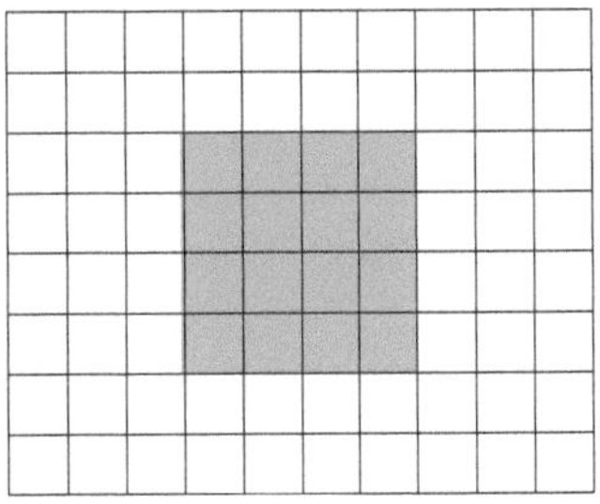

Fraction __________

Decimal __________

Percent __________

2.

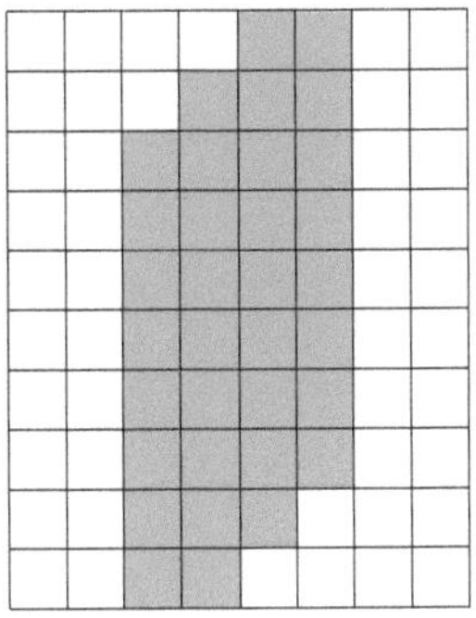

Fraction __________

Decimal __________

Percent __________

3.

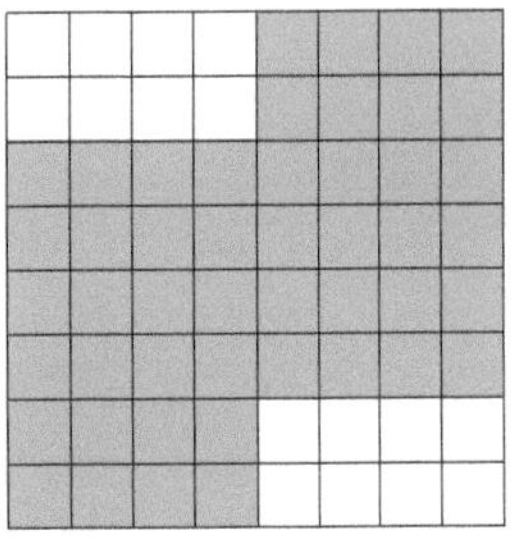

Fraction __________

Decimal __________

Percent __________

4.

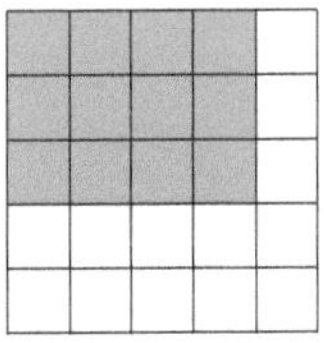

Fraction __________

Decimal __________

Percent __________

This activity has been adapted from Linda Cooper Foreman and Albert B. Bennett Jr. *Visual Mathematics Course II*. Salem, OR: Math Learning Center, 1996.

Representing Shaded Areas of Rectangular Grids

5.

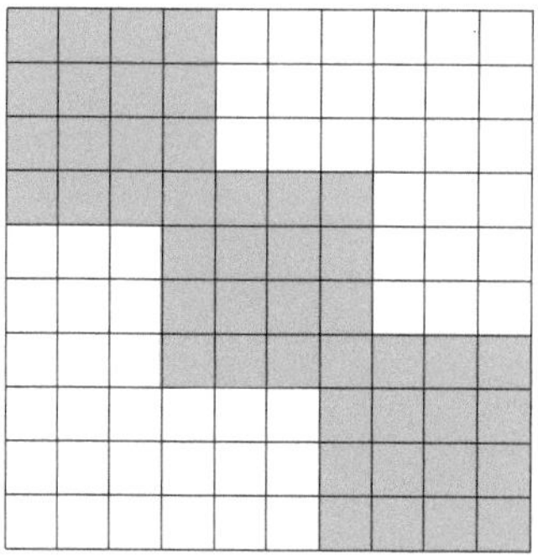

Fraction ______

Decimal ______

Percent ______

6.

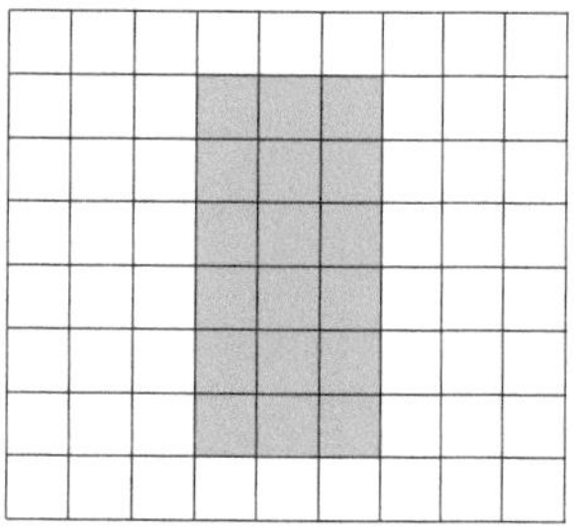

Fraction ______

Decimal ______

Percent ______

7.

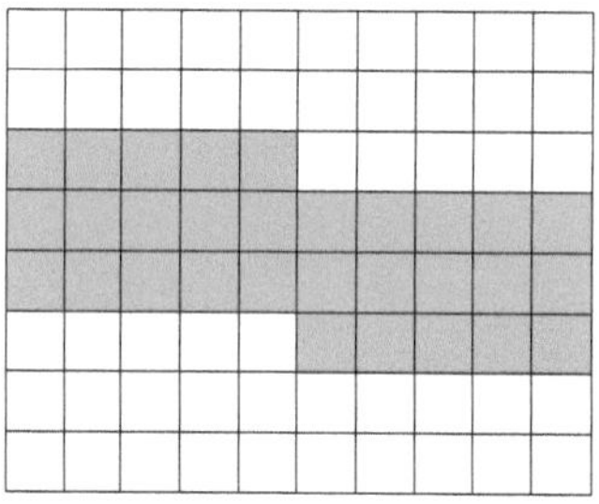

Fraction ______

Decimal ______

Percent ______

8.

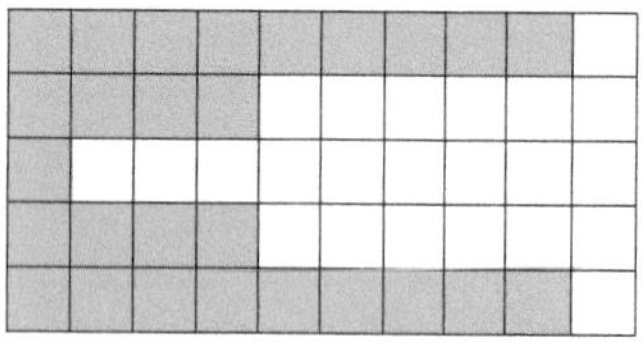

Fraction ______

Decimal ______

Percent ______

Shading Areas of Rectangular Grids

Use what you know about fractions, decimals, and percentages to solve the following problems.

1. *a.* Shade the portion of the area of the rectangle that represents 0.725.

   b. What fractional part of the area did you shade?

   c. What percentage of the area did you shade?

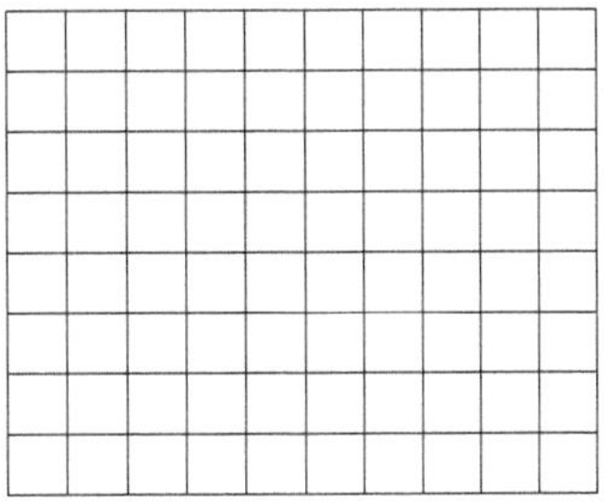

2. *a.* Shade 3/8 of the area of the rectangle.

   b. What percentage of the area did you shade?

   c. What decimal number does the shaded portion of the rectangle represent?

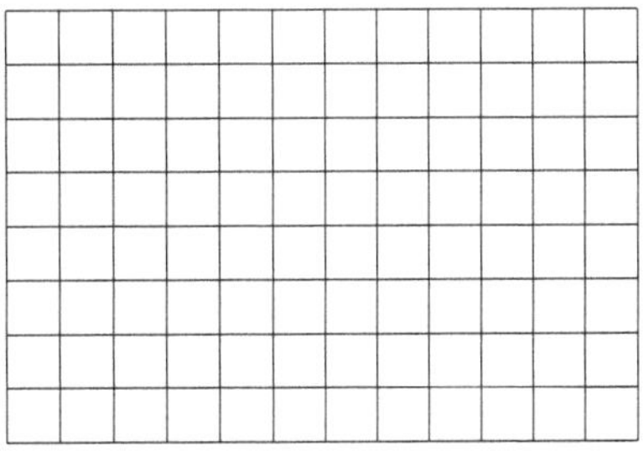

3. *a.* Shade 87.5% of the area of the rectangle.

   b. What fractional part of the area did you shade?

   c. What decimal number does the shaded portion of the rectangle represent?

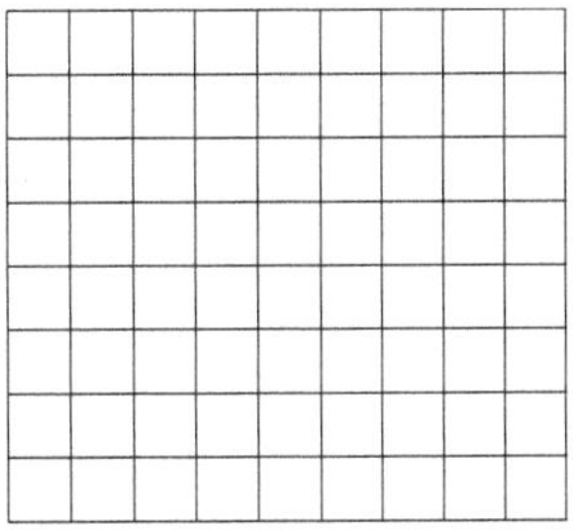

This activity has been adapted from Linda Cooper Foreman and Albert B. Bennett Jr. *Visual Mathematics Course II.* Salem, OR: Math Learning Center, 1996.

Using a Unit Rate to Solve Problems

1. Marcus runs around the track every day after school. He believes that with practice he can be a track star. He can run 12 laps around the school's track in 30 minutes.

   a. What are the two possible rates for this situation?

   b. Rewrite each rate as a unit rate.

   c. What does each unit rate tell you?

   d. Suppose someone asks you, "At this rate, how long will it take Marcus to run 14 laps?" Which unit rate will you use to answer the question? ____________ Explain why you chose that unit rate, and then use it to answer the question.

   e. Suppose someone then asks, "At this rate, how many laps can Marcus run in 5 minutes?" Which unit rate will you use to answer the question? _____________ Explain why you chose that unit rate, and then use it to answer the question.

Using a Unit Rate to Solve Problems

2. Michelle, an exchange student from France, will be in the United States for the next four months. In France, she buys everything in euros. When she came to the United States, she had to exchange her euros for U.S. dollars. She went to the bank and exchanged her money at the rate of 4.5 euros for 5 dollars.

   a. What are the two possible rates for this situation?

   b. Rewrite each rate as a unit rate.

   c. What does each unit rate tell you?

   d. Suppose someone asks you, "At this rate, how many euros will Michelle receive for $500?" Which unit rate will you use to answer the question? ____________ Explain why you chose that unit rate, and then use it to answer the question.

   e. Suppose someone then asks, "At this rate, how many dollars did Michelle receive for 135 euros?" Which unit rate will you use to answer the question? ____________ Explain why you chose that unit rate, and then use it to answer the question.

Using a Unit Rate to Solve Problems

3. The Martinez family is planning to drive from New York to Florida during winter break to visit the Kennedy Space Center. The scale on the map that they are using to plan their trip is 2.5 cm = 125 miles.

   a. What are the two possible rates for this situation?

   b. Rewrite each rate as a unit rate.

   c. What does each unit rate tell you?

   d. Write two questions that you can use a unit rate to answer about the Martinez family's trip to Florida. Use a different unit rate for each question. Answer both your questions, and explain which unit rate you used to find the answer.

From Stories to Graphs

1. In a walking experiment, Josephine walked a total distance of 40 feet. At the halfway point, she had walked for 25 seconds. She stopped for 5 seconds to tie her shoe and then continued walking for 25 more seconds. Sketch a graph that shows Josephine's distance from the starting point over time.

---

2. You are gathering data in the school cafeteria from 8:00 A.M. to 3:00 P.M. Sketch a graph that tells a story about the number of cans of soda in a vending machine over that time. Write a paragraph that tells the same story in words.

---

3. You are mowing the lawn. As you mow, the amount of grass to be cut decreases. You mow at the same rate until about half the grass has been cut. Then you take a break for a while. Then, mowing at the same rate as before, you finish cutting the grass. Sketch a graph that shows how much uncut grass is left as you mow, take your break, and finish mowing.

From Graphs to Stories

1. John and his father participate in a 100-meter race. John started the race 3 seconds after his father began to run. The graph provides information about how far John and his father ran over time. Write a story about who won the race; be descriptive about how the race was run. If the two lines describing how each person ran were parallel, what would the graph tell you about who won the race?

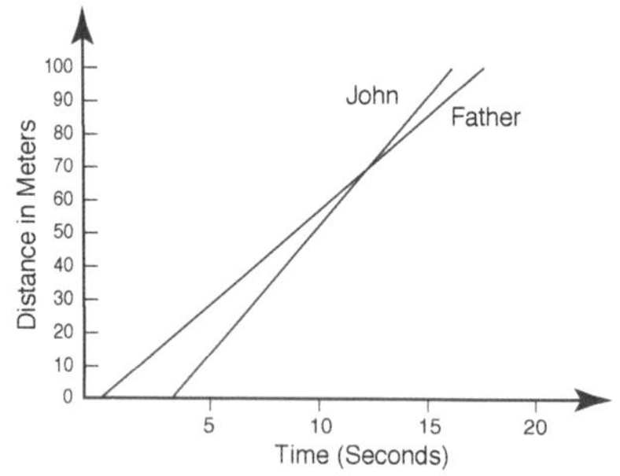

2. The graph represents the relationship between the profit and the amount of lemonade sold at a lemonade stand. Write a story about how the lemonade stand's profit is determined. Include an explanation of what is indicated when the line is below zero and when the line crosses the horizontal axis. (This graph assumes that the seller is not paid and that there is no overhead.)

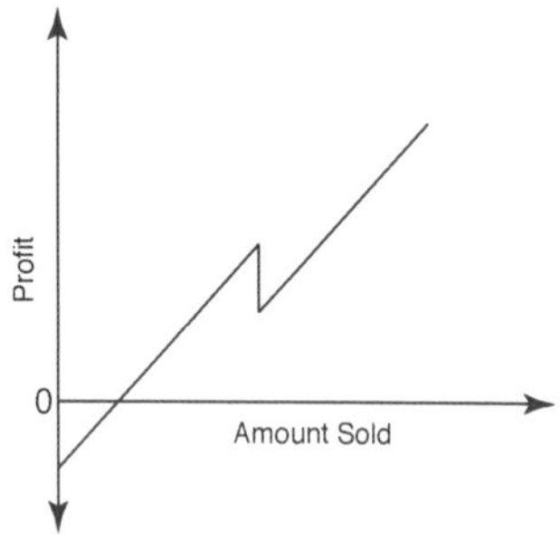

3. The graph represents a flag being raised on a flagpole. Write a story that describes what is happening to the flag, gives an estimate of the height of the flagpole, and explains the shape of the graph.

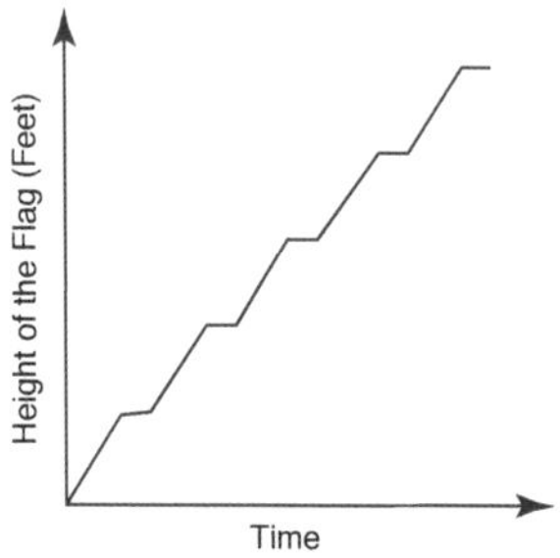

4. Graphs can be used to depict the story of a race. Here is a graph that represents a swimming race that occurred between two middle-grades students. Write a story that describes what happened in this race.

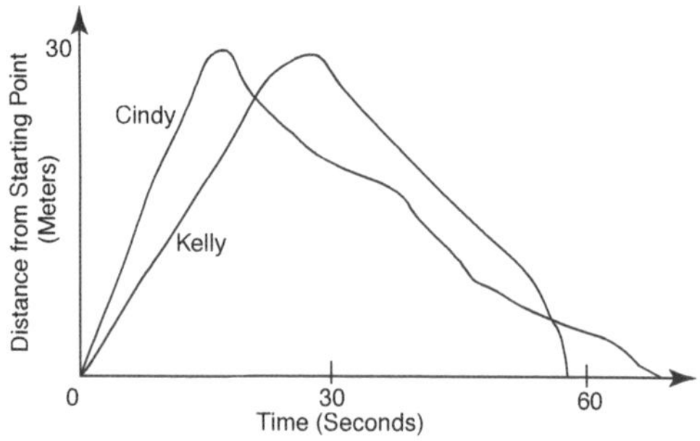

Tiling Tubs

Hot tubs and in-ground swimming pools are sometimes surrounded by borders of tiles. This drawing shows a square hot tub with sides of length *s* feet. This tub is surrounded by a border of square tiles. Each border tile measures 1 foot on each side.

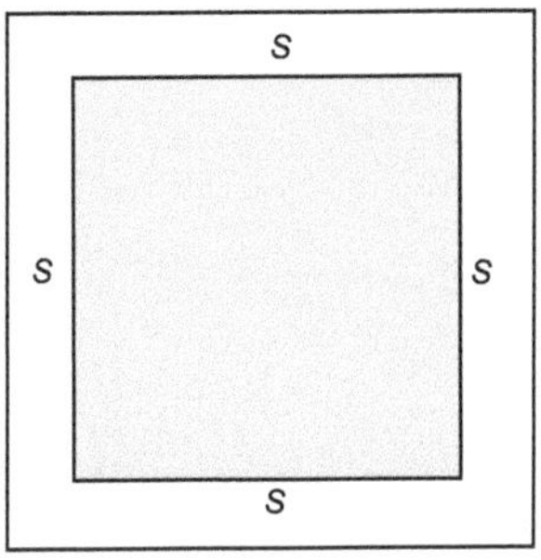

1. How many 1-foot square tiles will be needed for the border of a square hot tub that has edge length *s* feet?________________________________

2. Express the total number of tiles in as many ways as you can. ____________________

    ____

    ____

    ____

3. Be prepared to convince your classmates that the expressions are equivalent.

Plotting Land

A gardener has divided a plot of land into two sections.The shaded section is to be used for growing vegetables, and the unshaded portion is for growing flowers.

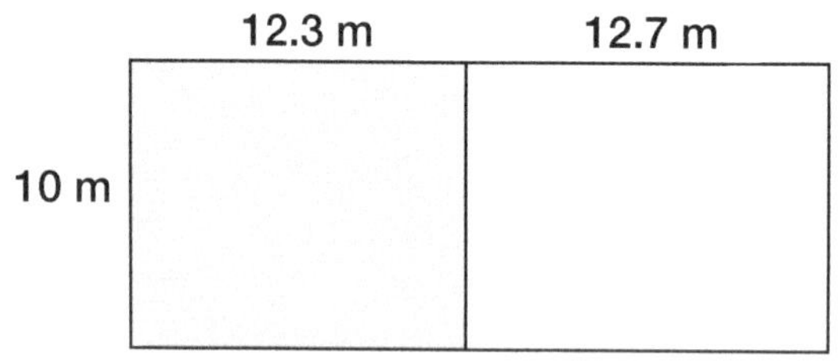

1. What is the area of the shaded portion of the plot of land? ______________________

2. What is the area of the unshaded portion of the plot of land? ______________________

3. What is the area of the entire plot of land? ______________________

4. Suppose the gardener wanted to divide the plot of land so that 3/5 of the land was used for vegetables and 2/5 of the land was used for flowers.

   (*a*) What would be the dimensions of the shaded and unshaded portions? ____________

   ____

   (*b*) What would be the areas of the shaded and unshaded portions of the plot of land? ________

   ____

   (*c*) What would be the area of the entire plot of land? ______________________

Plotting Land

5. For each of the following garden designs, show two ways to calculate the total surface area.

(a)

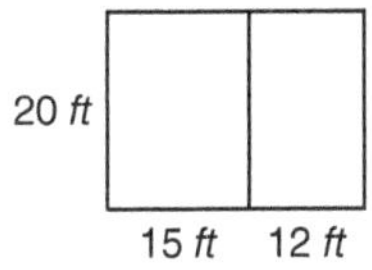

(b)

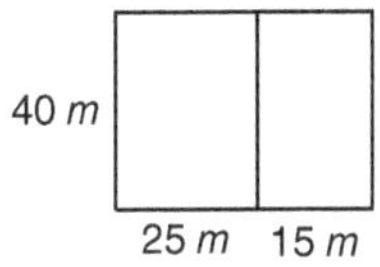

(c)

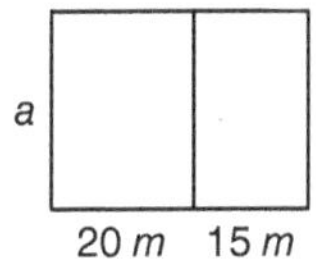

(d)

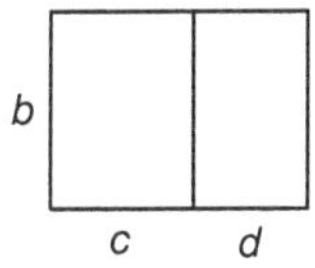

Plotting Land

6. Which of the following have an area of $8\ (5 + x)$? ________________

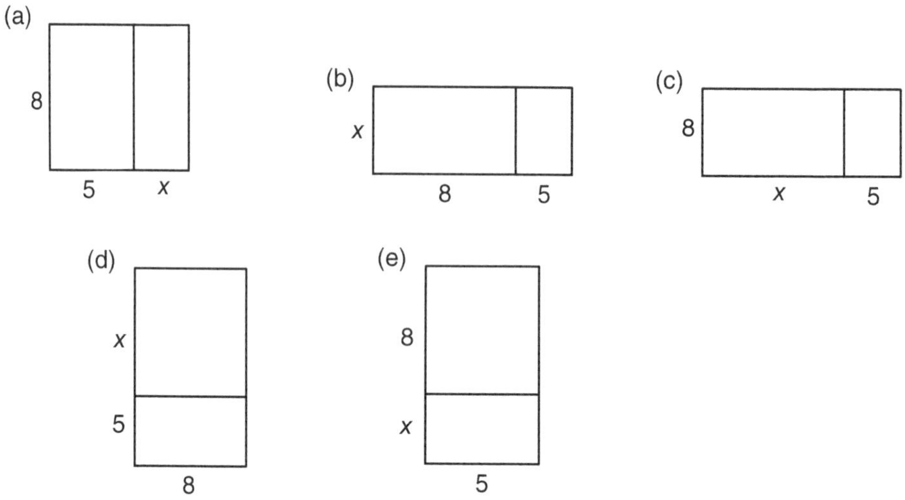

7. Which rectangles above have an area of $8x + 5x$? ______________

8. Draw a diagram using rectangles to show that $8x + 16$ and $8\ (x + 2)$ are equivalent.

Scale It Up, Scale It Down

Six geometric figures appear below on dot grids. Scale each figure up or down as the activity sheet Perimeters and Areas of Similar Figures directs.

A.

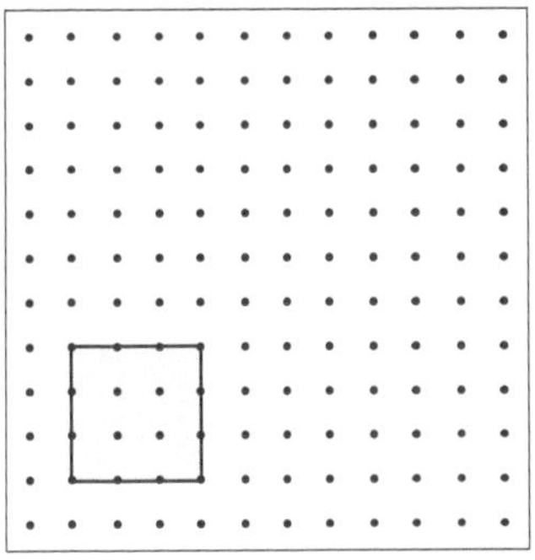

B.

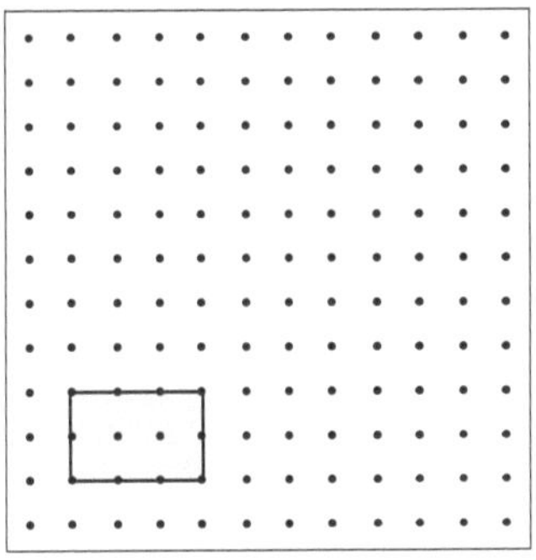

C.

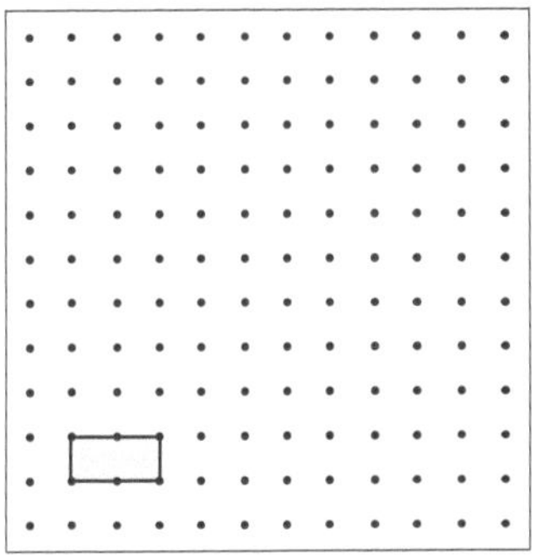

D.

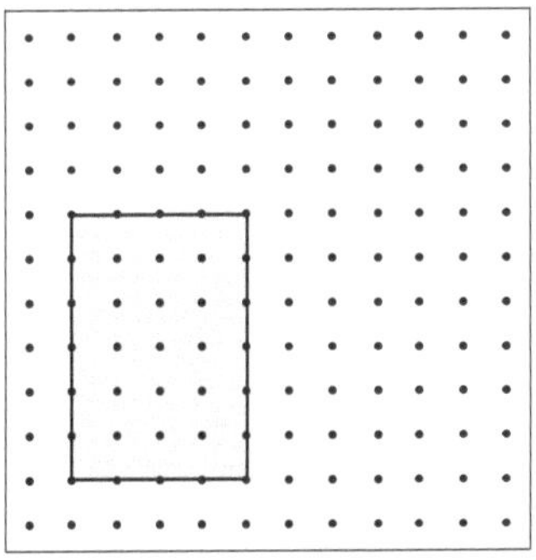

E.

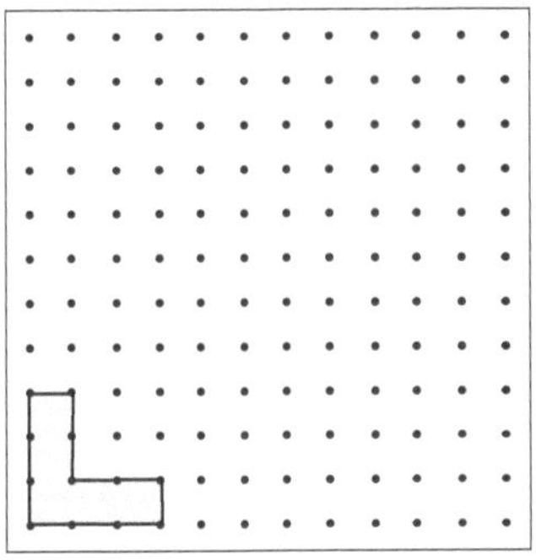

F.

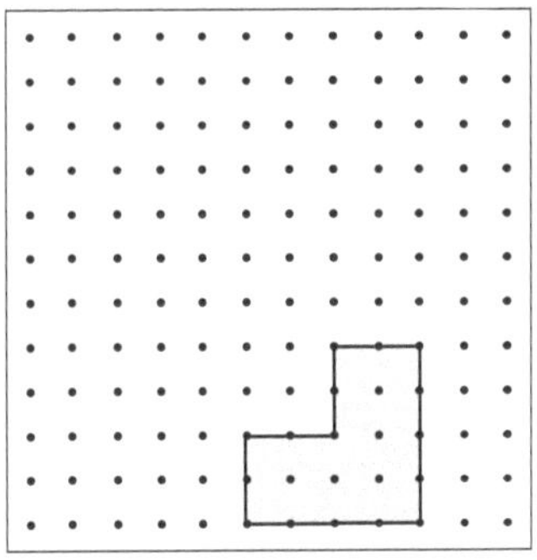

Perimeters and Areas of Similar Figures

1. The activity sheet Scale It Up, Scale It Down shows six geometric figures on dot grids. Column 2 in the table below shows scale factors for all the figures.

Measurements of Preimages and Images

Figure	Scale Factor	Length of Longest Side in Preimage (linear units)	Length of Corresponding Side in Image (linear units)	Perimeter of Preimage (linear units)	Perimeter of Image (linear units)	Area of Preimage (square units)	Area of Image (square units)
A	2						
B	3						
C	4						
D	$\frac{1}{2}$						
E	2						
F	$\frac{3}{2}$						

a. For each figure (called a *preimage*), locate the appropriate scale factor, and use it to draw a similar figure (called an *image*) on the same grid as the preimage on Scale It Up, Scale It Down.

b. Complete the table:

- Identify the longest side in each preimage, and determine its length. Find the corresponding side in each image, and determine its length. Record your results.
- Determine the perimeter of each preimage. Then determine the perimeter of each image. Record your results.
- Determine the area of each preimage. Then determine the area of each image. Record your results.

Perimeters and Areas of Similar Figures

2. *a.* For each figure, find the ratio of the length of the longest side of the image to the length of the longest side of the preimage.

A________________ D ________________

B________________ E ________________

C________________ F ________________

b. What patterns do you observe in the ratios? ____

____

____

3. *a.* For each figure, find the ratio of the perimeter of the image to the perimeter of the preimage.

A________________ D ________________

B________________ E ________________

C________________ F ________________

b. What patterns do you observe in the ratios? ____

____

____

4. *a.* For each figure, find the ratio of the area of the image to the area of the preimage.

A________________ D ________________

B________________ E ________________

C________________ F ________________

b. What patterns do you observe in the ratios? ____

____

____

Perimeters and Areas of Similar Figures

5. Consider the patterns that you observed in steps 2–4.

   a. What conclusions can you draw about corresponding sides, perimeters, and areas of similar figures? (*Hint*: Use the scale factor in your explanation.)

   b. Suppose that a figure has a perimeter of 13 units and an area of 16 square units and you are going to enlarge it on a copy machine by using a scale factor of 250%. What will the perimeter and area of your enlarged figure be?

   $P=$ ____________________

   $A=$ ____________________

   How did you get your answers?

6. (Optional) A pizza restaurant sells two different sizes of pizza – a small one that is 6 inches in diameter and a large one that is 12 inches in diameter. The small pizza costs $5. If the restaurant prices its pizzas proportionally by their areas, what should the price of the large pizza be?

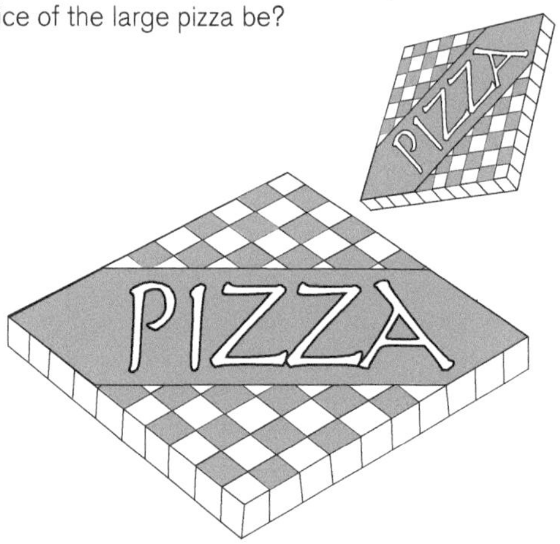

Surface Areas and Volumes of Similar Figures

1. *a.* Use centimeter cubes to build the geometric figure A, whose dimensions (*length* × *width* × *height*, in centimeters) appear in column 2 in the table. The figure is a three-dimensional box—a *rectangular prism*. Use the scale factor given in column 3 to build a second rectangular prism that is the *image* of figure A (the *preimage*). Find the surface areas and volumes of the preimage and image and enter them to complete the row for figure A.

Measurements of Preimages and Images

Figure (Preimage)	Dimensions of Preimage (centimeters)	Scale Factor	Surface Area of Preimage (square centimeters)	Surface Area of Image (square centimeters)	Volume of Preimage (cubic centimeters)	Volume of Image (cubic centimeters)
A	1 × 2 × 3	2				
B	1 × 2 × 1	3				
C	1 × 1 × 1	4				
D	2 × 2 × 4	$\frac{1}{2}$				
E	4 × 2 × 4	$\frac{3}{2}$				

b. Repeat the process that you followed in (*a*), this time building figure B and its image, as specified in the table. Then complete the row for figure B by finding and recording the surface areas and volumes of your new preimage and image.

c. Repeat the process, building figures C, D, and E in turn and completing the respective rows in the table. You may need to dismantle figures and images that you built earlier to have enough cubes to build new ones.

Surface Areas and Volumes of Similar Figures

2. *a.* For each figure, find the ratio of the surface area of the image to the surface area of the preimage.

   A________________ D________________

   B________________ E________________

   C________________ F________________

   b. What patterns do you observe?

3. *a.* For each figure, find the ratio of the volume of the image to the volume of the preimage.

   A________________ D________________

   B________________ E________________

   C________________ F________________

   b. What patterns do you observe?

4. Consider the patterns that you observed in steps 2 and 3. What conclusions can you draw about the surface areas and volumes of similar figures? (*Hint:* Use the scale factor in your explanation.)

5. Suppose that a building has a volume of 100,000 cubic feet and you have been assigned to build a scale model of the building by using a scale factor of $\frac{1}{100}$. What will the volume of your scale model be?

   $V =$ ____________________________

   How did you arrive at your answer?

Scale Models

People who make models of objects use a *scale factor* to determine the size of each part that they make for the model. The scale factor is a ratio that gives the mathematical relationship between lengths in the model and corresponding lengths in its life-sized counterpart. For instance, an O gauge model train has a scale factor of 1:48, or $\frac{1}{48}$, which means that each inch of the model corresponds to 48 inches on the original train. Makers of models use scale factors to ensure that a replica is like the original object in all of its proportions.

Suppose that you buy a model train engine and you see on the package that 1 inch in the model equals 10 feet in the actual engine. What is the scale factor? Remember that a scale factor is a ratio and has no units. You can convert one of these measurements to express both in the same units. Ten feet equals 120 inches, so you can express the relationship this way:

$$\frac{1 \text{ inch}}{10 \text{ feet}} = \frac{1 \text{ inch}}{120 \text{ inches}} = \frac{1}{120}.$$

1. In an HO model train set, 1 inch is 7.25 feet. What is the scale factor?

   Explain your thinking.

2. The scale on a county map reads, "1 inch equals 25 miles." What is the scale factor?

   Explain your thinking.

Scale Models

3. In Jonathan Swift's great classic, *Gulliver's Travels*, the shipwrecked hero, Gulliver, washes up in Lilliput, an island nation of people who are perfectly proportioned but not quite 6 inches high. Suppose that a Lilliputian is exactly 6 inches tall and Gulliver is exactly 6 feet.

   a. What is the scale factor between the Lilliputian and Gulliver?

   Explain your thinking.

   b. Imagine a mattress on which Gulliver could sleep comfortably in his own house after a sea voyage. Imagine a scaled-down mattress on which the Lilliputian could sleep with equal room. What are the dimensions of the two mattress tops, and how do their areas compare?

   Explain your thinking.

   c. Imagine Gulliver at home in his living room — which he might call his "parlor" or "sitting room." What might the room's dimensions be? What would the dimensions of a scaled-down room for the Lilliputian be? How would the volume of Gulliver's room compare to the volume of the Lilliputian's room?

   Explain your thinking.

Scale Models

4. On grid paper, draw a person or object or create a design. Choose a scale factor that you can use to make an image of your drawing on the same sheet of grid paper. Estimate the areas of your drawing and its image. Provide the following information about your similar figures.

Scale factor: ______________________

Approximate area of preimage: ______________________

Approximate area of image: ______________________

Comparison of areas: ______________________

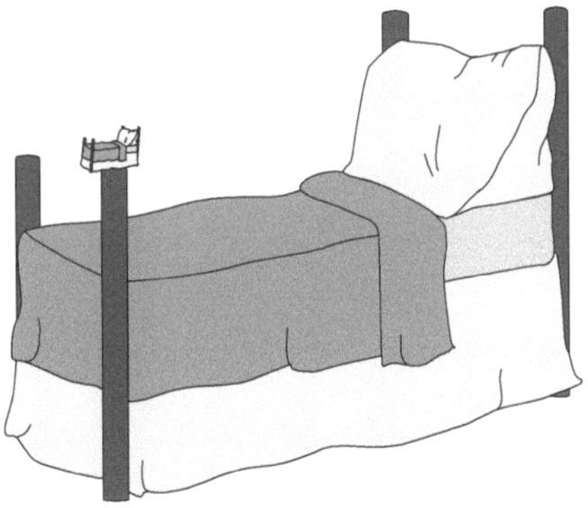

Block Buildings Set 1—A Constant Footprint

1. Stack centimeter cubes to create five block buildings. Each building should be one unit taller than the previous one. The drawing at the right shows the first two buildings.

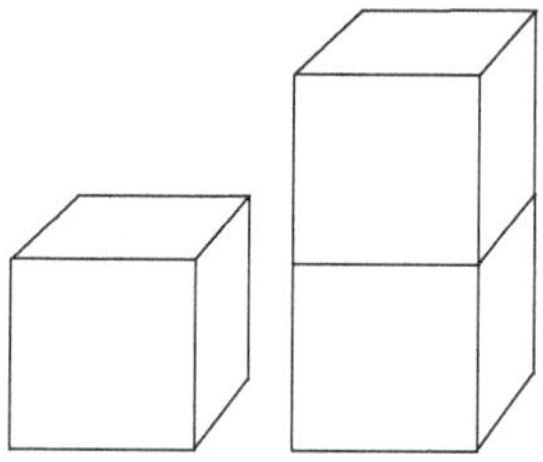

2. Find the perimeter, surface area, and volume of each building that you made in step 1, and then complete the table below. Leave the column under "*n*" blank for now.

Block Buildings, Set 1						
	Number of the Block Building					
	1	2	3	4	5	*n*
Perimeter (linear units)						
Surface area (square units)						
Volume (cubic units)						

3. Discuss the relationship between the numbers of the buildings in set 1 and the measurements of their perimeters, surface areas, and volumes. Describe each relationship in words:
   a. The relationship between a building's number and its perimeter:

   b. The relationship between a building's number and its surface area:

   c. The relationship between a building's number and its volume:

Block Buildings Set 1—A Constant Footprint

Suppose that n stands for the number of any building. Can you use n in a symbolic expression, or a formula or general rule, for the perimeter, surface area, or volume of building n? If you can, enter your work in the last column under "n" in table 1.

4. Predict what a graph of each group of measurements (perimeters, surface areas, and volumes), plotted against the building numbers, would look like:

   a. A graph of the perimeters:

   b. A graph of the surface areas:

   c. A graph of the volumes:

5. On grid paper, make each of the graphs that you described in step 4.

6. A composite picture puts different pictures, or pieces of pictures, together in one picture. On grid paper, make a composite picture of the measurements of the buildings in set 1 by showing all three measurements in different colors on one graph. To do this, let your y-axis—the vertical axis—show "Number of Units in a Measurement"—regardless of whether they are linear units (in the perimeters), square units (in the surface areas) or cubic units (in the volumes). Let your x-axis—the horizontal axis—show "Building Number."

Block Buildings Set 2— A Constant Height

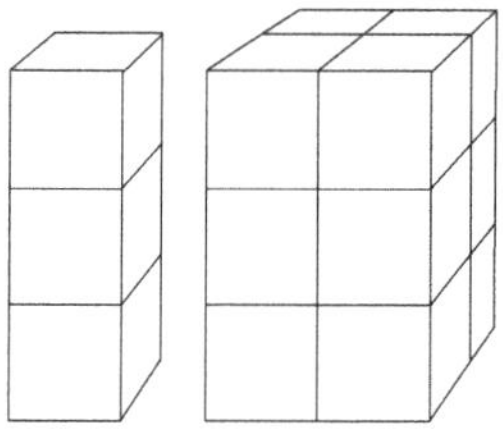

1. Stack centimeter cubes to make a new set of five buildings. This time, let the number of square units in the bases of the buildings be equal to the squares of consecutive numbers (1×1, 2×2, 3×3, etc.). Make the height of each structure exactly three units. The first two buildings are shown at the right.
2. Find the perimeter, surface area, and volume of each building that you made in step 1, and then complete the table below. Leave the column under "*n*" blank for now.

Block Buildings, Set 2						
	Number of the Block Building					
	1	2	3	4	5	*n*
Perimeter (linear units)						
Surface area (square units)						
Volume (cubic units)						

3. Discuss the relationship between the numbers of the buildings in set 2 and the measurements of their perimeters, surface areas, and volumes. Describe each relationship in words:

   a. The relationship between a building's number and its perimeter:

   b. The relationship between a building's number and its surface area:

   c. The relationship between a building's number and its volume:

Block Buildings Set 2—A Constant Height

Suppose that *n* stands for the number of any building. Can you use *n* in a symbolic expression, or a formula or general rule, for the perimeter, surface area, or volume of building *n*? If you can, enter your work in the last column under "*n*" in table 2.

4. Predict what a graph of each group of measurements (perimeters, surface areas, and volumes), plotted against the building numbers, would look like:

   a. A graph of the perimeters:

   b. A graph of the surface areas:

   c. A graph of the volumes:

5. On grid paper, make each of the graphs that you described in step 4.

6. A *composite* picture puts different pictures, or pieces of pictures, together in one picture. On grid paper, make a composite picture of the measurements of the buildings in set 2 by showing all three measurements in different colors on one graph. To do this, let your *y*-axis – the vertical axis – show "Number of Units in a Measurement" – regardless of whether they are linear units (in the perimeters), square units (in the surface areas) or cubic units (in the volumes). Let your *x*-axis – the horizontal axis – show "Building Number."

Block Buildings Set 1—Constantly Cubes

1. Stack centimeter cubes to create a set of five buildings that are successively larger cubes ($1 \times 1 \times 1$, $2 \times 2 \times 2$, etc.). The first two buildings are shown at the right.
2. Find the perimeter, surface area, and volume of each building that you made in step 1, and then complete the table below. Leave the column under "*n*" blank for now.

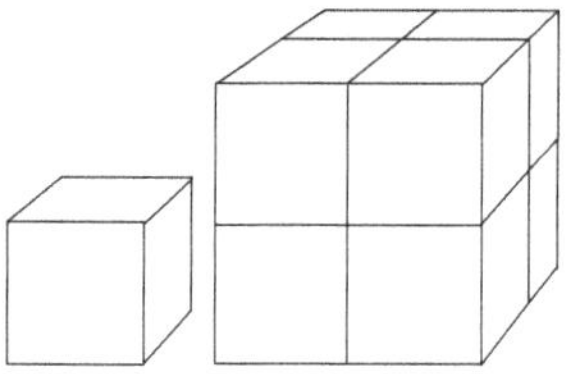

Block Buildings, Set 3						
	Number of the Block Building					
	1	2	3	4	5	*n*
Perimeter (linear units)						
Surface area (square units)						
Volume (cubic units)						

3. Discuss the relationship between the numbers of the buildings in set 3 and the measurements of their perimeters, surface areas, and volumes. Describe each relationship in words:
   a. The relationship between a building's number and its perimeter:

   b. The relationship between a building's number and its surface area:

   c. The relationship between a building's number and its volume:

Block Buildings Set 1—Constantly Cubes

Suppose that *n* stands for the number of any building. Can you use *n* in a symbolic expression, or a formula or general rule, for the perimeter, surface area, or volume of building *n*? If you can, enter your work in the last column under "*n*" in table 3.

4. Predict what a graph of each group of measurements (perimeters, surface areas, and volumes), plotted against the building numbers, would look like:

   a. A graph of the perimeters:

   b. A graph of the surface areas:

   c. A graph of the volumes:

5. On grid paper, make each of the graphs that you described in step 4.

6. A composite picture puts different pictures, or pieces of pictures, together in one picture. On grid paper, make a composite picture of the measurements of the buildings in set 3 by showing all three measurements in different colors on one graph. To do this, let your *y*-axis—the vertical axis—show "Number of Units in a Measurement"—regardless of whether they are linear units (in the perimeters), square units (in the surface areas) or cubic units (in the volumes). Let your *x*-axis—the horizontal axis—show "Building Number."

Measuring Shapes

Area of a Rectangle

The area of a rectangle is the number of unit squares that fill the rectangle with no gaps or overlaps.

1. Explain why the area of the rectangle below is 20 square units.

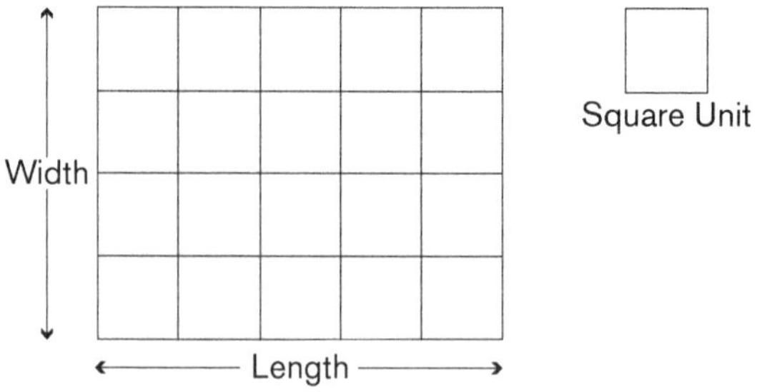

2. How can you use the dimensions of the rectangle in step 1 to find its area?

3. In general, how can you find the area of a rectangle when you know its length and width?

Base, Altitude, and Height in a Triangle

Any side of a triangle can be its *base*. An *altitude* of a triangle is a line segment that is perpendicular to the base and joins a point on it, or on an extension of it, to the opposite vertex. The illustration below on the right shows an altitude that joins a point on an extension to the base to the opposite vertex. Note that some altitudes are inside the triangle, and others, like the one in the illustration on the right, are outside. The *height* of a triangle is the length of one of its altitudes.

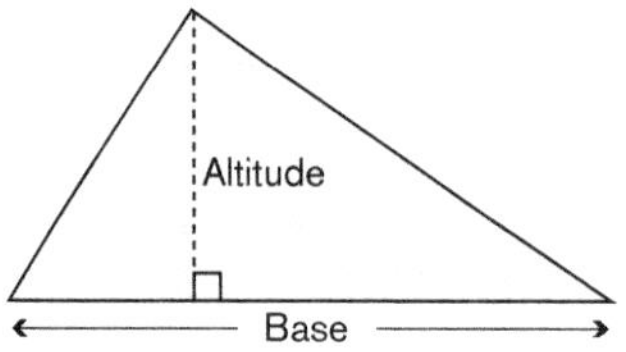

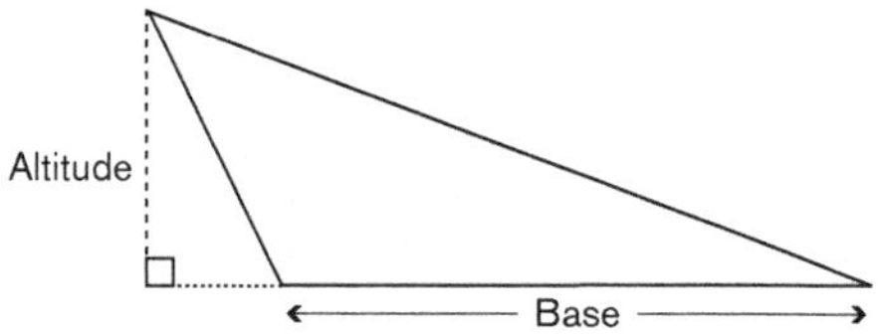

4. How many altitudes does a triangle have?

Measuring Shapes

Base and Altitude in a Parallelogram

Any side of a parallelogram can be its *base*. An *altitude* of a parallelogram is a line segment that is perpendicular to the base and joins a point on it, or on an extension of it, to a point on the opposite side, or an extension of it. The illustration below shows altitudes of the parallelogram.

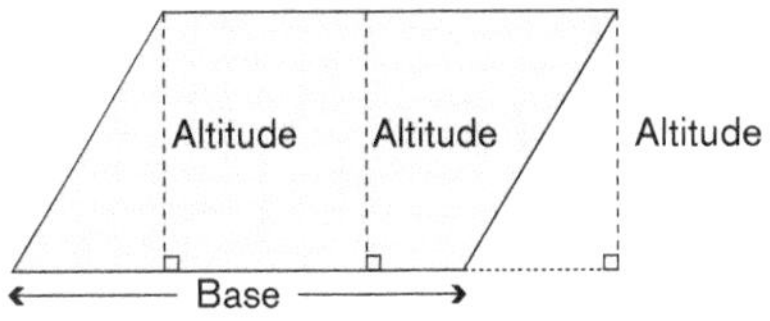

5. How many altitudes does a parallelogram have?

Base and Altitude in a Trapezoid

A trapezoid has two parallel sides. Either of these sides can be its *base*. An *altitude* of a trapezoid is a line segment that is perpendicular to the base and joins a point on it, or an extension of it, to the opposite side, or an extension of it. The illustration below shows altitudes of the trapezoid.

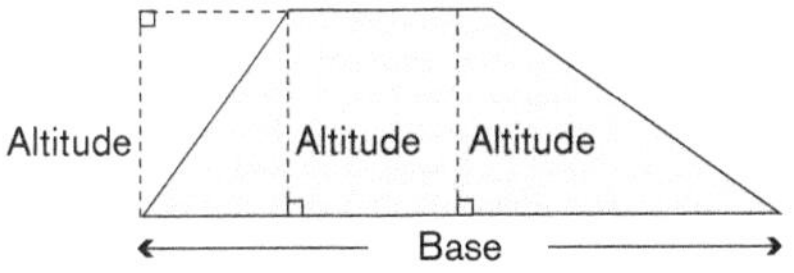

6. How many altitudes does a trapezoid have?

Make a Rectangle from That Parallelogram

1. *a.* On each parallelogram below, draw a line segment that divides the parallelogram into two pieces that you could rearrange to form a rectangle. To simplify the problems, be sure that all the end points of each of your line segments are on grid dots. Mark the drawings to show how you would form a rectangle from the two pieces of each parallelogram.

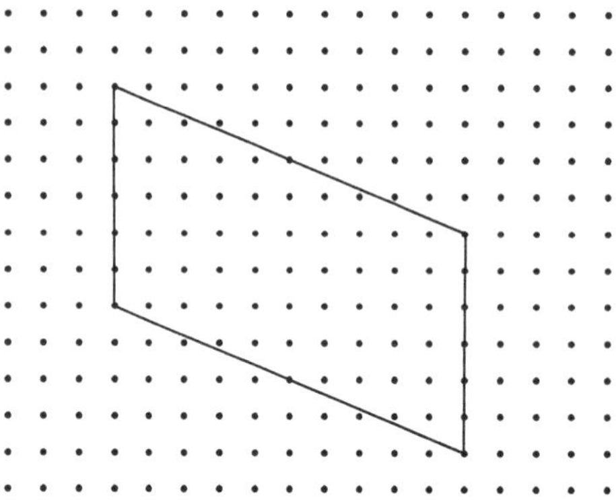

Parallelogram 1

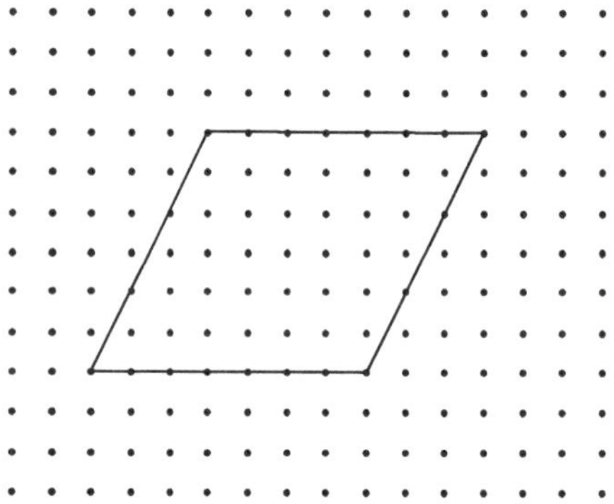

Parallelogram 2

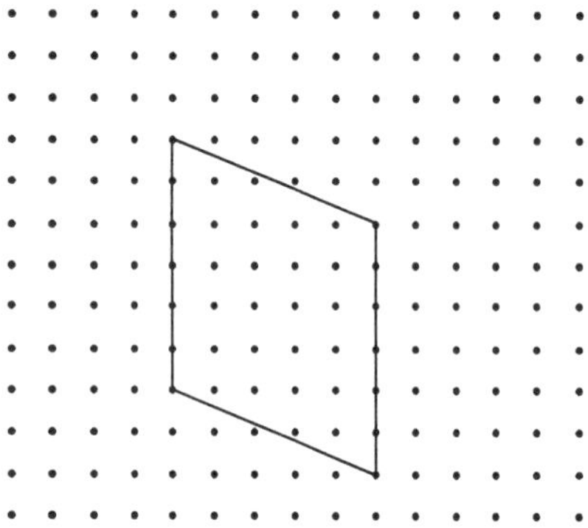

Parallelogram 3

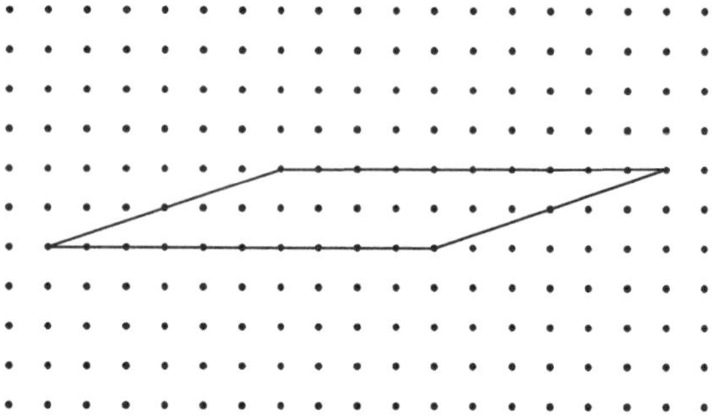

Parallelogram 4

b. Check your ideas by actually cutting out the pieces and rearranging them or by using the 2-D Shape Decomposition Tool on a computer.

Make a Rectangle from That Parallelogram

2. *a.* Draw a line segment that divides the parallelogram below into two pieces that you could rearrange to form a rectangle. Mark on the drawing to show how you would form the rectangle from the two pieces of the parallelogram.

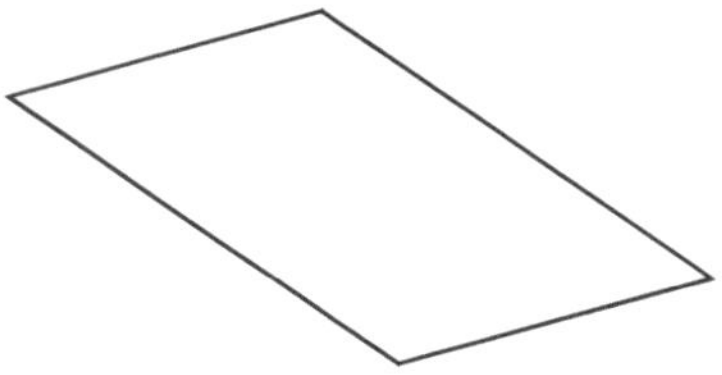

   b. Check your ideas by cutting out the pieces and reassembling them or by using the 2-D Shape Decomposition Tool on your computer.

3. The formula for the area of a parallelogram is

$$Area = base \times height.$$

Use your experimentation in steps 1 and 2 to help you explain this area formula.

Compare That Triangle with That Rectangle

For any triangle, you can construct a rectangle that shares a base and an altitude with the triangle, as shown below.

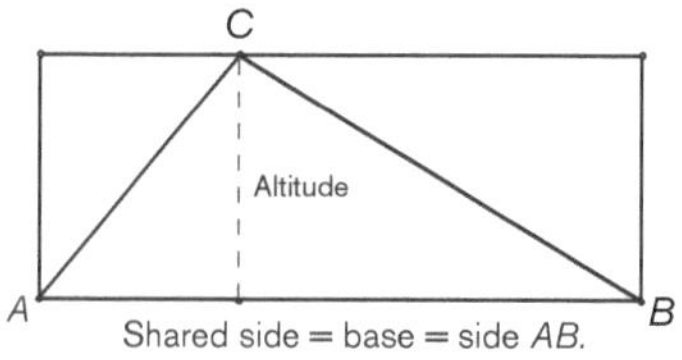

1. *a.* For each triangle below, draw a rectangle that shares a side with the triangle and has the triangle's remaining vertex as a point on the rectangle's opposite side. To simplify the problems, be sure that all the sides of your rectangles are horizontal or vertical line segments, with end points on grid dots.

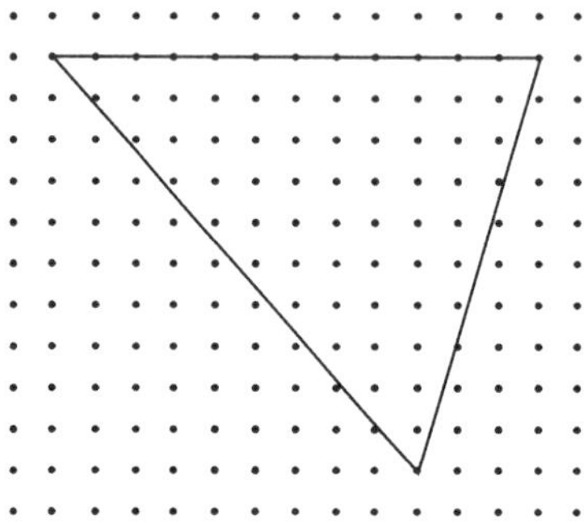

Triangle 1

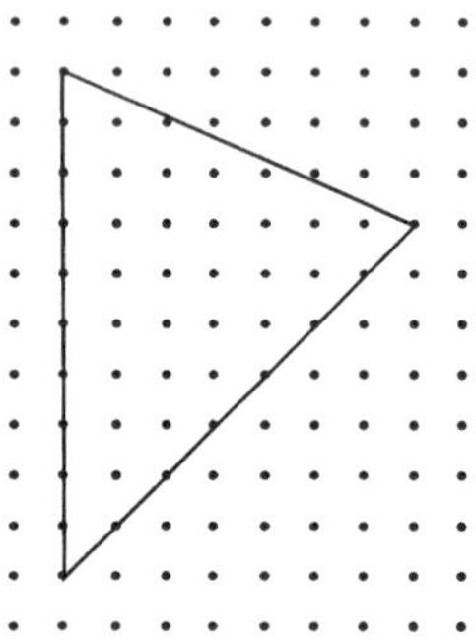

Triangle 2

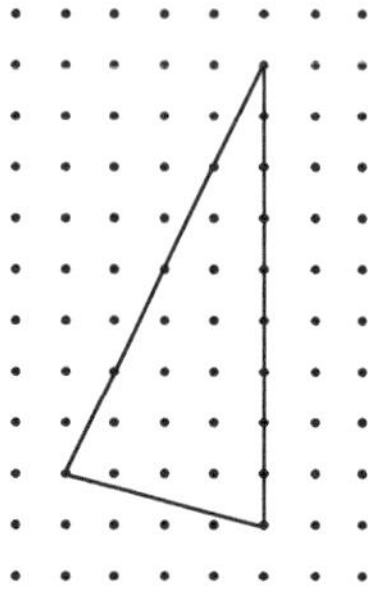

Triangle 3

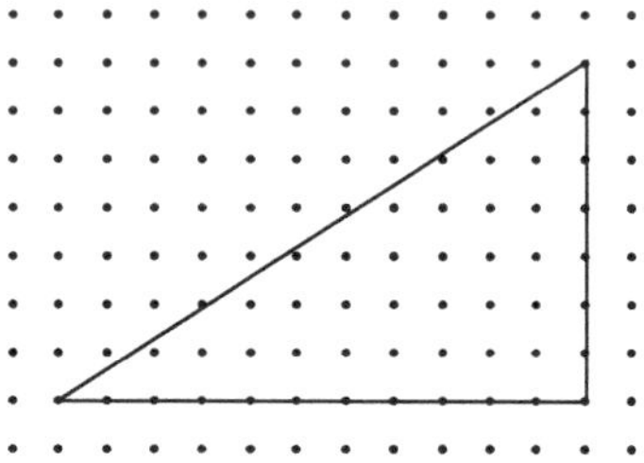

Triangle 4

b. For each rectangle that you have drawn, consider how the area of the triangle compares with the area of the rectangle. Share your ideas with your partner.

Compare That Triangle with That Rectangle

c. Show that your ideas are correct by actually cutting out the figures and manipulating them or by using the 2-D Shape Decomposition Tool on a computer.

2. *a.* Draw a rectangle that shares a side with the triangle below and contains the triangle's remaining vertex as a point on its opposite side.

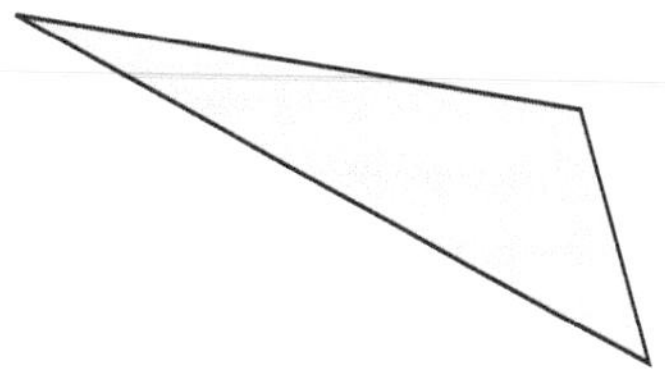

b. Describe how the area of the triangle compares with that of the rectangle.

3. The formula for the area of a triangle is

$$Area = \frac{1}{2}\ base \times height.$$

Use your experimentation in steps 1 and 2 to help you explain this area formula.

Compare That Trapezoid with That Parallelogram

The illustration below shows a trapezoid and marks the midpoint of one of its nonparallel sides.

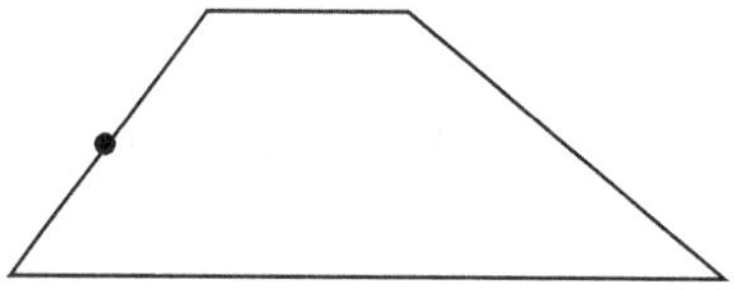

Suppose that you made an exact copy of the trapezoid and stacked it on top of your original trapezoid. Then imagine that you put a pin through both the original and your copy precisely at the marked midpoint and rotated the copy one-half turn (180 degrees). The original trapezoid and its copy – or *rotation image* – would then form the parallelogram shown below.

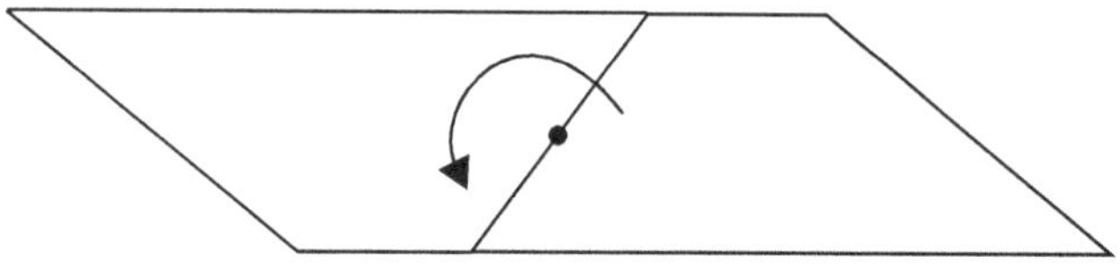

1. *a.* For each of the two trapezoids below, draw a parallelogram that you could form in the manner described above. (The midpoint is marked in the first case.)

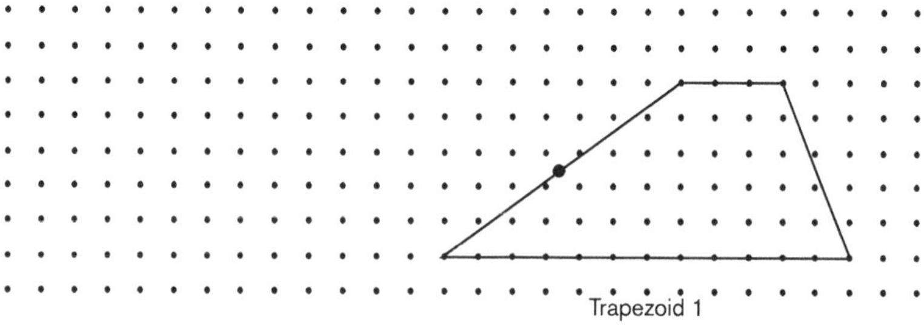

Trapezoid 1

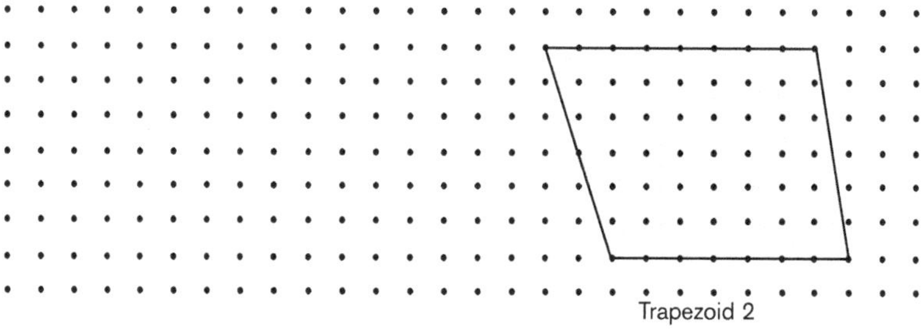

Trapezoid 2

Compare That Trapezoid with That Parallelogram

b. How does the area of each trapezoid compare with the area of the parallelogram that you created?

c. Check your ideas by cutting out your parallelograms and the component trapezoids or by working with the 2-D Shape Decomposition Tool.

2. The formula for the area of a trapezoid is

$$\textit{Area} = \frac{1}{2} \times (\textit{base}\ 1 + \textit{base}\ 2) \times \textit{height}.$$

Discuss the process that you followed in step 1 to help you explain the area formula to your partner. Illustrate your explanation by using the diagram below to draw a parallelogram in the same way.

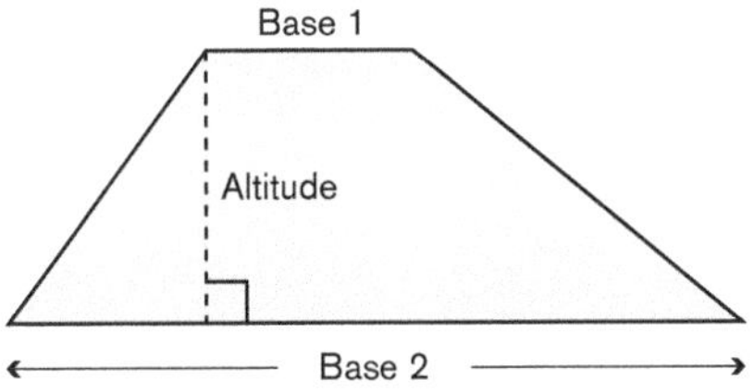

Cross Sections of Three-Dimensional Shapes

For each of the solids below, draw the cross section formed when the plane indicated by the lines intersects the figure.

1.
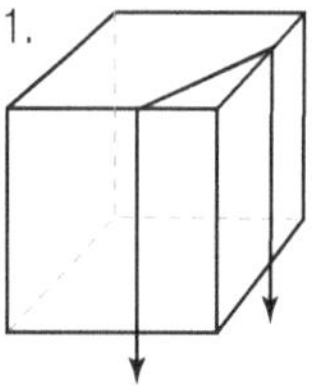

2.
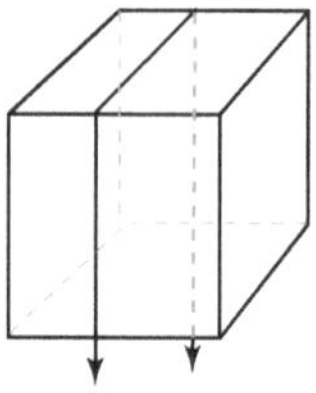

3.
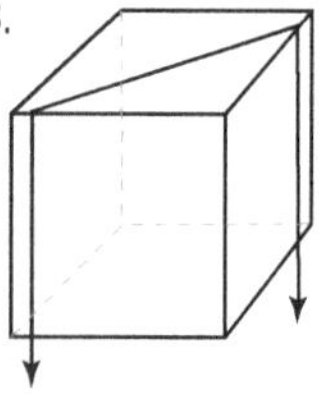

4.
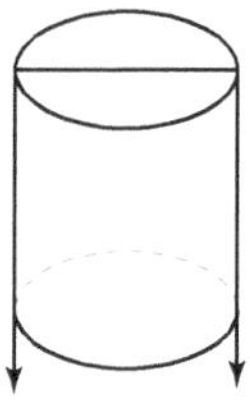

5.
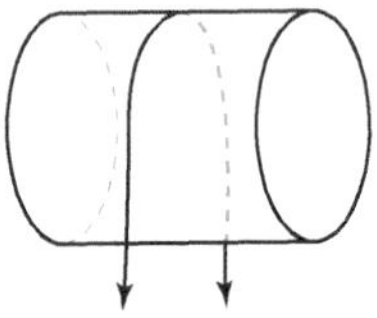

6.
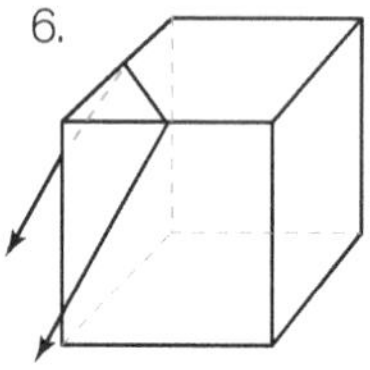

7.
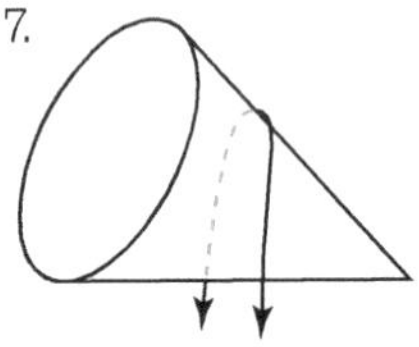

8.
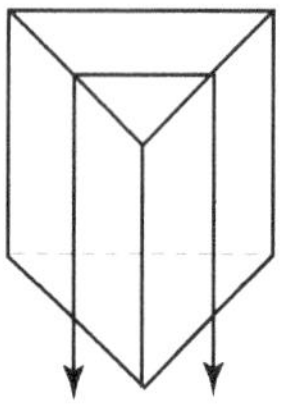

9.
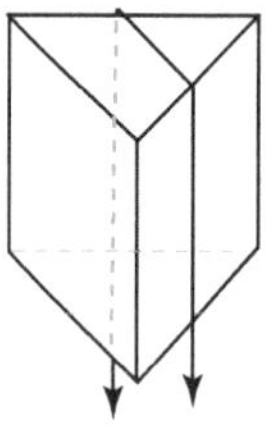

10.
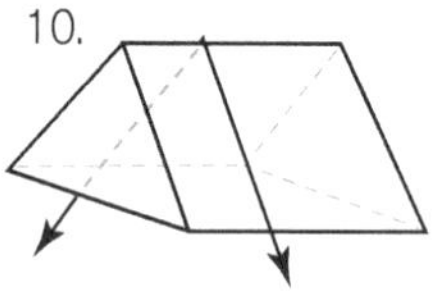

11.
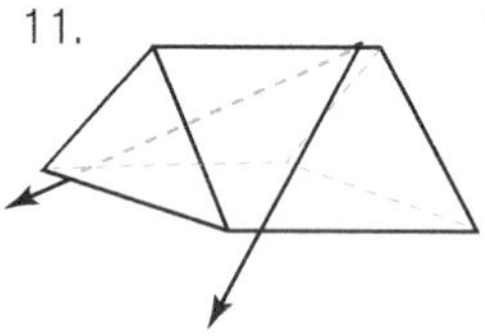

12.
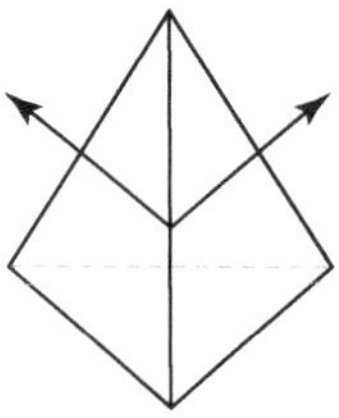

13.
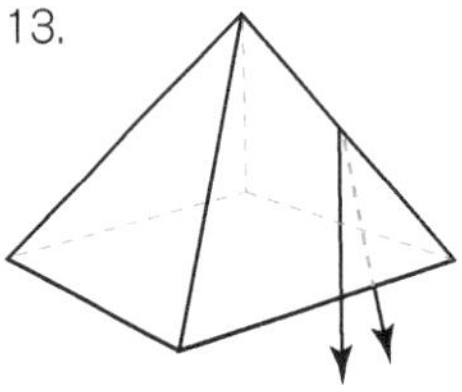

14.
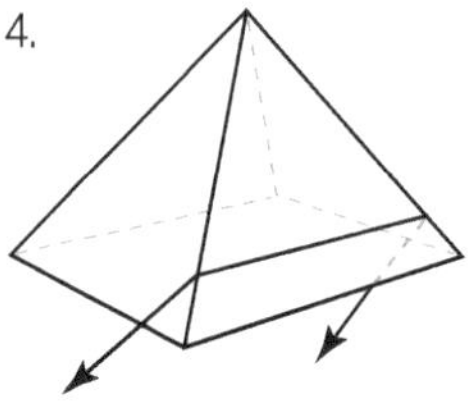

15.
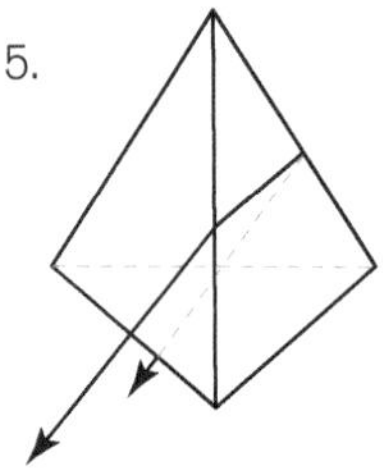

Constructing Three-Dimensional Figures

Use the materials your teacher supplies to complete the following tasks:

1. A picture of a solid (a triangular prism) is shown.

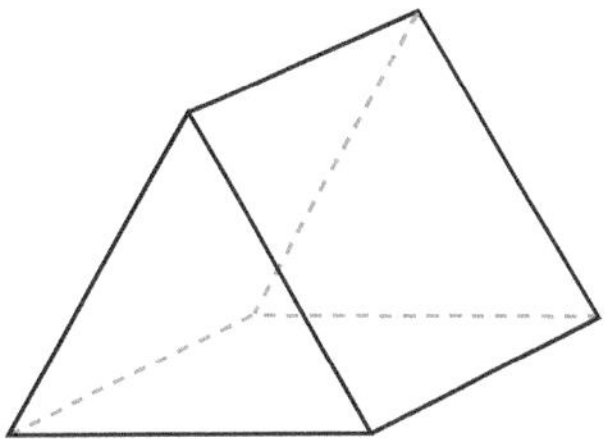

   (*a*) Use your materials to build the solid.

   (*b*) Count the number of vertices, edges, and faces.

   (*c*) Record the data in the table at the end of the activity sheet.

   (*d*) Open your solid to form a net. Draw the net on a separate piece of paper.

   (*e*) Draw a different net that can be used to make the solid.

   (*f*) Describe the relationship between the nets you have drawn and the solid.

____

____

____

____

2. A picture of another solid (a hexagonal pyramid) is shown.

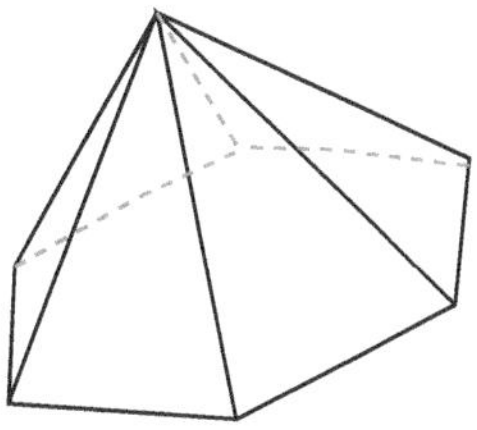

   (*a*) Use your materials to build the solid.

   (*b*) Count the number of vertices, edges, and faces.

   (*c*) Record the data in the table below.

   (*d*) Open your solid to form a net. Draw the net on a separate piece of paper.

   (*e*) Draw a different net that can be used to make the solid.

   (*f*) Describe the relationship between the nets you have drawn and the solid.

____

____

____

____

Constructing Three-Dimensional Figures

3. Construct, draw, and describe some additional solids:

   (*a*) Build a prism different from the one you have already made.

   (*b*) Draw a sketch of your solid.

   (*c*) Build a different solid that is a pyramid.

   (*d*) Sketch your solid.

   (*e*) Can you build a solid with exactly 8 faces or Polydron pieces? Sketch any you find.

   (*f*) Count the number of vertices, faces, and edges on the solids you built. Record your data in the table. Can you find any patterns in the data?

Solid	Number of Vertices	Number of Faces	Number of Edges
1			
2			
3			
4			
5			
6			
7			

The Platonic Solids

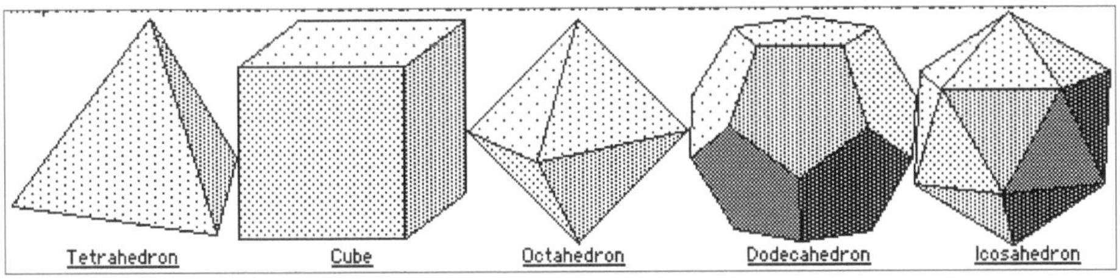

Shape of face	Angle measure of each angle of the face	Number of faces at each vertex	Total angle measure at each vertex	Name of polyhedron	Number of faces	Number of vertices	Number of edges

General Principles

For all polyhedra:

- At least three faces must intersect at each vertex.
- The sum of the face angles surrounding each vertex must be less than 360 degrees.

For regular polyhedra:

- All faces are identical.
- Every face is a regular polygon.

Nets of Polyhedra

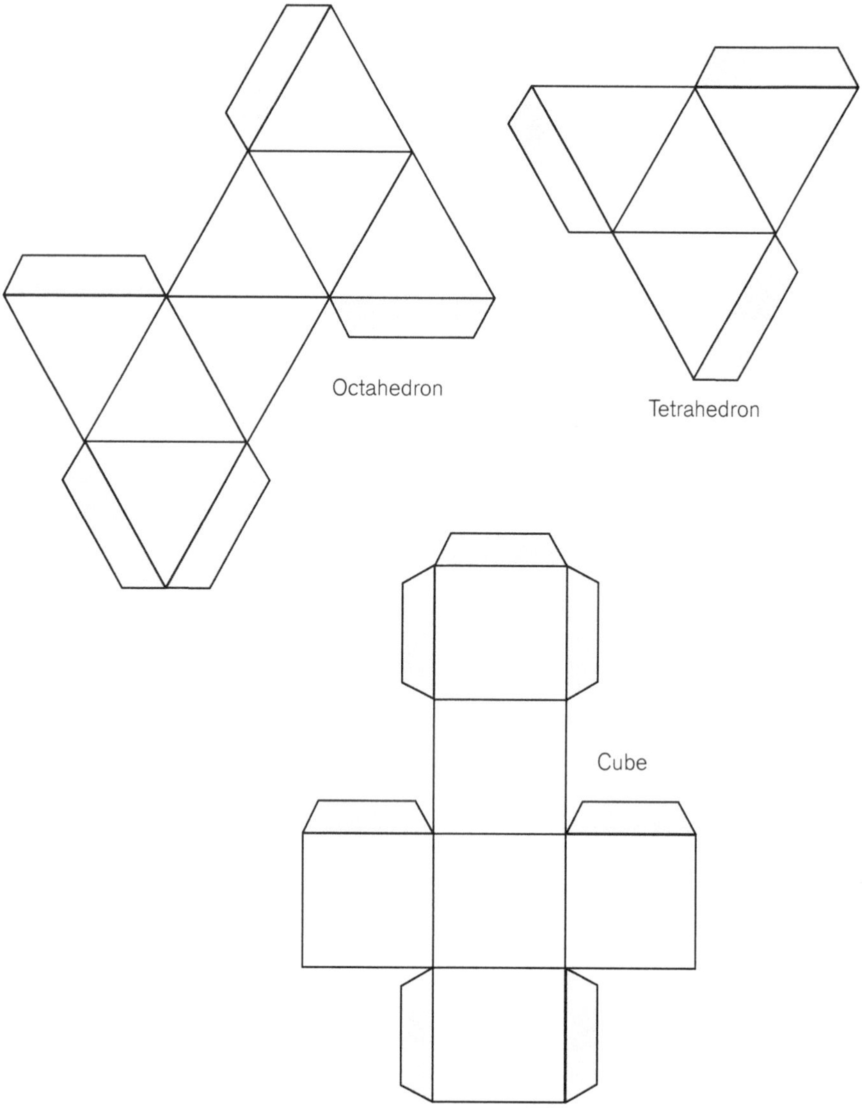

Nets of Polyhedra

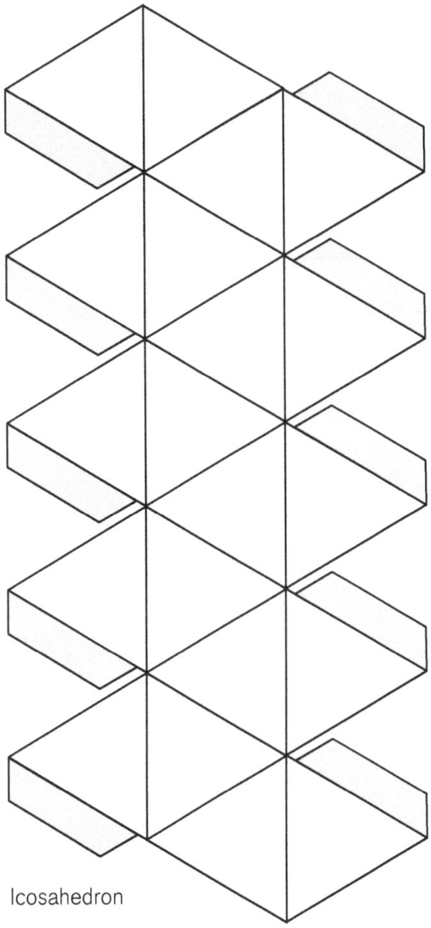

Icosahedron

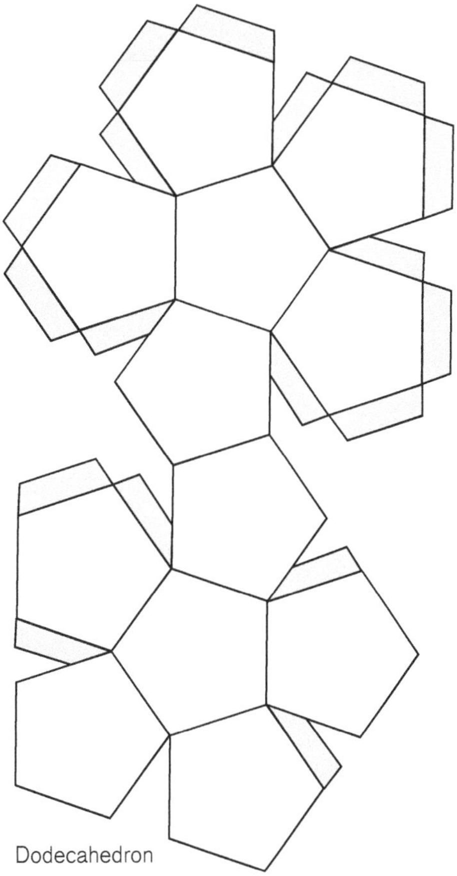

Dodecahedron

Isometric Explorations

1. Which isometric drawing shows the view from the left front corner of the building represented by the base plan below? _______

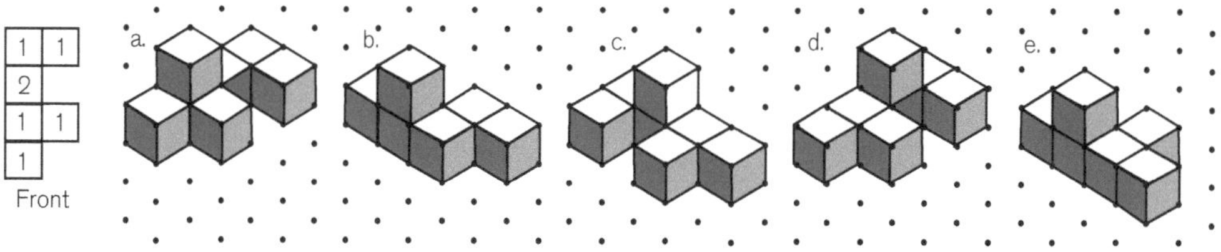

2. Which isometric drawing shows the view from the back left corner of the building represented by the base plan below? _______

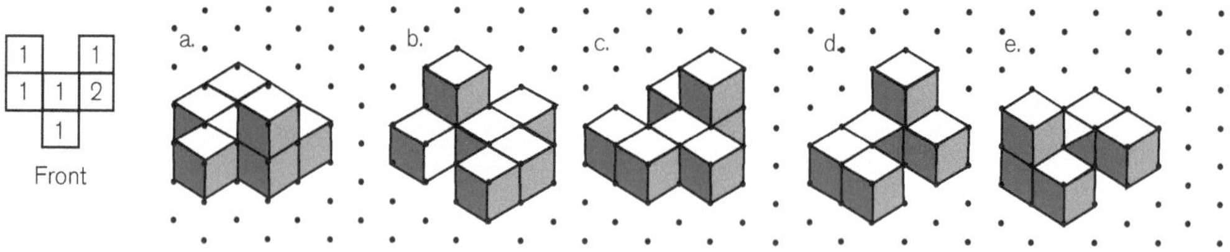

3. Which drawings are views of the building shown below? _______

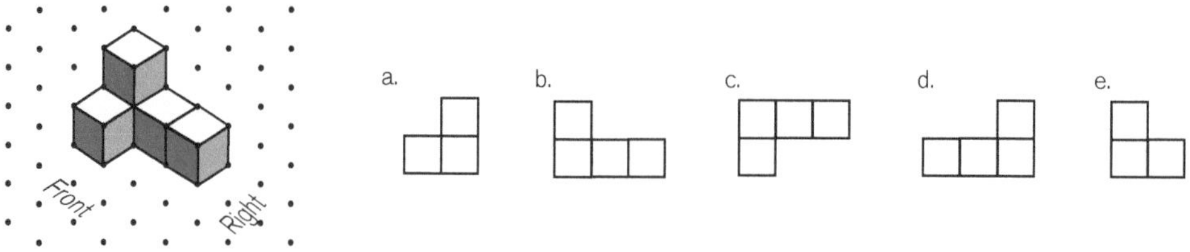

This activity is from *Ruins of Montarek* (Lappan et al. 1996, pp. 87–88). Used with permission.

Isometric Explorations

4. The isometric drawing below shows a building from the front right corner. Which drawing shows the back view of the building? ________

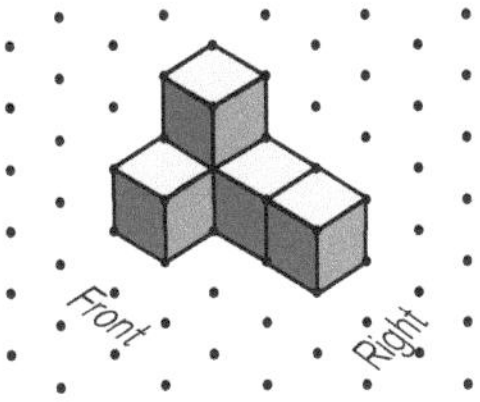

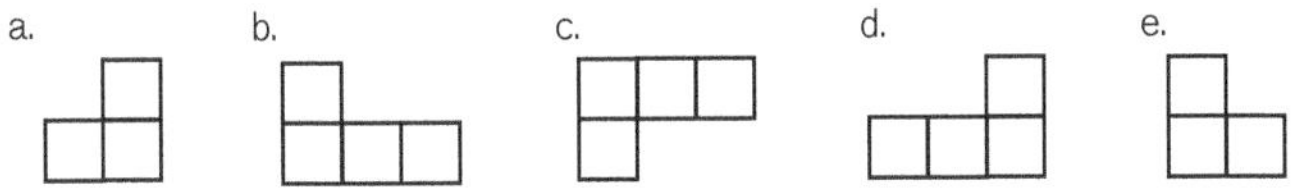

5. The isometric drawing below shows a building from the front right corner. Which drawing shows the right view of the building? ________

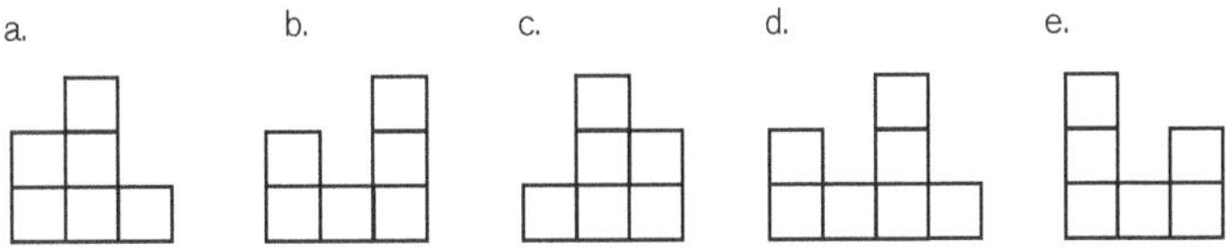

6. Draw the isometric view from the right back corner of the building represented by the base plan below.

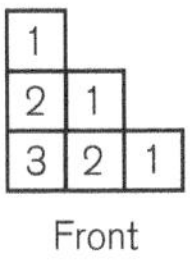

This activity is from *Ruins of Montarek* (Lappan et al. 1996, pp. 87–88). Used with permission.

Translations, Reflections, and Rotations

Complete the following steps for a translation:

1. Draw an arrow (vector) on one sheet of translucent paper. Use less than half the sheet to allow enough room for the translated figure. Make sure the point and the arrow are dark enough to be seen through a second sheet of paper.

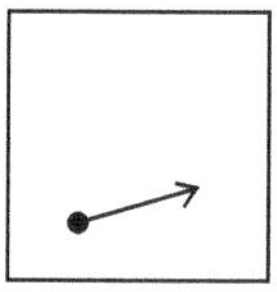

2. Draw an original shape on the sheet of paper.

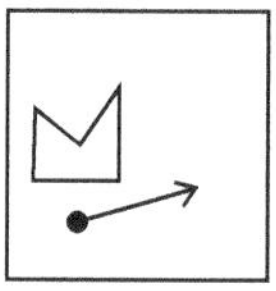

3. Place a second translucent sheet over the first sheet. On sheet 2, trace the endpoint of the arrow and draw a line that extends beyond the endpoint and head of the original arrow. Without moving sheet 2, trace the original figure.

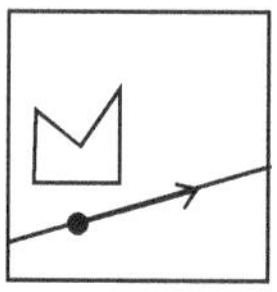

4. Place the second sheet under the original sheet. Align the line on the second sheet and the arrow (vector) on the first sheet. Slide sheet 2 until the point you drew on the line is under the tip of the arrow.

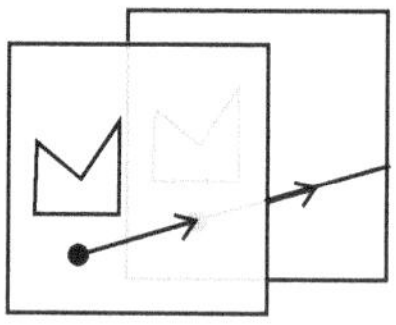

5. Trace the image from sheet 2 onto sheet 1. Label the original figure and the translated figure.

This activity has been adapted from the Shapes and Measurement Module (pp. 198–201), developed by the Reconceptualizing Mathematics Project, Center for Research in Mathematics and Science Education, San Diego State University.

Translations, Reflections, and Rotations

Complete the following steps for a reflection:

1. Draw a shape using less than half a sheet of translucent paper. Draw a line of reflection so that your paper is divided into two areas. Draw a heavy point on the line to use as a reference point.

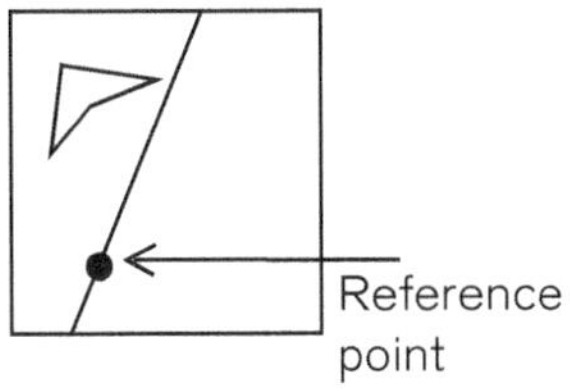

2. Place a second sheet of translucent paper on top of the original, and trace the figure, the line of reflection, and the reference point.

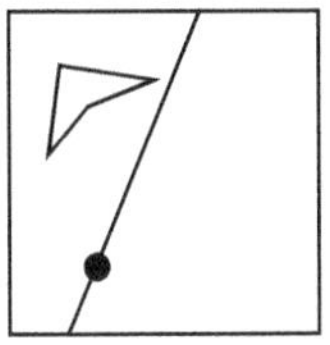

3. Flip sheet 2 over, and put it under the original sheet. Align the lines of reflection and the reference points.

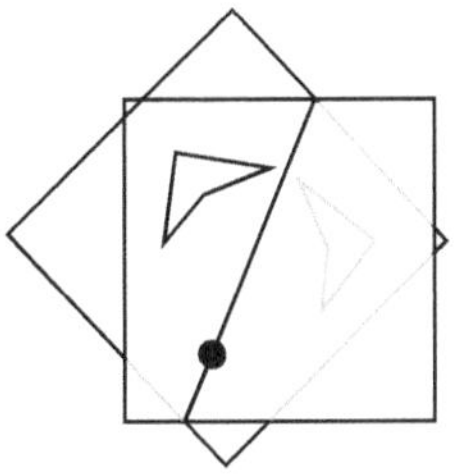

4. Trace the image from sheet 2 onto the original sheet. Label the original figure and the reflected figure.

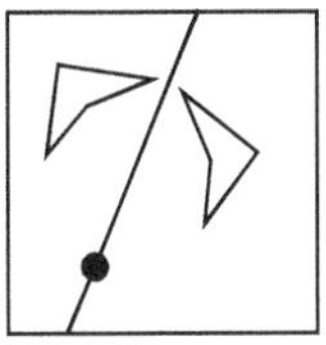

This activity has been adapted from Shapes and Measurement Module (pp. 198–201), developed by the Reconceptualizing Mathematics Project, Center for Research in Mathematics and Science Education, San Diego State University.

Translations, Reflections, and Rotations

Complete the following steps for a rotation:

1. Draw a shape on less than half a sheet of translucent paper. On the other half of the paper, draw a point to serve as the center of rotation and draw the angle of the rotation, with the center of rotation as the vertex of the angle. Don't make the angle too large, or you will not have enough room on the paper to draw the rotated figure. A clockwise rotation is illustrated.

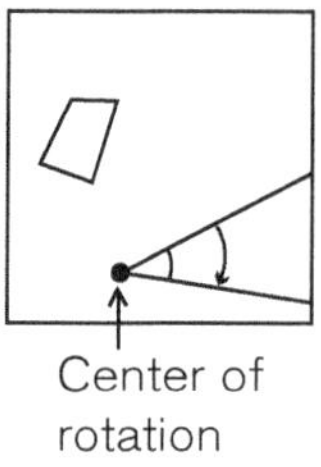

2. Place a second sheet of translucent paper on top of the original. Trace the figure, the vertex (point) of the angle of reflection, and one ray of the angle, as indicated.

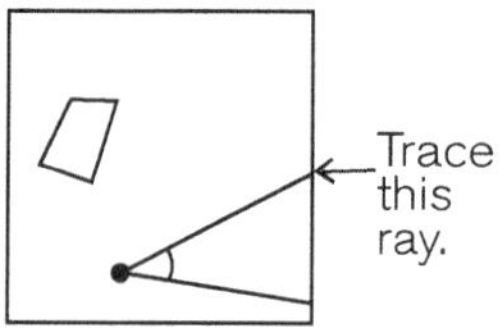

3. Place the second sheet under the original so that everything is aligned. Place your pencil tip on the vertex of the angle (the center of rotation). Turn sheet 2 until the ray is aligned with the other ray of the angle on sheet 1.

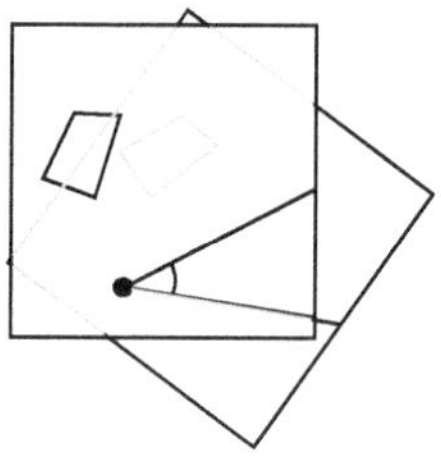

4. Trace the image onto the original sheet. Label the original figure and the rotated figure.

This activity has been adapted from Shapes and Measurement Module (pp. 198–201), developed by the Reconceptualizing Mathematics Project, Center for Research in Mathematics and Science Education, San Diego State University.

More Transformations

Use patty paper or other tracing paper to carry out each of the transformations described here.

1. Copy figure 1 onto tracing paper. Use that copy and additional tracing paper to rotate triangle *ABC*, using point *P* as the center of rotation. Rotate preimage *ABC* clockwise using angle *MPN* as the rotation angle. Label your image *A'B'C'* so that preimage and image points correctly correspond.

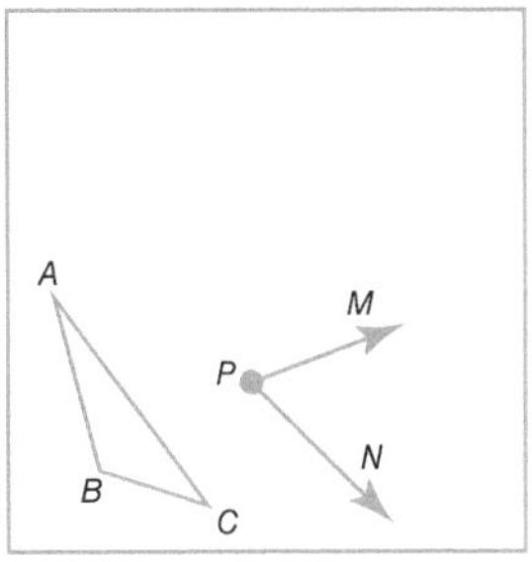

Figure 1

2. Copy figure 2 onto tracing paper. Use that copy and additional tracing paper to reflect your preimage, quadrilateral *WXYZ*, using line *j* as the mirror of reflection. Label your image *W'X'Y'Z'* so that preimage and image points correctly correspond.

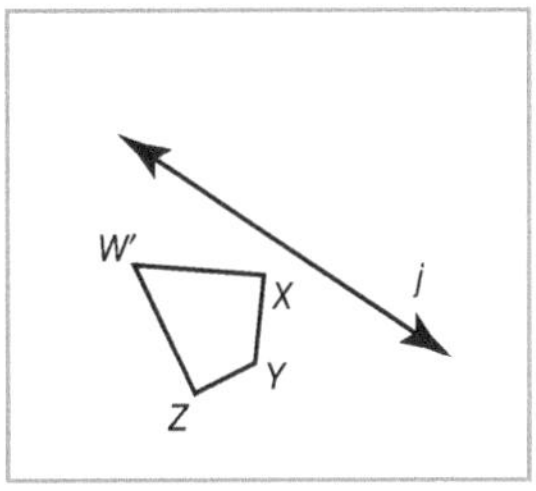

Figure 2

3. Copy figure 3 onto tracing paper. Use that copy and additional tracing paper to translate your preimage, polygon *TRAIN*, using vector *k* as the translation vector. Label your image *T'R'A'I'N'* so that preimage and image points correctly correspond.

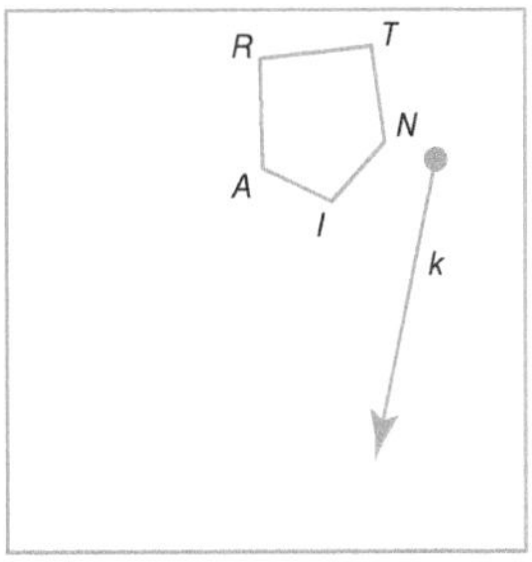

Figure 3

Reasoning about the Pythagorean Relationship

1. Using the distance between adjacent points of intersection on grid paper as units, draw a right triangle with sides measuring 3, 4, and 5 units. Let the legs be 3 units and 4 units and lie on grid lines. Place a second sheet of grid paper along the hypotenuse to verify that it has a length of 5 units.

2. Draw squares, using the sides of the triangle as sides of the squares, as illustrated at the right. Find the area of each square, and enter the information in the table below.

3. Similarly, draw a right triangle with sides measuring 5, 12, and 13 units. Draw squares on the sides of the new triangle. Find the area of each square, and enter the information in the table.

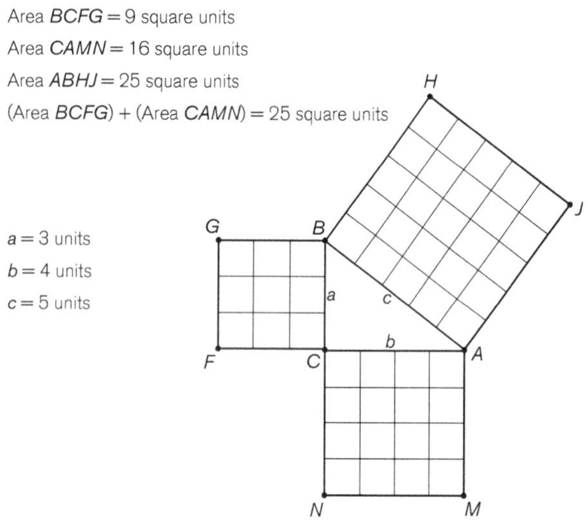

Triangle Number	Length of Side *a* (Units)	Length of Side *b* (Units)	Length of Side *c* (Units)	Area of Square with Length *a* (Square Units)	Area of Square with Length *b* (Square Units)	Area of Square with Length *c* (Square Units)
1	3	4	5	9	16	25
2	5	12	13			
3						
4						

4. Draw other triangles, as instructed by your teacher, and record the appropriate data in the table. Look for patterns in the data. Describe any relationships among the parts of the figure.

____

____

____

____

Take a Look at Those Squares

The triangle on the right is a *right triangle*. One of its angles is a right angle, which measures 90 degrees. The side that is opposite the right angle is called the *hypotenuse*. Each of the other two angles in the triangle is less than 90 degrees, and the sides that are opposite them are called the *legs* of the triangle.

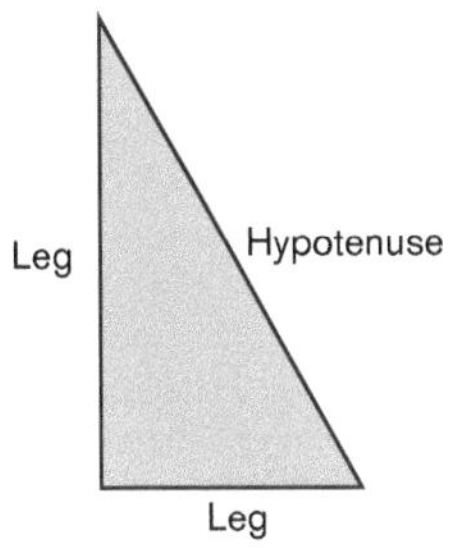

You could use the hypotenuse to form one side of a square adjacent to the triangle, and you could construct squares on the legs of the triangle in the same way, as in the diagram in step 1 below.

1. Consider the right triangle pictured and the squares constructed on each of its three sides.

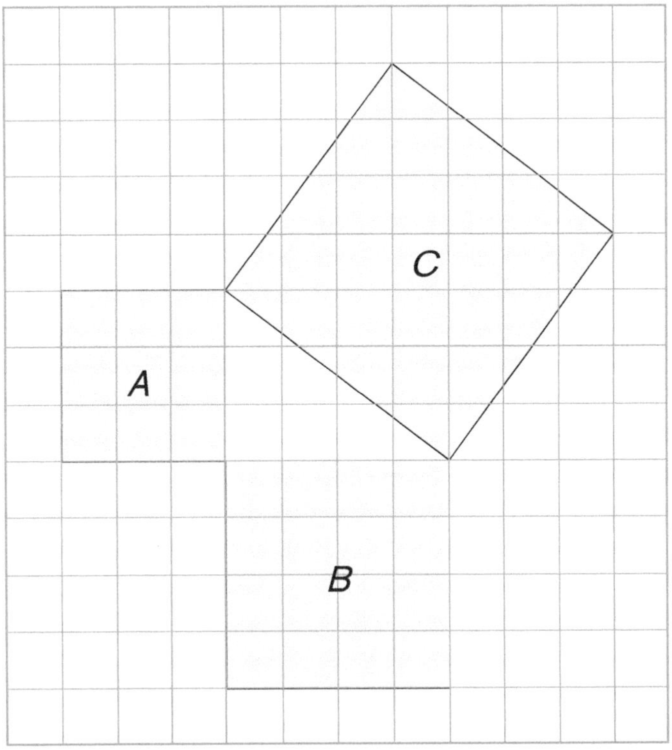

   a. What is the area of each square? (*Hint:* If you can't find the area of a square directly and immediately by counting grid units, then partition (or *decompose*) the square into triangles or other shapes whose areas you can find easily by using grid lines and grid units. Remember that the formula for the area of a triangle is $A = \frac{1}{2}bh$.

Area of $A =$ ____________ units^2

Area of $B =$ ____________ units^2

Area of $C =$ ____________ units^2

b. What is the side length of each square?

Side length of $A =$ ________ units

Side length of $B =$ ________ units

Side length of $C =$ ________ units

c. What do you notice about the areas of the three squares?

2. Consider a different right triangle and the squares constructed on its sides.

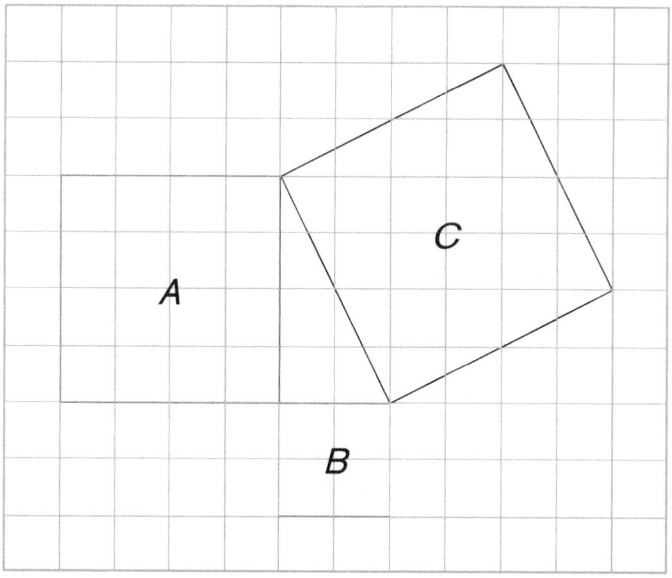

a. What is the area of each square? (*Hint:* If you can't determine the area of a square directly and immediately by counting grid units, decompose the square in the way that you did in step 1.)

Take a Look at Those Squares

Area of $A =$ ___________ units^2

Area of $B =$ ___________ units^2

Area of $C =$ ___________ units^2

b. What is the side length of each square? (If the side length is not a whole number of linear grid units, give the measurement to the nearest tenth of a unit.)

Side length of $A =$ _______ units

Side length of $B =$ _______ units

Side length of $C \approx$ _______ units

c. What do you notice about the areas of the three squares?

3. Consider the right triangle below and the squares constructed on its sides.

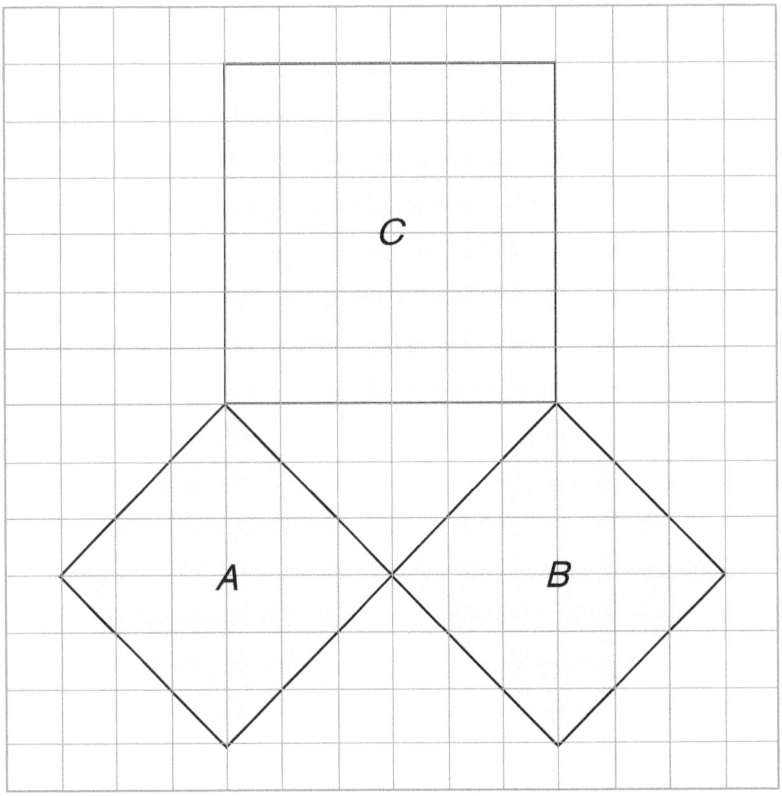

Take a Look at Those Squares

a. What is the area of each square? (If you can't count grid units easily, use the same strategy as before.)

Area of $A =$ ____________ units^2

Area of $B =$ ____________ units^2

Area of $C =$ ____________ units^2

b. What is the side length of each square? (If the side length is not an even number of grid units, give the measurement to the nearest tenth of a unit.)

Side of $A =$ ____________ units

Side of $B \approx$ ____________ units

Side of $C \approx$ ____________ units

c. What do you notice about the areas of the three squares?

4. Consider the right triangle on the following page and the squares constructed on its sides.

a. What is the area of each square? (Use the same strategy as before.)

Area of $A =$ ________ units^2

Area of $B =$ ________ units^2

Area of $C =$ ________ units^2

5. What is the side length of each square (to the nearest tenth of a grid unit)?

Side length of $A \approx$ ____________ units

Side length of $B \approx$ ____________ units

Side length of $C \approx$ ____________ units

6. What do you notice about the areas of the three squares?

Take a Look at Those Squares

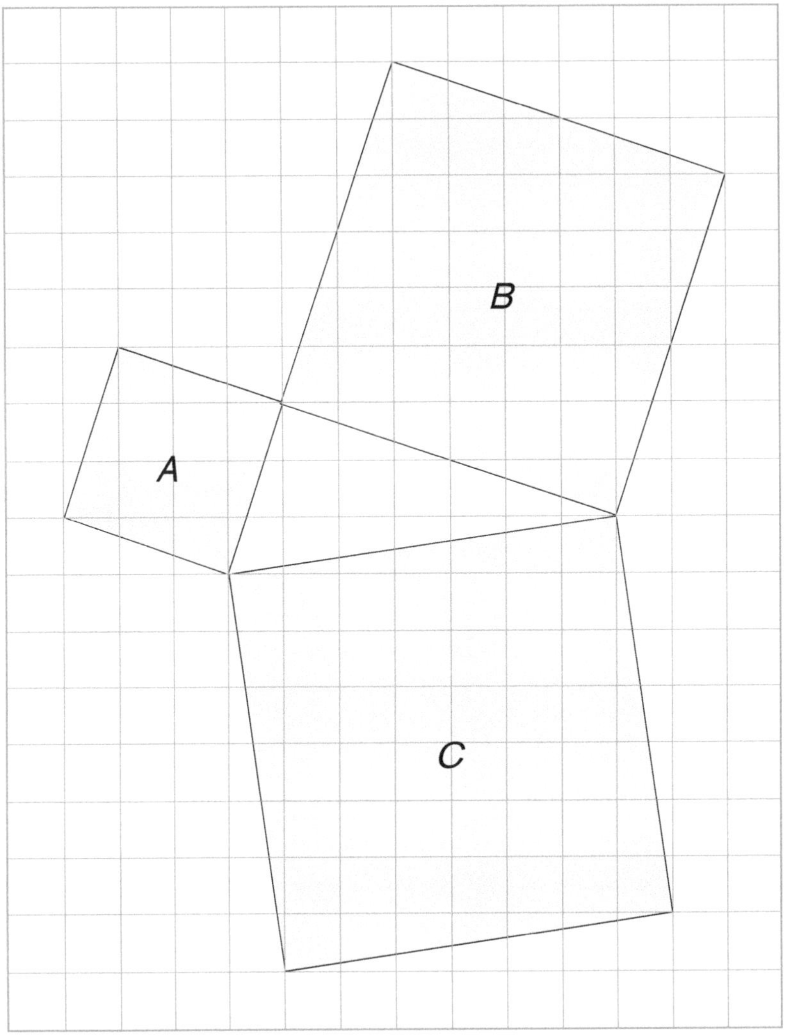

5. A screen image from the applet Squaring the Triangle appears at the top of the next page. The right-hand side of the screen shows a right triangle *ABC* with a square on each of its three sides. The left-hand side of the screen presents data on the triangle. Leg *AC* of the pictured triangle measures 9 linear units on the grid, leg *BC* also measures 9 units, and *AB*, the hypotenuse, measures 12.728 units. The displayed data also include measurements for the angles of the right triangle and the areas of the squares on its sides. All values of length represent linear units, and all values of area represent square units.

Take a Look at Those Squares

Note the two buttons that appear below the image of triangle and the squares. By sliding these buttons, applet users can adjust the lengths of legs *BC* and *AC*. At the same time, they will change the length of the hypotenuse *AB*, the area of right triangle *ABC*, and the areas of the squares on its sides. The screen will show the new right triangle and squares, as well as the accompanying data.

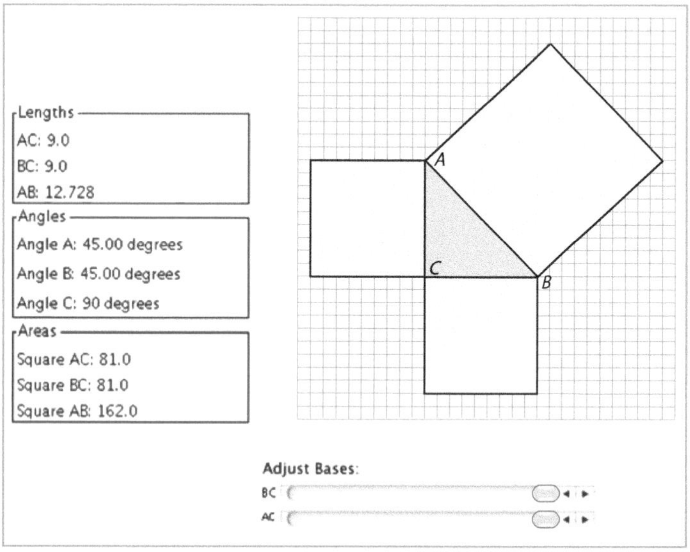

a. Use the applet to explore different right triangles and their corresponding squares. Keep records on five of your triangles in the table below. *If you don't have access to the applet*, draw five different right triangles on grid paper. Position all vertices at intersections of grid lines, and label the vertices *A*, *B*, and *C*, with *AB* as the hypotenuse, as in the screen image from the applet. Complete the chart below for the triangles that you have drawn.

Lengths (linear grid units)			Areas (square grid units)		
AC	*BC*	*AB*	$(AC)^2$	$(BC)^2$	$(AB)^2$

Take a Look at Those Squares

b. What do you notice about the areas of the three squares in each of your examples?

6. On the basis of all your work up to this point, can you make a general statement about the relationship among the areas of the squares constructed on the two legs of a right triangle and the area of the square constructed on the hypotenuse? Use the diagram and its labels to help you write a clear statement

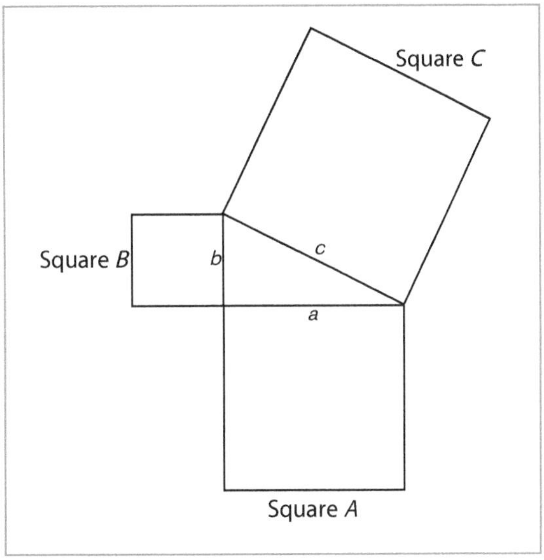

Can You Prove It?

1. Cut out each of the three sets of four right triangles on the accompanying sheet, Sets of Right Triangles for "Can You Prove It?"

2. Work with the sets one at a time on a sheet of centimeter grid paper. Arrange each set of four right triangles in such a way that their legs line up with grid lines to form a square whose side length is equal to $a + b$. The hypotenuses of these triangles will "frame" a smaller square with side length is c, as shown at the right.

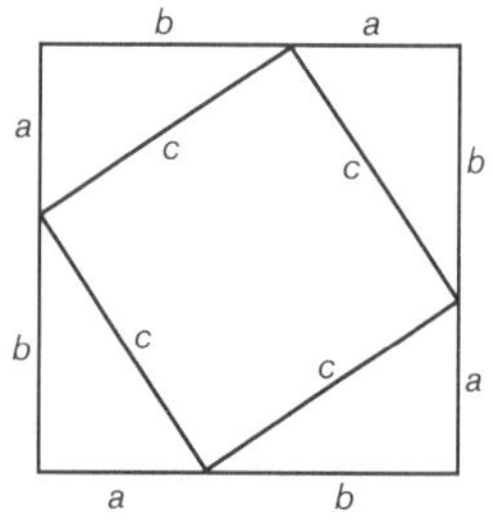

3. Draw each arrangement of triangles on the grid paper, producing three figures that look like the one above but match the triangles that you use to make them. Note that each figure has two squares—an outer, *circumscribed*, square with a side length of $a + b$ and an inner, *inscribed*, square with a side length of c. (Observe that a, b, and c are different lengths in each figure.)
4. Look at the three outer squares (side lengths $a + b$) that you have constructed from the different sets of right triangles. Identify the square formed from the right triangles in which leg a is longer than leg b.
   a. What expression can you write for the area of this outer square if you think about it just as a square with a side length of $a + b$ and ignore everything else in the figure?

   $A =$ ____________________________

   b. You can think about the area of the outer square in another way. What expression can you write for the area of the square if you think about it as the sum of the areas of the four right triangles with legs a and b and the area of the inner square with side length c?

   $A =$ ____________________________

   c. The expressions that you have written in parts (*a*) and (*b*) both give the area of the outer square, so you know that they are equivalent. Set your two expressions equal to each other and simplify them. What remains?

   ____________________________ = ____________________________

Can You Prove It?

5. Examine the outer square in which a is equal to b in the side length $a + b$. Repeat the process from step 4:

   a. What expression can you write for the area of this outer square if you think about it just as a square with a side length of $a + b$ and ignore everything else in the figure?

   $A =$ ________________________________

   b. What expression can you write for the area of the outer square if you think about it as the sum of the areas of the four right triangles with legs a and b and the area of the inner square with side length c?

   $A =$ ________________________________

   c. Set your expressions from parts (*a*) and (*b*) for the area of the outer square equal to each other and simplify them. What remains?

   ________________________________ = ________________________________

6. Examine the outer square in which a is less than b in the side length $a + b$. Repeat the process from steps 4 and 5:

   a. What expression can you write for the area of this outer square if you think about it just as a square with a side length of $a + b$ and ignore everything else in the figure?

   $A =$ ________________________________

   b. What expression can you write for the area of the outer square if you think about it as the sum of the areas of the four right triangles with legs a and b and the area of the inner square with side length c?

   $A =$ ________________________________

   c. Set your expressions from parts (*a*) and (*b*) for the area of the outer square equal to each other and simplify them. What remains?

   ________________________________ = ________________________________

7. Compare the results of your work up to this point with the statement that you wrote in step 8 in Take a Look at Those Squares. How can you relate what you wrote earlier to your discoveries here? Explain your thinking.

Sets of Right Triangles for Can You Prove It?

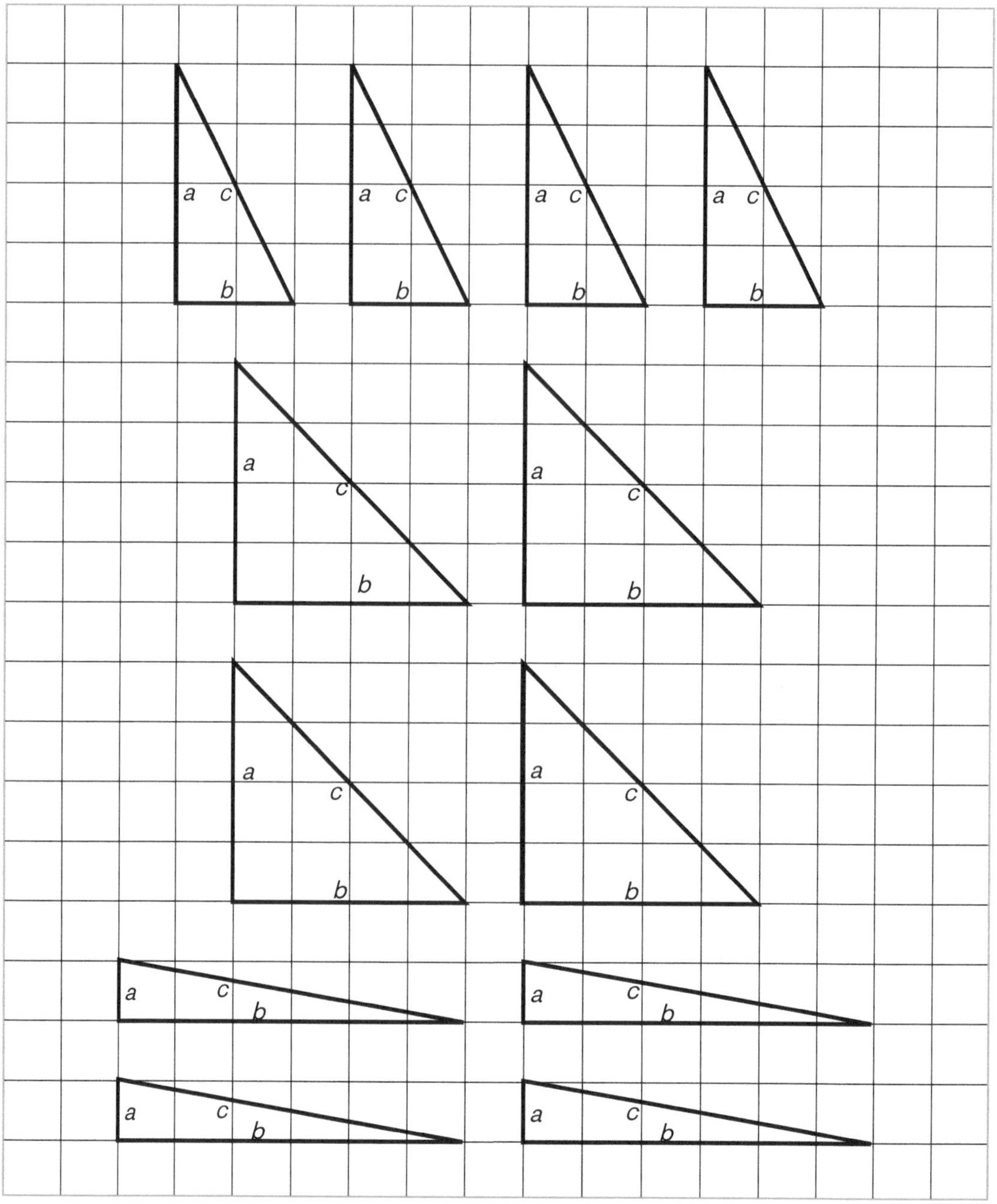

Pick's Theorem

1. Find the area in square units for each shape below. In the space next to the shapes, explain how you arrived at your answers.

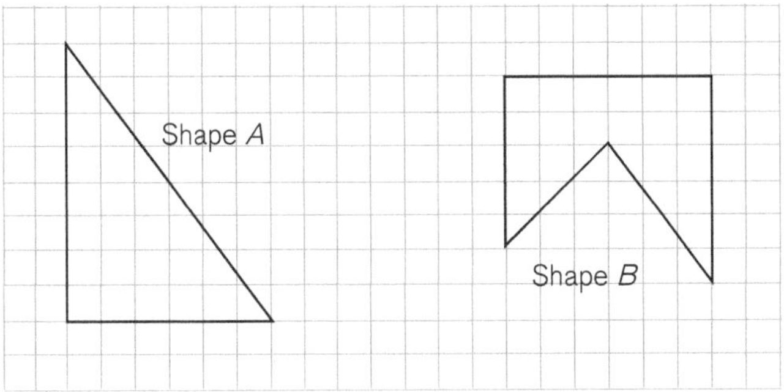

Area of shape *A*
______ square units
How did you arrive at your answer?

Area of shape *B*
______ square units
How did you arrive at your answer?

2. Look at the polygons below and complete the chart on the next page.

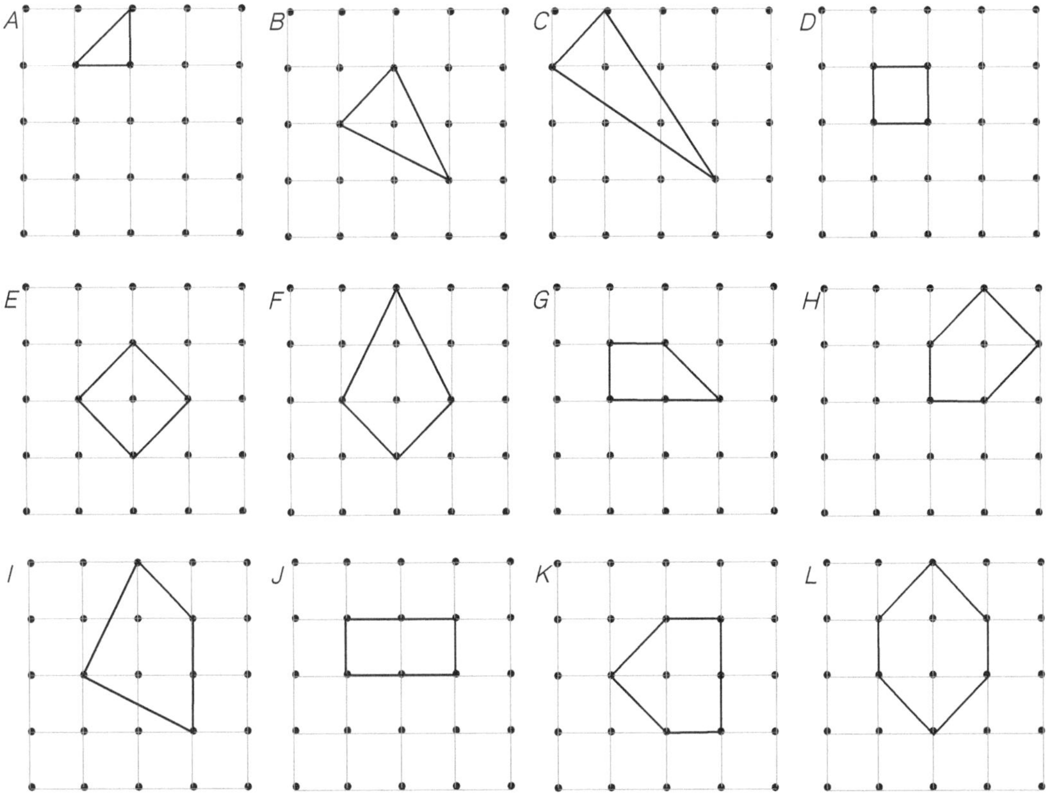

Pick's Theorem

Polygon	Number of Points on the Boundary (Sides) (B)	Number of Points in the Interior (I) of the Figure	Area in Square Units (A)
A			
B			
C			
D			
E			
F			
G			
H			
I			
J			
K			
L			

3. What patterns do you notice in the data in the chart?

4. As the number of boundary points (B) increases, what happens to the value of the area?

5. As the number of interior points (I) increases, what happens to the value of the area?

The chart below shows the data from Dani and LaNika's work:

Polygon	B	$B/2$	I	Area in Square Units
1	6	$6 \div 2 = 3$	4	6
2	6	$6 \div 2 = 3$	6	8
3	8	$8 \div 2 = 4$	1	4
4	8	$8 \div 2 = 4$	2	5
5	8	$8 \div 2 = 4$	3	6
6	7	$7 \div 2 = 3\ 1/2$	2	4 1/2

6. What is the relationship of $B/2$ and I to the area of each figure?

7. Write a rule for finding the area of any polygon when you know the number of boundary points and the number of interior points. Test your rule with the figures in question 1. Then draw your own closed figure on the dot paper your teacher has given you—making sure that the vertices of your figure fall on dots—and test your rule.

Exploring Pick's Rule

Case 1: Rectangles Aligned with Lattice Lines	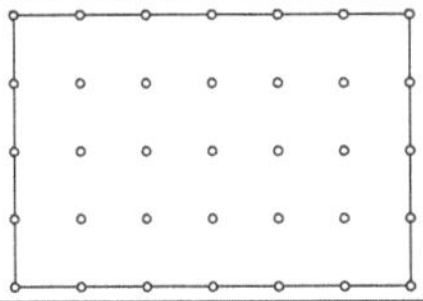	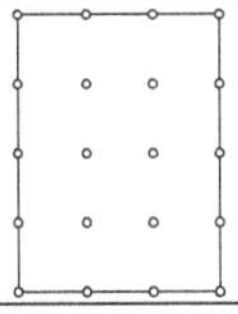
a) Length of horizontal side: b) Length of vertical side: c) Points on horizontal side: d) Points on vertical side: e) Total boundary points (B): f) Total interior points (I): g) Area calculated by Pick's rule: $A = B/2 + I - 1$ h) Area calculated by formula: $A = b \cdot h$	a) _____ b) _____ c) _____ d) _____ e) _____ f) _____ g) _____ sq. units h) _____ sq. units	a) _____ b) _____ c) _____ d) _____ e) _____ f) _____ g) _____ sq. units h) _____ sq. units
	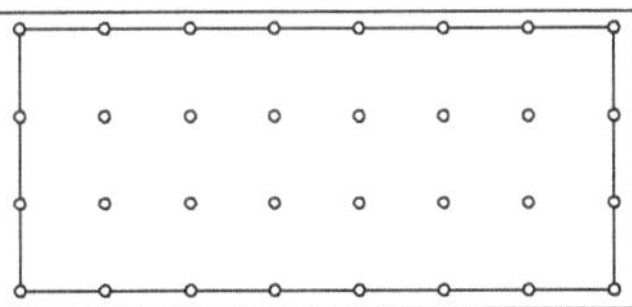	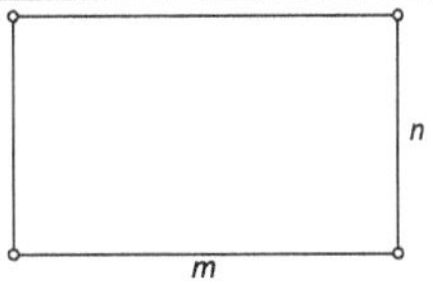
a) Length of horizontal side: b) Length of vertical side: c) Points on horizontal side: d) Points on vertical side: e) Total boundary points (B): f) Total interior points (I): g) Area calculated by Pick's rule: $A = B/2 + I - 1$ h) Area calculated by formula: $A = b \cdot h$	a) _____ b) _____ c) _____ d) _____ e) _____ f) _____ g) _____ sq. units h) _____ sq. units	a) _____ b) _____ c) _____ d) _____ e) _____ f) _____ g) _____ sq. units h) _____ sq. units

What do you conclude about Pick's formula applied to rectangles?________________

____

Exploring Pick's Rule

Case 2: Right Triangles Aligned with Lattice Lines	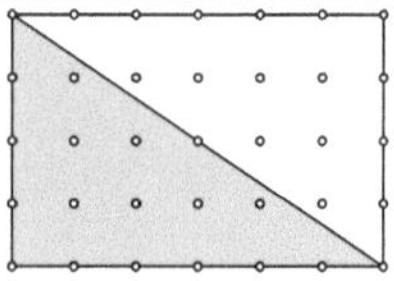	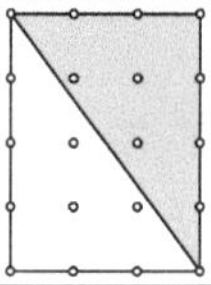
a) Length of horizontal side:	a) ______	a) ______
b) Length of vertical side:	b) ______	b) ______
c) Points on horizontal side:	c) ______	c) ______
d) Points on vertical side:	d) ______	d) ______
e) Points on hypotenuse, not including endpoints (*h*)	e) ______	e) ______
f) Total boundary points (*B*):	f) ______	f) ______
g) Total interior points (*I*):	g) ______	g) ______
h) Area calculated by Pick's rule: $A = B/2 + I - 1$	h) ______ sq. units	h) ______ sq. units
i) Area calculated by formula: $A = ½ (b \cdot h)$	i) ______ sq. units	i) ______ sq. units
	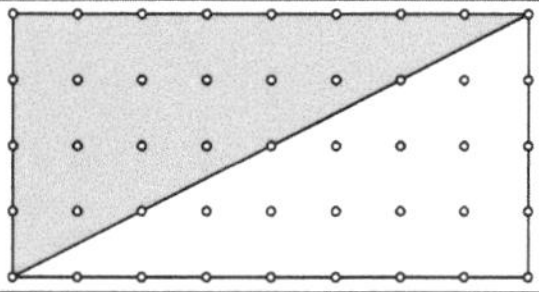	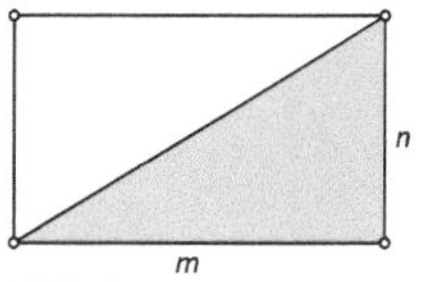
a) Length of horizontal side:	a) ______	a) ______
b) Length of vertical side:	b) ______	b) ______
c) Points on horizontal side:	c) ______	c) ______
d) Points on vertical side:	d) ______	d) ______
e) Points on hypotenuse, not including endpoints (*h*)	e) ______	e) ______
f) Total boundary points (*B*):	f) ______	f) ______
g) Total interior points (*I*):	g) ______	g) ______
h) Area calculated by Pick's rule: $A = B/2 + I - 1$	h) ______ sq. units	h) ______ sq. units
i) Area calculated by formula: $A = ½ (b \cdot h)$	i) ______ sq. units	i) ______ sq. units

What do you conclude about Pick's formula applied to right triangles? ____________

____

Exploring Pick's Rule

Case 3: **Triangles with One Side Aligned with Lattice Lines**	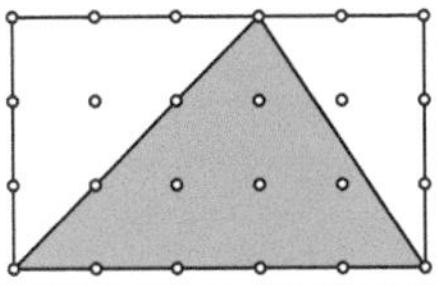	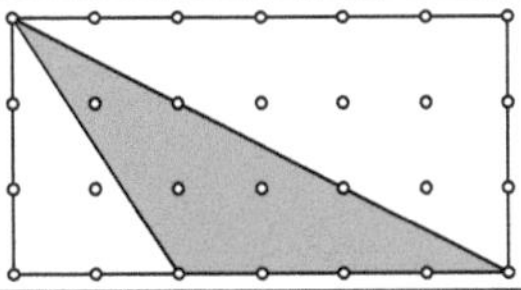
a) Length of triangle base: b) Length of triangle altitude: c) Triangle boundary points (B): d) Triangle interior points (I): e) Area calculated by Pick's rule: $A = B/2 + I - 1$ f) Area calculated by formula: $A = \frac{1}{2}(b \cdot h)$	a) ________ b) ________ c) ________ d) ________ e) ________ sq. units f) ________ sq. units	a) ________ b) ________ c) ________ d) ________ e) ________ sq. units f) ________ sq. units
	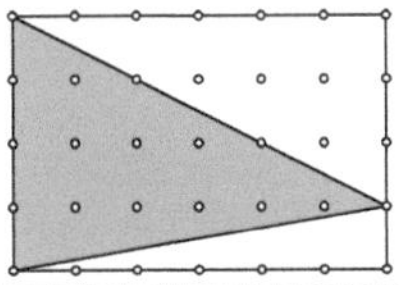	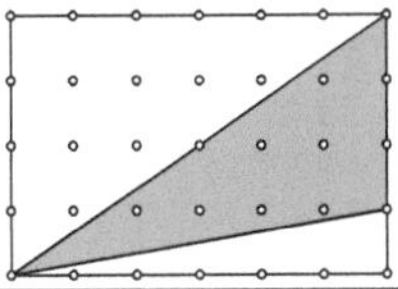
a) Length of triangle base: b) Length of triangle altitude: c) Triangle boundary points (B): d) Triangle interior points (I): e) Area calculated by Pick's rule: $A = B/2 + I - 1$ f) Area calculated by formula: $A = \frac{1}{2}(b \cdot h)$	a) ________ b) ________ c) ________ d) ________ e) ________ sq. units f) ________ sq. units	a) ________ b) ________ c) ________ d) ________ e) ________ sq. units f) ________ sq. units

What do you conclude about Pick's formula applied to triangles with one aligned side?

____

____

Exploring Pick's Rule

Case 4: Triangles with no sides aligned with the lattice

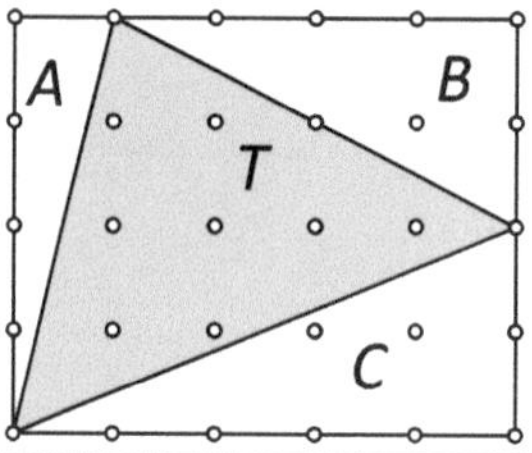

a) Area of rectangle R: ____________

b) Area of triangle A: ____________

c) Area of triangle B: ____________

d) Area of triangle C: ____________

e) Boundary points of ΔT: ____________

f) Interior points of ΔT: ____________

g) Area ΔT from Pick's rule:

$A = B/2 + I - 1$ ____________ sq. units

h) Area ΔT from

$A(R) - A(\Delta A) - A(\Delta B) - A(\Delta C)$

____________ sq. units

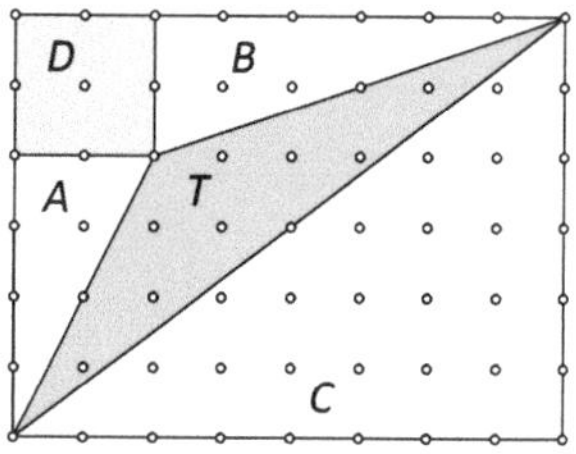

a) Area of outer rectangle R: ____________

b) Area of triangle A: ____________

c) Area of triangle B: ____________

d) Area of triangle C: ____________

e) Area of rectangle D: ____________

f) Boundary points of ΔT: ____________

g) Interior points of ΔT: ____________

h) Area ΔT from Pick's rule:

$A = B/2 + I - 1$ ____________ sq. units

i) Area ΔT from

$A(R) - A(\Delta A) - A(\Delta B) - A(\Delta C) - A(D)$

____________ sq. units

What do you conclude about Pick's formula applied to triangles with no aligned sides?

____

____

What's the Area?

Use Pick's formula to find the area of the following polygons.

Pick's Theorem—The Hole Truth

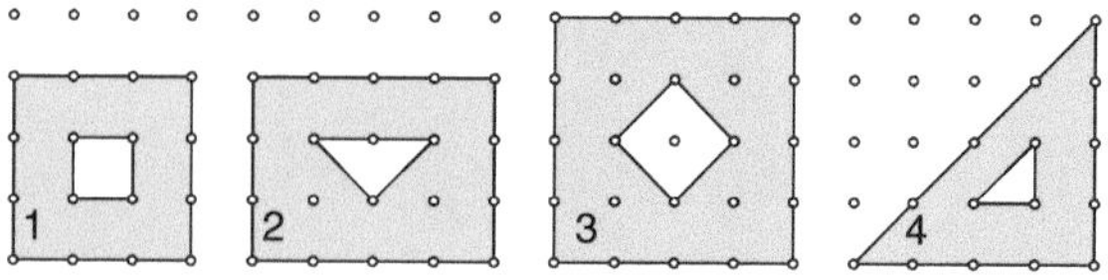

1. The polygons shown above each contain a hole. Complete the following table for the area of these "holey" polygons.

Polygon	Area Outer Shape (sq. units)	Area of Hole (sq. units)	Outer Area Minus Area of Hole	Boundary Points	Interior Points	Area by Pick's Formula $A = B/2 + I - 1$	"Error"
1							
2							
3							
4							

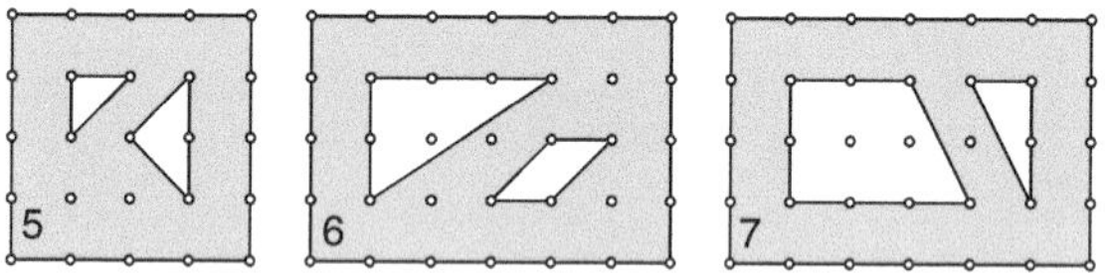

2. The polygons shown above each contain two holes. Complete the following table for the area of these "holey" polygons.

Polygon	Area Outer Shape (sq. units)	Area of Holes (sq. units)	Outer Area Minus Area of Holes	Boundary Points	Interior Points	Area by Pick's Formula $A = B/2 + I - 1$	"Error"
5		1) 2)					
6		1) 2)					
7		1) 2)					

Pick's Theorem—The Hole Truth

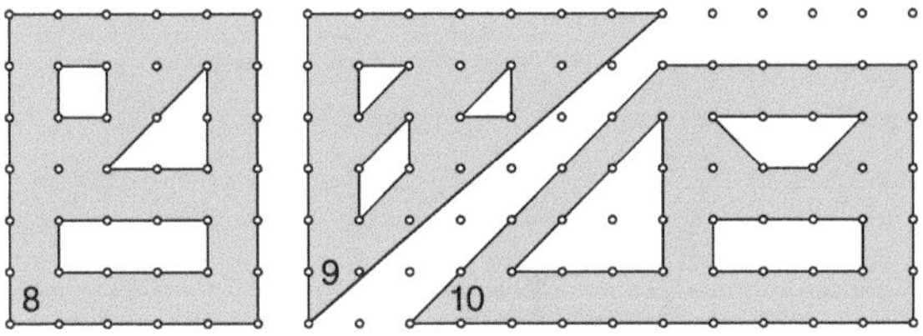

3 The polygons shown above each contain three holes. Complete the following table for the area of these "holey" polygons.

Polygon	Area Outer Shape (sq. units)	Area of Holes (sq. units)	Outer Area Minus Area of Holes	Boundary Points	Interior Points	Area by Pick's Formula $A = B/2 + I - 1$	"Error"
8		1) 2) 3)					
9		1) 2) 3)					
10		1) 2) 3)					

4. What patterns do you notice in the data in the previous three charts?

5. As the number of holes increases, what happens to the discrepancy between the area calculated by subtracting the area of the holes and the area calculated by Pick's rule?

6. Pick's theorem is known to be valid for lattice polygons that do not contain holes. Write an adjusted formula that will extend Pick's theorem to also include polygons with holes.

Ratios

1. Roll two dice, and find the sum of the values indicated on the top faces. Decide whether the sum is prime or not prime. Put an *X* in the appropriate column. Then compute the ratio of "number of prime sums" to "cumulative number of rolls," and enter the ratio in the chart. Repeat the process 20 times.

Roll	Numbers Rolled and Sum	Prime Sum?	Not a Prime Sum?	Ratio of "Number of Prime Sums" to "Cumulative Number of Rolls"
1				
2				
3				
4				
5				
6				
7				
8				
9				
10				
11				
12				
13				
14				
15				
16				
17				
18				
19				
20				

Ratios

2. Graph the data on the following axes:

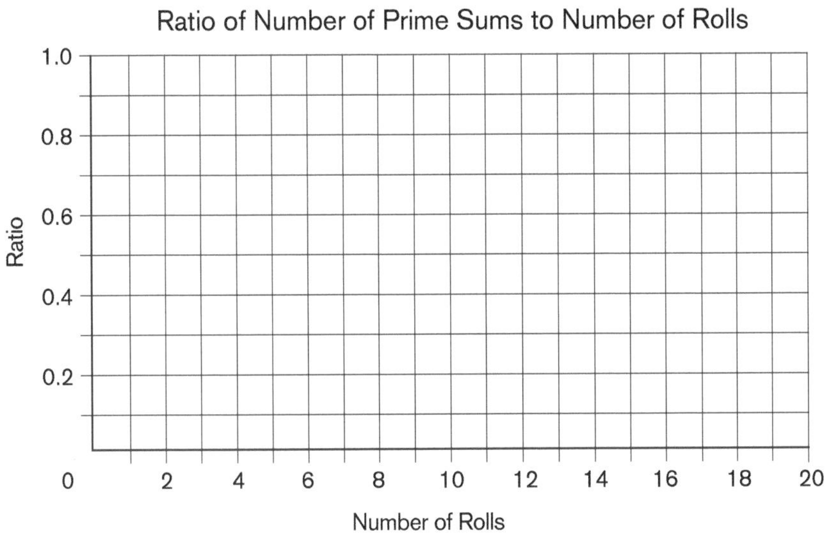

3. What patterns do you see in the graph? ______________________________

____

____

How does the graph of the first ten rolls differ from the graph as the number of rolls increases?

____

____

4. If you rolled the dice many times, about what ratio of sums do you think would be prime? __________

Explain your answer. ______________________________

____

____

Ratios

5. Roll two dice, and multiply the values indicated on the top faces each time. Observe whether the product is a two-digit number or not. Put an *X* in the appropriate column. Then compute the ratio of "number of two-digit products" to "cumulative number of rolls," and enter the ratio in the chart. Repeat the process 20 times.

Roll	Numbers Rolled and Product	Two-Digit Product?	Not a Two-Digit Product?	Ratio of "Number of Two-Digit Products" to "Cumulative Number of Rolls"
1				
2				
3				
4				
5				
6				
7				
8				
9				
10				
11				
12				
13				
14				
15				
16				
17				
18				
19				
20				

Ratios

6. Graph the data on the following axes:

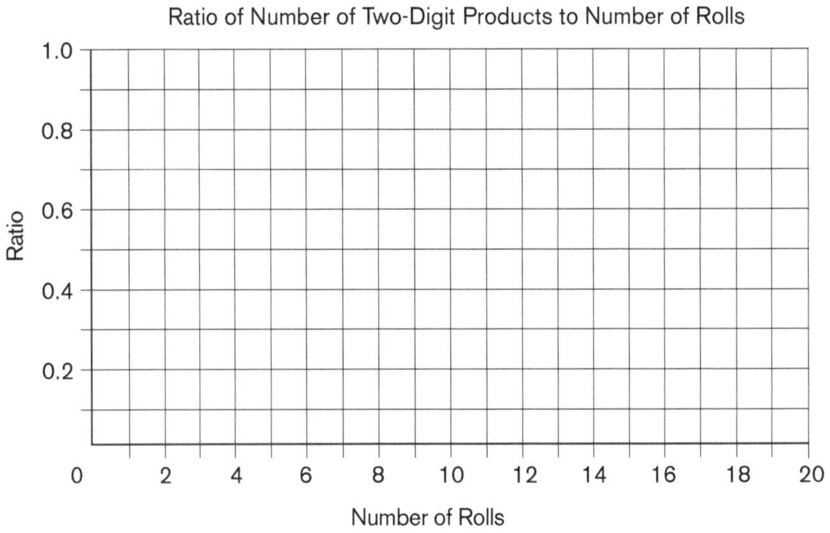

7. What patterns do you see in the graph? ____

____

____

How does the graph of the first 10 rolls differ from the graph as the number of rolls increases?

____

____

8. If you rolled the dice many times, about what ratio of products do you think would be two-digit numbers? ____________________ Explain your answer. ______________________________

____

____

Test Guessing

Suppose that you have to take a true-or-false test with three questions and you have forgotten to study. You take the test, but you have to guess on each question.

1. Since there are only two choices for each question (true or false), what is the probability that you will guess the correct answer for the first question? ______________ For the second question? ______________ For the third question? ______________
2. Using C for a correct guess and W for a wrong guess, list all the possible outcomes of answering the three questions on the test. For example, you would record CCC to indicate the possibility of getting all three questions correct. *Hint:* Eight outcomes are possible.
3. If you are truly guessing, what is the probability associated with each of the eight outcomes? ______________

   Describe two ways to explain your answer. ______________
4. If 70 percent is the lowest passing grade, what is the probability that you will pass the test by guessing? ______________
5. Repeat the analysis (questions 1–4) for a true-or-false test of five questions.
6. If time permits, repeat the analysis (questions 1–4) for a three-question multiple-choice test with three options for each answer.

First Head

Exploration 1

1. Use any fair coin. Toss it repeatedly, recording the outcome of each toss as H or T, until the first head appears. Then record the number of the toss on which the first H appears. Repeat this process 20 times.

Trial	String of Hs and Ts	Number of Tosses to Get First Head
Sample	T T T H	4
1	________	____
2	________	____
3	________	____
4	________	____
5	________	____
6	________	____
7	________	____
8	________	____
9	________	____
10	________	____
11	________	____
12	________	____
13	________	____
14	________	____
15	________	____
16	________	____
17	________	____
18	________	____
19	________	____
20	________	____

2. Estimate the probability of each event by computing relative frequencies:

Event	Estimate of Probability	Event	Estimate of Probability
First H on toss 1	______	First H on toss 7	______
First H on toss 2	______	First H on toss 8	______
First H on toss 3	______	First H on toss 9	______
First H on toss 4	______	First H on toss 10	______
First H on toss 5	______	No H in 10 tosses	______
First H on toss 6	______		

3. What surprised you about the number of times you tossed a coin before you got a heads?__________

____

____

____

First Head

Exploration 2

1. Tape a small wad of paper to the tail side of the coin. Repeat the trials.

Trial	String of Hs and Ts	Number of Tosses to Get First Head
Sample	T T T T T H	6
1	____________	____
2	____________	____
3	____________	____
4	____________	____
5	____________	____
6	____________	____
7	____________	____
8	____________	____
9	____________	____
10	____________	____
11	____________	____
12	____________	____
13	____________	____
14	____________	____
15	____________	____
16	____________	____
17	____________	____
18	____________	____
19	____________	____
20	____________	____

2. Estimate the probability of each event by computing relative frequencies:

Event	Estimate of Probability	Event	Estimate of Probability
First H on toss 1	________	First H on toss 7	________
First H on toss 2	________	First H on toss 8	________
First H on toss 3	________	First H on toss 9	________
First H on toss 4	________	First H on toss 10	________
First H on toss 5	________	No H in 10 tosses	________
First H on toss 6	________		

3. How were the results of these two explorations the same? ______________________________

____

____

____

How were they different? ____

____

____

Strings of Heads

Exploration 1

1. Use any fair coin. Toss it ten times. Record the longest string of heads in the ten tosses. For example, if the tosses are H H T H H H T T T T, the longest string of heads is 3. Repeat this process 20, making 10 tosses each time.

Trial	Tosses	Longest String of Heads
Sample	H H T H H H T T T T	3
1	__________	______
2	__________	______
3	__________	______
4	__________	______
5	__________	______
6	__________	______
7	__________	______
8	__________	______
9	__________	______
10	__________	______
11	__________	______
12	__________	______
13	__________	______
14	__________	______
15	__________	______
16	__________	______
17	__________	______
18	__________	______
19	__________	______
20	__________	______

2. Estimate the probability of each event by computing relative frequencies:

Event	Estimate of Probability	Event	Estimate of Probability
Length of longest string = 0	______	Length of longest string = 5	______
Length of longest string = 1	______	Length of longest string = 6	______
Length of longest string = 2	______	Length of longest string = 7	______
Length of longest string = 3	______	Length of longest string = 8	______
Length of longest string = 4	______	Length of longest string = 9	______
		Length of longest string = 10	______

Strings of Heads

3. Are you surprised by any of your results? ____________ What surprised you? ____________

4. Do you think the length of the longest string of heads would be different if you tossed the coin 20 times in each trial? ____________
Explain. ____________

Exploration 2

1. Use any fair coin. Toss it 20 times. Record the longest string of heads in the 20 tosses. Repeat this process 20 times, making 20 tosses each time.

Trial	Tosses	Longest String of Heads
1		
2		
3		
4		
5		
6		
7		
9		
10		
11		
12		
13		
14		
15		
16		
17		
18		
19		
20		

Strings of Heads

2. Estimate the probability of each event by computing relative frequencies:

Event	Estimate of Probability
Length of longest string = 0	______
Length of longest string = 1	______
Length of longest string = 2	______
Length of longest string = 3	______
Length of longest string = 4	______
Length of longest string = 5	______
Length of longest string = 6	______
Length of longest string = 7	______
Length of longest string = 8	______
Length of longest string = 9	______
Length of longest string =10	______
Length of longest string = 11	______
Length of longest string = 12	______
Length of longest string = 13	______
Length of longest string = 14	______
Length of longest string = 15	______
Length of longest string = 16	______
Length of longest string = 17	______
Length of longest string = 18	______
Length of longest string = 19	______
Length of longest string = 20	______

3. How were the results of the 20-toss exploration similar to the results of the 10-toss exploration?

____

____

____

How were they different? ____

____

____

____

Strings of Heads

Exploration 3

1. Get the results of all the games that your favorite baseball or basketball team played last year. List each game as a win (W) or a loss (L). Record the longest string of wins in each set of 10 games during the season (e.g., games 1–10, games 11–20).

Games	Wins/Losses	Longest String of Wins
1–10	______________	_____
11–20	______________	_____
21–30	______________	_____
31–40	______________	_____
41–50	______________	_____
51–60	______________	_____
61–70	______________	_____
71–80	______________	_____
81–90	______________	_____
91–100	______________	_____
101–110	______________	_____
111–120	______________	_____
121–130	______________	_____
131–140	______________	_____
141–150	______________	_____
151–160	______________	_____

2. Estimate the probability of each event by computing relative frequencies:

Event	Estimate of Probability	Event	Estimate of Probability
Length of longest string = 0	____________	Length of longest string = 6	____________
Length of longest string = 1	____________	Length of longest string = 7	____________
Length of longest string = 2	____________	Length of longest string = 8	____________
Length of longest string = 3	____________	Length of longest string = 9	____________
Length of longest string = 4	____________	Length of longest string = 10	____________
Length of longest string = 5	____________		

3. Do the data look like the data for a coin toss? ____________ Explain. ______________________________

____

____

4. What difference between the sports situation and the coin-toss situation might account for the differences you observed in the results? ____

____

____

____

Migraines: Histograms

Below are data collected from patients who suffer from migraine headaches. The patients were instructed to take their assigned drugs as soon as their headaches began and to record how much time passed before the drugs gave relief. Drug *A* is a traditional drug, and drug *B* is an experimental drug. Each value is the number of minutes (rounded to the nearest two minutes) that elapsed before a patient got relief.

Drug *A* (106 patients)

16, 18, 18, 20, 22, 22, 24, 24, 26, 26, 28, 28, 30, 30, 32, 32, 34, 36, 36, 36, 38, 38, 40, 42, 44, 44, 46, 46, 48, 50, 54, 56, 56, 58, 58, 58, 62, 62, 64, 64, 66, 68, 68, 70, 70, 70, 72, 72, 74, 76, 76, 76, 78, 78, 80, 80, 80, 82, 82, 84, 84, 84, 86, 86, 88, 88, 88, 88, 90, 90, 90, 90, 90, 92, 92, 92, 92, 94, 94, 94, 96, 96, 98, 98, 98, 98, 100, 100, 100, 100, 102, 102, 102, 104, 104, 106, 106, 108, 108, 108, 110, 110, 112, 114, 118, 120

Drug *B* (47 patients)

18, 20, 20, 22, 24, 24, 24, 26, 26, 30, 30, 30, 34, 34, 34, 36, 36, 36, 38, 38, 40, 40, 44, 44, 46, 50, 52, 52, 56, 56, 58, 62, 62, 66, 74, 74, 78, 88, 94, 98, 98, 100, 104, 106, 110, 116, 120

1. From examining these data, which drug do you think gave faster relief from headache pain? ________

   Explain. ____

   ____

   ____

2. Construct a histogram for each data set on the axes below. Title your display, and specify an appropriate scale on the horizontal axis.

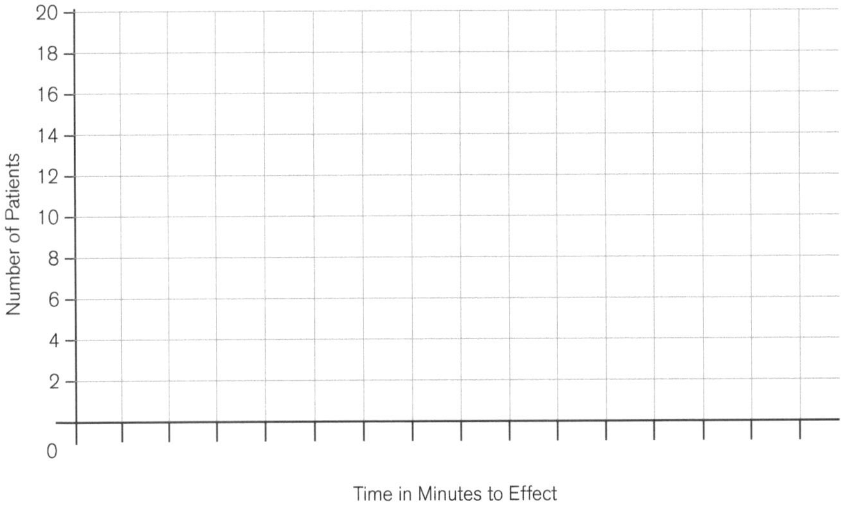

Migraines: Histograms

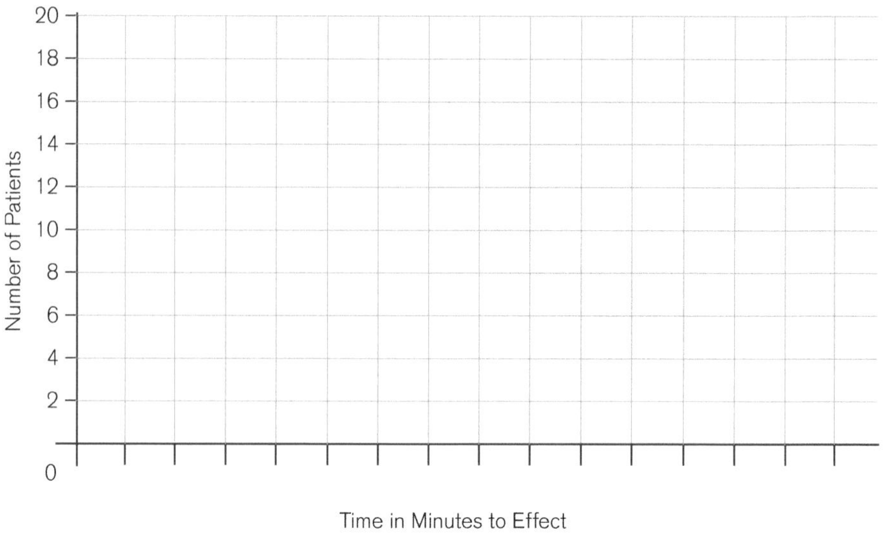

3. From examining the histograms, which drug do you think was more effective in giving fast relief from headache pain? ________ Explain. ____
____
____

4. Construct a relative-frequency histogram on the axes below.

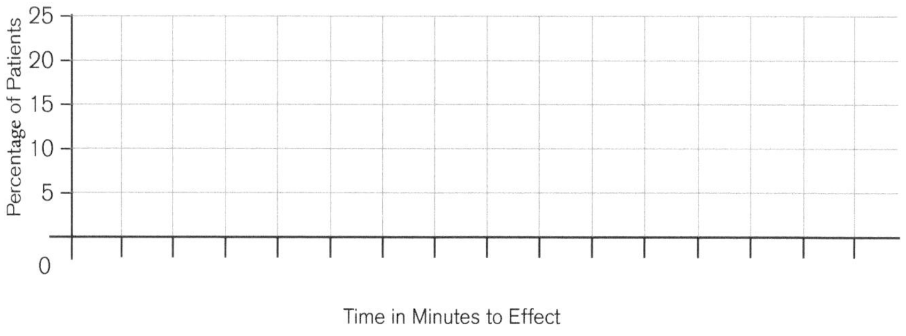

Migraines: Histograms

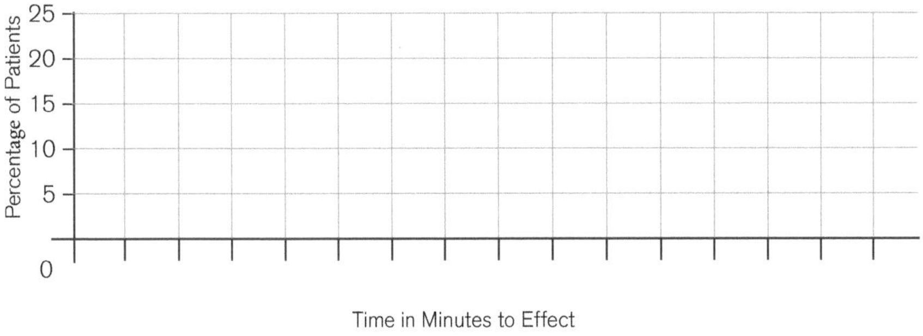

5. On the basis of your examination of the relative-frequency histograms, which drug do you think gave faster relief from headache pain? ______________ Explain. ______________________________

6. Some students get different answers for questions 3 and 5. Why do you think that happens? ________

7. How does changing the display change the information you can read from the graph?

8. What advantage does the histogram have over the relative-frequency histogram? ______________

9. What advantage does the relative-frequency histogram have over the histogram? ______________

Migraines: Box Plots

The data below show the number of minutes that elapsed before patients, some taking drug *A* and some taking drug *B*, got relief from migraine headaches.

Drug *A* (106 patients)

16, 18, 18, 20, 22, 22, 24, 24, 26, 26, 28, 28, 30, 30, 32, 32, 34, 36, 36, 36, 38, 38, 40, 42, 44, 44, 46, 46, 48, 50, 54, 56, 56, 58, 58, 58, 62, 62, 64, 64, 66, 68, 68, 70, 70, 70, 72, 72, 74, 76, 76, 76, 78, 78, 80, 80, 80, 82, 82, 84, 84, 84, 86, 86, 88, 88, 88, 88, 90, 90, 90, 90, 90, 92, 92, 92, 92, 94, 94, 94, 96, 96, 98, 98, 98, 98, 100, 100, 100, 100, 102, 102, 102, 104, 104, 106, 106, 108, 108, 108, 110, 110, 112, 114, 118, 120

Drug *B* (47 patients)

18, 20, 20, 22, 24, 24, 24, 26, 26, 30, 30, 30, 34, 34, 34, 36, 36, 36, 38, 38, 40, 40, 44, 44, 46, 50, 52, 52, 56, 56, 58, 62, 62, 66, 74, 74, 78, 88, 94, 98, 98, 100, 104, 106, 110, 116, 120

One way to represent these data is with dot plots like those below.

Time to Effect of Drug *A*

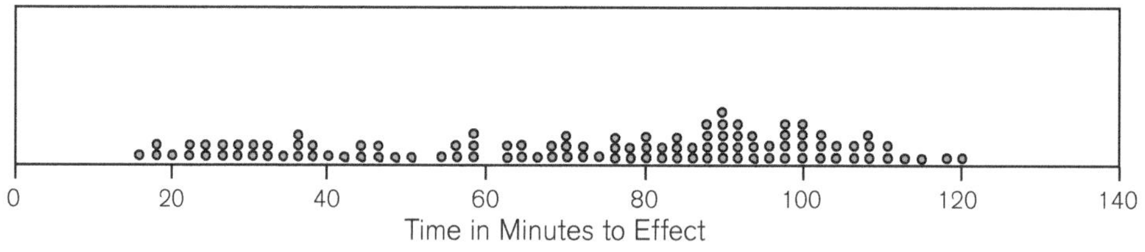

Time to Effect of Drug *B*

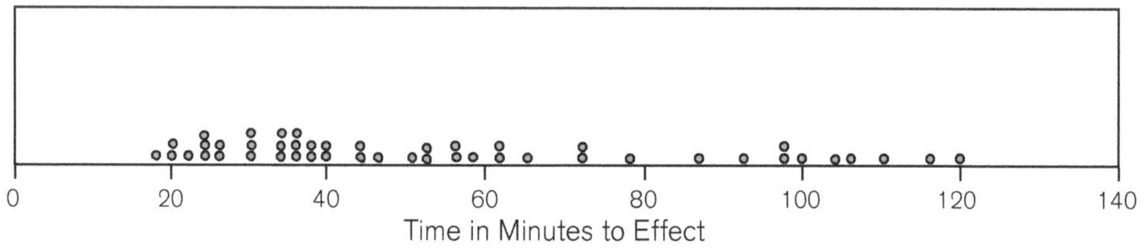

1. Use a vertical line segment that intersects the horizontal axis to mark the median of each data set.
2. What do you know about the number of data values on either side of the median? ______________________________

____

____

Migraines: Box Plots

3. On the basis of a comparison of only the medians, which drug appears to provide faster relief? ______
Explain your answer. ____

____

____

4. Use a vertical line segment that intersects the horizontal axis to mark the median of each half of each set of data. You should now have three vertical line segments drawn on the dot plot for each data set. The two new values that you have identified are called the *lower quartile* (or *first quartile*) and the *upper quartile* (or *third quartile*).
5. What do you know about the number of data elements in each of the four intervals for drug *A*? ______
______________________ For drug *B*? ______________________
6. Look again at the lower quartiles, the medians, and the upper quartiles that you marked on the dot plots. On the basis of a comparison of these three values in the data sets, which drug appears to provide faster relief? ______________________ Explain your answer.

____

____

7. Use a vertical line segment to mark each extreme (least and greatest) value in each data set. You should now have five values marked in each data set. These five values are called the *five-point summary* of a data set.
8. Use the five-point summaries and the axis below to make two box plots. Label the axis and title your display.

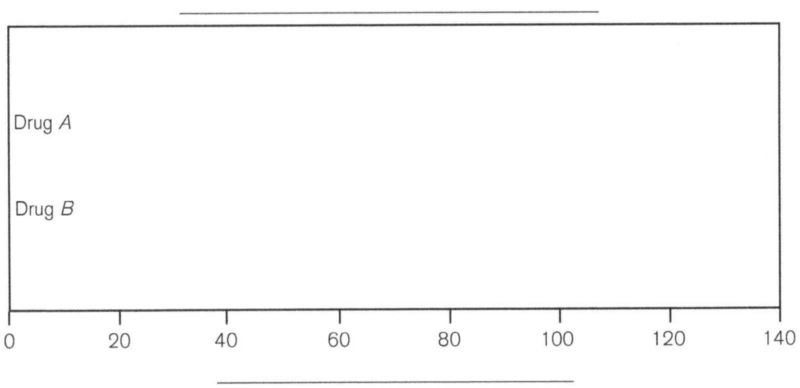

9. What can you say about the data for drug *A* in the first interval compared with the data for drug *A* in the fourth interval? ____

____

Migraines: Box Plots

10. What can you say about the data for drug *B* in the first interval compared with the data for drug *B* in the fourth interval? ______________________________

____

____

11. What does the distance between the vertical line segments tell you about how the data are spread out?

____

12. The lower quartile for drug *A* is about the same as the median for drug *B*. What does that information tell you about how the speeds of the drugs compare? ______________________________

____

____

13. The median for drug *A* is about the same as the upper quartile for drug *B*. What does that information tell you about how the speeds of the drugs compare? ______________________________

____

____

14. On the basis of all the information, which drug seems to provide faster relief? ______________

Explain your answer. ______________________________

____

____

Two Data Sets

Set A	16, 18, 18, 20, 22, 22, 24, 24, 26, 26, 28, 28, 30, 30, 32, 32, 34, 36, 36, 36, 38, 38, 40, 42, 44, 44, 46, 46, 48, 50, 54, 56, 56, 58, 58, 58, 62, 62, 64, 64, 66, 68, 68, 70, 70, 70, 72, 72, 74, 76, 76, 76, 78, 78, 80, 80, 80, 82, 82, 84, 84, 84, 86, 86, 88, 88, 88, 88, 90, 90, 90, 90, 90, 92, 92, 92, 92, 94, 94, 94, 96, 96, 98, 98, 98, 98, 100, 100, 100, 100, 102, 102, 102, 104, 104, 106, 106, 108, 108, 108, 110, 110, 112, 114, 118, 120
Set B	18, 20, 20, 22, 24, 24, 24, 26, 26, 30, 30, 30, 34, 34, 34, 36, 36, 36, 38, 38, 40, 40, 44, 44, 46, 50, 52, 52, 56, 56, 58, 62, 62, 66, 74, 74, 78, 88, 94, 98, 98, 100, 104, 106, 110, 116, 120

Batteries

Mrs. Brewer uses graphing calculators in her mathematics classes. She wants to use longer-lasting batteries so that a minimum of time is lost because of dead batteries. She searched the Internet and found the following data on the life, in hours, of two brands of batteries.

Battery Life in Hours

Always Ready Batteries			Tough Cell Batteries		
96	111	110	101	95	103
115	95	115	91	121	106
106	86	110	104	121	111
115	63	84	84	110	114
44	110	52	103	94	107
110	111	107	121	97	99
115	116	89	107	109	96
113	92	93	97	105	110
74	117	101	103	112	110
115	175	101	115	115	98
114	31	105	140	102	108
19	105	99	130	91	110
86	22		86	95	
203	96		100	88	

1. On grid paper, make two graphical representations that illustrate the differences between these two brands of batteries.
2. What are the quartiles for each set of data? ____________________

   ____

   What do these values indicate about the two brands? ____________________

   ____

   ____
3. Which brand of batteries seems to have the longer life? ____________________

   Explain the reasons for your answer. ____________________

   ____

   ____
4. Suppose that Mrs. Brewer puts new batteries of the brand you named in question 3 in all the calculators at the beginning of the school year. About when during the year will she need to have replacements available? ____________________ Explain the reasons for your answer. ____________________

   ____

   ____

   ____

Centimeter Grid Paper

Quarter-Inch Grid Paper

Geodot Paper

Isodot Paper

References

Bakker, Arthur, Rolf Bieler, and Cliff Konold. 2004. "Should Young Students Learn about Box Plots?" In *Curricular Development in Statistics Education,* edited by Gail Burrill and Mike Camden, pp. 163–173. Voorburg, the Netherlands: International Statistics Institute.

Beneduce, Ann Keay. 1996. *Gulliver's Adventures in Lilliput.* New York: Putnam and Grosset.

Berry, Robert Q., III. 2019. "Examining Equitable Teaching Using the Mathematics Teaching Framework." NCTM *President's Message,* May 2019. https://www.nctm.org/News-and-Calendar/Messages-from-the-President/Archive/Robert-Q_-Berry-III/Examining-Equitable-Teaching-Using-the-Mathematics-Teaching-Framework/.

Briggs, Raymond. 1997. *Jim and the Beanstalk.* New York: Putnam and Grosset Group.

Carpenter, Thomas P., Megan Loef Franke, and Linda Levi. 2003. *Thinking Mathematically: Integrating Arithmetic and Algebra in Elementary School.* Portsmouth, NH: Heinemann.

Del Grande, John. 1990. "Spatial Sense." *Arithmetic Teacher* 37, no. 6 (February): 15.

Foreman, Linda Cooper, and Albert B. Bennett Jr. 1996. *Visual Mathematics Course II.* Salem, OR: Math Learning Center.

Haldane, J. B. S. 1926. "On Being the Right Size." http://www.phys.ufl.edu/courses/phy3221/spring10/HaldaneRightSize.pdfhttp://www.phys.

Heritage, Margaret. 2008. *Learning Progressions: Supporting Instruction and Formative Assessment.* Washington, DC: Council of Chief State School Officers.

Hodges, Margaret. 1995. *Gulliver in Lilliput.* New York: Holiday House.

House, Peggy A. 1980. *Interactions of Science and Mathematics.* Columbus, OH: ERIC Clearinghouse for Science, Mathematics, and Environmental Education.

Kader, Gary, and Jim Mamer. 2008. "Statistics in the Middle Grades: Understanding Center and Spread." *Mathematics Teaching in the Middle School* 14, no. 1 (August): 38–43.

Kader, Gary D., and Mike Perry. 2006. "A Framework for Teaching Statistics within the K–12 Mathematics Curriculum." *Proceedings of the Seventh International Conference on Teaching Statistics,* Salvador, Bahia, Brazil, 2006. Edited by Allan Rossman and Beth Chance. Voorburg, The Netherlands: International Statistical Institute. https://www.stat.auckland.ac.nz/~iase/publications/17/2B3_KADE.pdf.

Koirala, Hari P., and Phillip M. Goodwin. 2000. "Teaching Algebra in the Middle Grades Using Mathmagic." *Mathematics Teaching in the Middle School* 5 (May 2000): 563–566.

Lamon, Susan J. 2001. "Presenting and Representing: From Fractions to Rational Numbers." In *The Role of Representations in School Mathematics*, 2001 Yearbook of the National Council of Teachers of Mathematics (NCTM), edited by Albert A. Cuoco, pp. 146–165. Reston, VA: NCTM.

Lappan, Glenda, James T. Fey, William M. Fitzgerald, Susan N. Friel, and Elizabeth Difanis Phillips. 1998. *Say It with Symbols*. Menlo Park, CA: Dale Seymour Publications.

National Council of Teachers of Mathematics (NCTM). 1980. *An Agenda for Action*. Reston, VA: NCTM.

_____. 1989. *Curriculum and Evaluation Standards for School Mathematics*. Reston, VA: NCTM.

_____. 1991. *Professional Standards for Teaching Mathematics*. Reston, VA: NCTM.

_____. 1995. *Assessment Standards for School Mathematics*. Reston, VA: NCTM.

_____. 2000. *Principles and Standards for School Mathematics*. Reston, VA: NCTM.

_____. 2001. *Navigating through Algebra in Grades 6–8*. Reston, VA: NCTM.

_____. 2002. *Navigating through Geometry in Grades 6–8*. Reston, VA: NCTM.

_____. 2003a. *Navigating through Data Analysis in Grades 6–8*. Reston, VA: NCTM.

_____. 2003b. *Navigating through Probability in Grades 6–8*. Reston, VA: NCTM.

_____. 2005. *Navigating through Measurement in Grades 6–8*. Reston, VA: NCTM.

_____. 2006a. *Curriculum Focal Points for Prekindergarten through Grade 8 Mathematics : A Quest for Coherence*. Reston, VA: NCTM.

_____. 2006b. *Navigating through Number and Operations in Grades 6–8*. Reston, VA: NCTM.

_____. 2008. *Navigating through Discrete Mathematics in Grade 6–12*. Reston, VA: NCTM.

_____. 2009a. *Focus in High School Mathematics: Reasoning and Sense Making*. Reston, VA: NCTM.

_____. 2009b. *Navigating through Problem Solving and Reasoning in Grade 6*. Reston, VA: NCTM.

_____. 2009c. *Navigating through Problem Solving and Reasoning in Grade 6–8*. Reston, VA: NCTM.

_____. 2014. *Principles to Actions: Ensuring Mathematical Success for All*. Reston, VA: NCTM.

_____. 2019. *Activity Gems for the PK–2 Classroom*. Reston, VA: NCTM.

National Governors Association Center for Best Practices (NGA Center) and Council of Chief State School Officers (CCSSO). 2010. *Common Core State Standards for Mathematics*. Washington, DC: NGA Center and CCSSO.

National Research Council. 2001. *Adding It Up: Helping Children Learn Mathematics*. Edited by Jeremy Kilpatrick, Jane Swafford, and Bradford Findell, Mathematics Learning Study Committee, Center for Education, Division of Behavioral and Social Sciences and Education. Washington, DC: National Academies Press.

O'Connor, Peggy. 2000. "Uncovering the Magic." *Teaching Children Mathematics* 7, no. 1 (September): 16–21.

Petersen, Jean. 1983. "Why We Still Need to Teach Geometry." In *Proceedings of the Fourth International Congress on Mathematical Education,* pp. 158–159. Boston: Birkhauser Boston.

Pohl, Victoria. 1987. "Visualizing Three Dimensions by Constructing Polyhedra." In *Learning and Teaching Geometry, K–12,* 1987 Yearbook of the National Council of Teachers of Mathematics (NCTM), edited by Mary Montgomery Lindquist, 144–154. Reston, VA: NCTM.

Riehl, Suzanne M., and Olof Bjorg Steinthorsdottir. 2014. "Revisiting Mr. Tall and Mr. Short." *Mathematics Teaching in the Middle School* 20, no. 4 (November): 221–228.

Silverstein, Shel. 1974. "One Inch Tall." In *Where the Sidewalk Ends: The Poems and Drawings of Shel Silverstein,* p. 55. New York: Harper and Row.

Smith, Margaret S., Edward A. Silver, Mary Kay Stein, Melissa Boston, Marjorie A. Henningsen, and Amy F. Hillen. 2005. *Improving Instruction in Rational Numbers and Proportionality: Using Cases to Transform Mathematics Teaching and Learning.* Vol. 1. New York: Teachers College Press.

Smith, Margaret S., and Mary Kay Stein. 2018. *5 Practices for Orchestrating Productive Mathematics Discussions.* 2nd ed. Reston, VA: National Council of Teachers of Mathematics.

Spiegelhalter, David. 2010. "Why Do People Find Probability So Difficult?" *NRICH Newsletter,* November 2010. https://nrich.maths.org/7326.

Stein, Mary Kay, Margaret Schwan Smith, Marjorie A. Henningsen, and Edward A. Silver. 2000. *Implementing Standards-Based Mathematics Instruction: A Casebook for Professional Development.* Reston, VA: National Council of Teachers of Mathematics; New York: Teachers College Press.

Sundby, Scott. 2000. *Cut Down to Size at High Noon.* Watertown, MA: Charlesbridge Publishing.

Wiles, Peter, Travis Lemon, and Alessandra King. 2019. "Transforming Middle School Geometry Instruction." *Mathematics Teaching in the Middle School* 24, no. 7 (May): 415–421.

Navigations Series

Navigating through Algebra in Grades 6–8. Reston, VA: NCTM, 2001.

Navigating through Data Analysis in Grades 6–8. Reston, VA: NCTM, 2003.

Navigating through Discrete Mathematics in Grade 6–12. Reston, VA: NCTM, 2008.

Navigating through Geometry in Grades 6–8. Reston, VA: NCTM, 2002.

Navigating through Measurement in Grades 6–8. Reston, VA: NCTM, 2005.

Navigating through Number and Operations in Grades 6–8. Reston, VA: NCTM, 2006.

Navigating through Probability in Grades 6–8. Reston, VA: NCTM, 2003.

Navigating through Problem Solving and Reasoning in Grade 6. Reston, VA: NCTM, 2009.

Navigating through Problem Solving and Reasoning in Grade 6–8. Reston, VA: NCTM, 2009.